PALACE OF HEALING

Books by Dorothy Clarke Wilson

THE BROTHER · THE HERDSMAN

PRINCE OF EGYPT · HOUSE OF EARTH

FLY WITH ME TO INDIA · JEZEBEL

THE GIFTS · THE JOURNEY

THE THREE GIFTS · DR. IDA

TAKE MY HANDS · TEN FINGERS FOR GOD

HANDICAP RACE · PALACE OF HEALING

Palace of Healing

THE STORY OF DR. CLARA SWAIN,
FIRST WOMAN MISSIONARY DOCTOR,
AND THE HOSPITAL SHE FOUNDED

Dorothy Clarke Wilson

McGRAW-HILL BOOK COMPANY
New York   Toronto   London   Sydney

Among the many source materials used for the writing of this book, the author is especially indebted to the following:

A Glimpse of India: Being a Collection of Extracts from the Letters of Dr. Clara N. Swain, James Pott and Company, New York, 1909.

Mrs. William Butler, by Clementina Butler, Methodist Book Concern, 1929.

"Northwestern Doctors at the Clara Swain Hospital," Three Parts, published in the *Quarterly Bulletin,* Northwestern University Medical School, Chicago, 1947.

ACKNOWLEDGMENTS

The author wishes to make grateful acknowledgment to the following:

To the Board of Missions Library of the Methodist Church, especially its librarian, Mrs. Elsie Lund, for cooperation in much historical research.

To Drs. Charles and Wilma Perrill, now at the Methodist hospital in Vrindaban, North India, for their generous sharing of biographical materials, including lengthy correspondence and personal interviews; also to the Northwestern University Medical School Alumni Association for permission to draw heavily on material published in their Quarterly Bulletin concerning the Perrills and their work.

To Dr. and Mrs. Ernest Sundaram for tireless cooperation in supplying personal reminiscences, printed materials, technical advice, criticism of the manuscript, and other services too numerous to mention.

To Miss Mary Gordon, R.N., Miss Theresa Lorenz, R.N., Miss Janette Crawford, Bishop J. Waskom Pickett, Mr. Henry Lacy, Miss Chanda Christdas, Mrs. Barney Thompson, for help in supplying material and in critical reading of the manuscript.

To other present and former members of the staff of Clara Swain Hospital who furnished invaluable help through correspondence and personal interviews, especially Dr. and Mrs. Eugene Riel, Dr. and Mrs. Robert Petersen, Dr. Villoo Anklesaria, and Miss Frances Allen, R.N., who was my hostess during the days of research at Clara Swain Hospital and gave invaluable help in seeking out information and arranging interviews with present members of the staff. Though the names of the latter are too many to mention here, they will appear at some point in the story.

To Miss Doris Franklin, Indian journalist, for her most able account of personal interviews with Mrs. Minnie Paul and Nizam Masih.

And to Nizam Masih, for tying together seventy years of this hundred-year story with bright threads of humor, pithy wisdom, and unswerving loyalty; in other words, just for being himself.

PROLOGUE

MISS CLARA A. SWAIN, M.D.
FIRST WOMAN PHYSICIAN TO COME
TO THE ORIENT
1869
SHE ERECTED THIS BUILDING IN 1873
FOUNDING THE FIRST HOSPITAL
FOR WOMEN AND CHILDREN IN ASIA
REMODELED 1951

Above these words in the old dispensary built nearly a hundred
years ago Clara Swain looks down serenely, hair drawn back
neatly atop patrician features, lips a bit stern, eyes soberly intent
behind gleaming glasses.

"If only you could come alive," I think, looking up at her,
"and see how this dream of yours has grown to such rich fulfillment!"

And suddenly, in my mind's eye, I see it happen. She steps
down from her frame, smooths the long full skirt of her black
dress with its high neck and ballooning sleeves, and, crossing the
worn floor to the door and out onto the porch, descends the
broad stone steps. Here she stops short, blinded by more than
the blazing Indian sunlight, at first bewildered, then startled into
incredulity; then, as she recognizes familiar landmarks, awed,
filled to overflowing with wonder and thanksgiving.

For there behind her, changed ever so little, is the building she
so carefully planned, with its two round columns, its square
posts now built into the framework of two new wings, and over
the portico its round window with a design like the points of a
star or the spokes of a wheel. There to the right is the long low
shape of the first hospital wing, distinguishable in spite of the ab-
sorption of its outer verandah into solid walls. There are the big
mango tree—or its offshoots—and surely some of the bamboos

she once planted. And to the left is the bungalow where she stayed on her last visit over sixty years ago, almost unchanged.

True, the old "palace," the beginning of it all, is gone, yet it seems to live on at the heart of the big compound, just as the original trunk of an ancient banyan, long since lost, lives in the forest of tree trunks sprung from its down-thrust tendrils. Even the amazing new signs of growth must hold a hint of familiarity, for are they not dreams of her own come to fulfillment?

"Come," I say to her, taking the slender surgeon's hand which started the long succession of healing miracles in this place. "Let me show you."

We walk through the compound, and her eyes sparkle behind the clear glasses as they see the changes nearly a hundred years have made. She marvels at the new dispensary, the dental and chest clinics, the maternity wing, the physical medicine unit, the nursing school buildings, the wonders being performed in the shining operating theaters. She stares incredulously at the dental and X-ray vans starting out on tours of ministry to school children and at a public health bus leaving on its mission of outreach in a distant village. Awed and radiant, she sees sixty-plus nursing students, lovely in their blue and white uniforms, sitting with heads devoutly bowed in chapel, performing dedicated and efficient service in the wards, learning new skills in classroom, laboratory, dispensary.

We look into the male and female chest wards, where one of India's most terrible scourges is being successfully combated.

"Men and women," she exclaims wonderingly, "all here in the hospital together!"

"Yes," I reply. "India has been changing too, and growing. It's no longer necessary to treat women in seclusion. For a quarter of a century your hospital has served both men and women."

We watch skillful fingers, darker than our own, perform delicate surgery, white-uniformed men and women of another race hurrying past us bound on important missions. I answer the amazement I see in her eyes.

"It's true. The helpless child you so tenderly nurtured has come of age. Most of the positions of leadership in your hospital are now held by highly trained and qualified nationals of a new free country."

"Such changes!" she murmurs with awed satisfaction.

"You see," I explain, "the story of the hundred years really has three parts. The first is all about you and the work you started for women and children, carried on for nearly seventy years. The second is a period of rapid growth, with men as well as women among staff and patients. The third, only beginning, is the best part of all, with the Christian leadership of an indigenous Indian church assuming more and more responsibility."

Tears of joy glisten behind the clear glasses. "Truly, God has been very good to us!"

She walks unnoticed through the once-familiar compound, for she belongs to a different era. But suddenly a figure comes hurrying toward her, face alight, a handsome man, tall, straight, with a proud carriage, thick hair barely streaked with gray in spite of his nearly seventy years. He is Nizam Masih, the only staff member left who ever saw Clara Swain in the flesh.

"Doctor Miss Sahiba!" Face beaming, hands upraised in *namaste*, he greets her joyfully in a booming voice which must reach the farthest bounds of the compound. "You come back! Remember me—Nizam?"

"Nizam?"

"Son of your old *khansama*, Mathru Masih, one of his twelve children, nine sons and three daughters."

"Of course. Dear Mathru, so fine and faithful! And you are his son."

"Remember? I saw Doctor Miss Sahiba when she last time return, at Jubilee, in 1906. I was then boy of eight years."

"I remember. How well I remember! Such a helpful, willing little fellow! And all this time you have been serving the hospital?"

"Forty-five years, Doctor Miss Sahiba." The broad shoulders assume an even prouder, more jaunty posture. "But not as cook. *Jihan*, no! In ca-capacities much more important!"

I smile, having sounded the full gamut of those truly remarkable capacities.

"Wonderful, Nizam. It would be worth it to come back, if only to see you. Connecting links we are, you and I, joining together these hundred years."

The man's keen eyes soften. "Ah, but did I say you come back? No, Doctor Miss Sahiba. For me and many, many others you have been here all the time."

It is all sheer imagination, of course. I walk alone through the compound, accumulating facts, taking pictures, interviewing

[ix]

doctors, nurses, patients, humbler but equally important workers like Nizam, trying to collect all the material needed to write the story of a hundred years. And Clara Swain, who started it all, dead more than half a century, is still in her frame on the wall of the first building she dreamed into being nearly a century ago.

Or—is she? No. A dream fulfilled cannot outlive the dreamer. Just as the "palace" lives on in the huge complex of buildings which have supplanted it, she is still the vital moving spirit of this continuing healing ministry. Nizam is right. She has been here all the time.

Bareilly, North India
November, 1966

PART ONE
Women

1

The story began over a hundred years ago on the banks of the Ganges River in north India. The year was 1856. Mrs. William Butler, wife of the first Methodist missionary to India, was taking her first long journey across the country from Calcutta to Bareilly. The party stopped one night at a government rest house overlooking the Ganges. Walking out to enjoy the sunset, Mrs. Butler looked down on the sandy shore and to her surprise saw people lying with their feet in the water.

"Who are they?" she inquired with her usual concern and curiosity.

Those? Oh, they were only women, she was told, women so sick they were certain to die soon; and since no man would be allowed to look on the face of a caste woman, they were denied the services of a physician. As an act of mercy they were brought here, close to the sacred river, that their misery might end as soon as possible. A male relative, husband, father, or son, waited close to the bank, going down occasionally to see if life remained in the body. No food was given, no medicine, only an occasional sip of water. When death mercifully came, the relative would push the body into the river, whose sacred waters would assure it the blessing of salvation.

Mrs. Butler was deeply shocked and distressed. When she had been sick, she had had the best medical skill available, as well as loving care and sympathy. Yet these her sisters were left to die here alone, their miseries unrelieved. Perhaps it was this experience which caused her to write back to America, "India is the land of breaking hearts."

During her nine years of service in India she was constantly confronted with the need of Indian women for doctors of their own sex, and constantly frustrated by her own medical ignorance. Because she was a Westerner and able to render assistance in so many ways, people seemed to feel she must be able to help their physical ills. Often her skill and ingenuity were taxed to the utmost. On one occasion an Indian preacher in Lucknow came, imploring her to come to the aid of his wife, who had been suffering long in labor. The native midwife was unable to help.

"I'm sorry," said Mrs. Butler, deeply sympathetic, "but I have no knowledge of midwifery. I could do nothing for her."

The man was more incredulous than dismayed. A white woman was supposed to know everything! But his persistence brought no results. Though she had given birth to two children of her own, Mrs. Butler knew her limitations. If she tried to help and the woman died, the non-Christians would say she had killed her. Far better to refuse to go, since she did not know the right things to do. Still the pastor pleaded. If she could not come, would she at least send some medicine?

She went to the medicine closet. It looked much like Mother Hubbard's cupboard. But there was a bottle of laudanum and another of a remedy very popular in the middle of the last century, Perry Davis Pain Killer. Taking a large glass, she put in a few drops of laudanum and some of the pain killer. Then, for its warming qualities, she added some Jamaica ginger. Filling the glass with strong hot tea, she gave it to the preacher.

In about an hour he returned, face wreathed in smiles. *Achchha*, good! The baby had come, a boy. His wife was much better, and, please, Memsahiba, could he have another dose?

Somewhat reluctantly Mrs. Butler made some fresh tea, rinsed out the laudanum bottle, added a few drops of the pain killer and some more Jamaica ginger, filled the glass again with the strong brown tea, and sent the man off. To her dismay and astonishment, in another hour he reappeared. *Achchha!* Very good medicine it was indeed. Another baby had come, two boys now, and his wife would like another dose. *No!* This time Mrs. Butler firmly declined. Bad enough to have twins attributed to her, without running the risk of triplets! At the same time she made another firm decision. Somehow, sometime, she would see to it that India had at least one woman doctor.

In the 1850s this seemed an impossible dream. Medical training for women was almost nonexistent, even in America. Less than a decade had passed since Elizabeth Blackwell, shocking the academic world by attempting to gain entrance to a medical school, had finally found a small college willing to receive her and graduated in 1849 with honors. Though in 1850 the Female Medical College of Philadelphia was opened in rented back rooms of a building in Arch Street and proceeded against tremendous odds to graduate a few hardy pioneers, the movement was encountering fierce opposition. In 1858, just about the time Mrs. Butler was concocting her surprisingly effective potion, the Philadelphia County Medical Society was recommending to members of the profession that they withhold all approval and support from both faculty and graduates of the new college.

Yet Mrs. Butler's seemingly impossible dream was shared by a few other farsighted women. As early as 1851 Mrs. Sarah J. Hale of Philadelphia organized a Ladies' Medical Missionary Society, the object of which was "to aid the work of foreign missions by sending out young women qualified as physicians to minister to the wants of women in heathen lands." Mrs. Hale wrote a number of editorials for *Godey's Lady's Book,* of which she was editor, and communicated with several eminent clergymen who lent more sympathy than encouragement to the cause. However, little was actually accomplished.

But, like these fellow pioneers, the wife of William Butler was as patient as she was determined. Ten years after the Lucknow preacher incident, having laid the foundations of Indian Methodism, the Butlers were back in America; and as a minister's wife in Chelsea, Massachusetts, a suburb of Boston, Mrs. Butler was attempting in every way possible to arouse church women to the needs of their sisters in India. A beginning of mission work for women by women had already resulted in the formation of a Woman's Union Missionary Society in New York and Philadelphia, but little interest had so far been shown in the Boston area.

One Monday morning in 1867, reports her daughter Clementina, Mrs. Butler was directing the laundering for her family of seven in the basement of the narrow, five-storied parsonage in Chelsea when the doorbell rang. Mounting the stairs in her yellow polka-dotted house dress, she opened the door to two elegantly silk- and fur-bedecked members of her husband's congregation. But her consternation vanished when they made known their errand.

"We heard you talking about that Woman's Union Missionary Society in New York, and we thought it was such a splendid idea! We wondered if we couldn't help start a branch of it here in Boston."

[5]

Silks and furs, cottons and polka dots faded into unimportance. However, the eager hopes aroused by the subsequent discussion failed to materialize. Certain denominations apparently were not ready for such cooperation. It was with diluted satisfaction that Mrs. Butler in the following January, 1868, assisted the Congregational women of Park Street Church in the organization of their denominational Woman's Board of Missions. Determined now that there should be a similar organization among her own Methodist women, she elicited from most of them only lukewarm enthusiasm and excuses. They were too busy. Even when the General Conference met that year in the Middle West, where Methodism was stronger and more energetic, the Butlers failed to arouse interest in the movement.

Another year passed, and now Mrs. Butler had a staunch and vigorous ally. Mrs. Edwin W. Parker, wife of a missionary who had gone to India in 1859, was in America on furlough, fortified by the appeals of other missionary wives to send back help to the women of India. Visiting the Butlers, she spoke to many women's groups around the Boston area, and donations of money were sent to the mission field.

"But that's no way to give permanent help," the two women agreed. "We need a responsible organization. And if the Congregational women can do it, we can!"

But *how?* And who would dare to start it?

On a trip west early in 1869 Mrs. Parker talked with many influential Methodist women. She returned in March with the pledges of several to unite in the movement as soon as the women in the East should organize.

On Sunday, March 14, Dr. Butler, now minister at Dorchester, preached a rousing missionary sermon. In the congregation were Mr. and Mrs. Lewis Flanders of the Tremont Street Church. After the meeting Mrs. Butler, Mrs. Parker, and Mrs. Flanders were stirred to action. They wrote to Dr. John P. Durbin, secretary of the Methodist Missionary Society, asking what steps they should take to organize a women's society to work in cooperation with the churchwide group. Dr. Durbin's reply was cautious. "By all means raise funds for some portion of mission work in India, in China too if you wish," he recommended, "but leave the selection of missionaries and the administration of the work to the Board of Managers here at home and the Mission in India."

"In other words," commented Mrs. Butler tartly, "you women raise the money, and we men will do all the spending."

The three women had other ideas. An invitation was extended to all the Methodist women of the Boston churches to attend a meeting at Tremont Street Church on March 23. The day brought a drenching rainstorm. Arriving at the church, Mrs. Butler and Mrs. Parker huddled in a cold vestibule outside a locked door, hopes draining with the water from their dripping umbrellas. But presently Mrs. Flanders appeared, bringing the sexton with a key.

"Men!" she fumed cheerfully. "Thinking a little rain would keep us from holding our meeting! When the Methodist women of Boston really make up their minds about something—!"

Mrs. Butler's face brightened. "Let's hope there are some others as courageous as you, Mrs. Flanders."

"There will be. I sent notices to twenty-six churches. And if I'm not mistaken, those who don't come will wish they had."

She led the way into a small room off the vestry. It was warm and cosy, with several comfortable upholstered chairs, a round table with a fringed cloth in the center, and a thick carpet on the floor. Rain drummed against the two arched windows at one end with a cheerful rather than ominous sound.

Mrs. Flanders' optimism was only modestly justified. Five other women arrived, Mrs. Rich, Mrs. Kingsbury, Mrs. Merrill, Mrs. Stoddard, and Mrs. Taylor. All were equally wet, equally undaunted, equally concerned.

"What a day! I suppose we were fools to come."

"But I kept thinking about those women in India you told us about, Mrs. Butler, and I decided that with all they have to put up with, I could stand a little rain."

"Fools are we? Maybe that means we'll have the courage to rush in where our angel husbands still fear to tread."

The three leaders of the group proceeded as if they had been eighty instead of eight. Mrs. Butler and Mrs. Parker spoke briefly but earnestly of the needs of women in India. Mrs. Butler displayed the constitution of the new Woman's Board of Missions of the Congregational Church and a copy of their magazine, *Life and Light*. Then Mrs. Flanders came straight to the point.

"Ladies, we all know why we are here—to plan the organization of a Woman's Foreign Missionary Society so our Methodist women can help meet some of these needs. Suppose we get down to business."

During the next few minutes history hung precariously in the balance.

"But—there are only eight of us. Don't you think perhaps we should wait?"

"We've waited too long already, years too long. Do you realize that our Congregational sisters are already supporting seven missionaries and nine Bible women?"

"Perhaps—if we called another meeting.... After all, the rain—and just eight women...."

"There were only twelve disciples. What if they'd argued that they were too few to get anything started?"

"You mean you think we should really organize—*right now?*"

"Why not?"

"But—what would our husbands say?"

"Too much. And, as usual, do too little."

"After all, what can men really know of the needs of women?"

"But—so few of us! Do we *dare* ..."

They dared. That rainy afternoon in Tremont Street Church eight women voted to organize the Woman's Foreign Missionary Society of the Methodist Episcopal Church. A nominating committee was appointed, and at a meeting called the following week on Tuesday, another stormy day, twenty-six women adopted a constitution and elected officers. The purpose of the society was stated: "to engage and unite the efforts of the women of the Methodist Episcopal Church in sending out and supporting female missionaries, native Christian teachers, and Bible readers, in foreign lands." Mrs. Osmon C. Baker was elected president. There were forty-four vice-presidents, including wives of the bishops and of the corresponding secretary of the Missionary Society. And Mrs. Lois S. Parker, Mrs. Jennie Fowler Willing, and Mrs. William F. Warren were named corresponding secretaries. Membership dues were set at "two cents a week and a prayer."

Events moved rapidly, too rapidly to suit some apprehensive brethren of the denomination. On May 7 Dr. Durbin and William L. Harris, secretaries of the churchwide Missionary Society, met members of the women's organization in the Bromfield Street Church, Boston, "for the purpose of coming to a more

[8]

definite understanding with regard to the object and aim of the new society." Dr. Durbin was kindly and a bit indulgent, like a parent confronted with unexpected perverseness in a child.

"Please understand, ladies, the society rejoices in the interest and zeal for missions displayed by your little organization, and we approve of it heartily. However, just a word of advice and caution." Here indulgence stiffened into firmness. *"You raise the money, we will administer."*

Silence met his words. "Let me give logical reasons," he continued, smiling. "For example, could you ladies make the necessary arrangements for Miss A. to go to India, obtain bills of exchange, take care of her on the voyage, provide a home for her when she arrives at her destination, and so forth? No, of course not. Your work is to forward the money for Miss A. to New York. We will credit it to your society, keep you informed as to her needs, take care of her in sickness and in health. I believe this must be the purpose of your constitution."

The women did not share his amusement. After some spirited discussion one of them rose to her feet. "Madam President."

"Yes, Mrs. Twombly?"

"We women feel that we have organized an independent society. We will be as dutiful children to the church authorities, but through our organization we may do a work which no other can accomplish. Madam President, I move that we administer our own funds."

The motion was seconded and passed with enthusiasm; and with good grace, if some reluctance, the secretaries gave the new society official approval and assumed responsibility of publishing to the church a statement of its object and plan of operation. They commended also the proposed publication of a paper in the interest of missions, and Dr. Harris with less reluctance received from the treasurer of the society its first contribution of money, appropriated for the support of a Bible woman in India.

The two church secretaries returned to New York chagrined but comforted by a certain cynical satisfaction. Let the ladies play around with their little society and handle their own money for a while. They would find out they needed the men soon enough. Later disapproval was expressed more caustically by one of the church bishops. "Utter nonsense! It usually takes three-fourths of their funds to pay the expenses of any ladies' organization!"

[9]

Little did any of them realize, least of all the founders, that the "little society" started by eight women on that rainy March day in a small Boston room was to become one of the largest and most efficient women's organizations in the world!

The fires of enthusiasm were white-hot for the forging of new plans and activities. On May 26 a public meeting was held at Bromfield Street Church in Boston, at which Governor Claflin presided. The large and responsive audience was addressed by President William Fairfield Warren of Boston University (later a distinguished bishop), Dr. Butler, and Mr. Parker. As the result of previous long discussion, objections from the more timorous, proddings from the more courageous, much prayer and soul-searching, it was voted with loud acclaim and thanksgiving to appoint Isabella Thoburn, a teacher from St. Clairsville, Ohio, as the society's first missionary to India. It was a historic decision. That same month appeared the first issue of the society's magazine, *The Heathen Woman's Friend,* edited for many years by Mrs. Warren. Its first subscription list was 3,600, its second year 21,000, and by 1874 it would reach 25,000. Later the name was changed, significantly, to *The Woman's Missionary Friend.*

But Mrs. Butler was not satisfied with Miss Thoburn's appointment. The picture of the women left to die on the banks of the Ganges was etched indelibly on her heart. Her Indian sisters needed teachers, yes, but were not life and health prerequisites to education? She would never be at ease in spirit until she had seen at least one woman doctor in India. She coveted this pioneer service for her new society.

Meanwhile there had been developments both in India and in America. Mrs. D. W. Thomas, wife of a fellow missionary who had charge of the girls' orphanage in Bareilly, had long shared Mrs. Butler's passionate desire for efficient medical aid for Indian women and children. She had even thought seriously of studying medicine herself. Back in 1867 she had organized a "medical class" among the older orphanage girls and attempted to instruct them in physiology and hygiene. But from the beginning she had run into difficulties.

"The girls haven't done anything yet in medicine," she had written to a friend, "because in the first place all but one, Piyari, could not manage the English physiology. Then we sent to Agra for some Urdu books on anatomy, but when they arrived they were such a combination of Persian, Arabic, and 'hifalutin' Urdu that we couldn't manage them without a Persian teacher!"

Even more important, Mrs. Thomas had been trying to rouse the interest of both Indian citizens of prominence and English officers in providing some medical help for women. One wealthy Indian had become so impressed by the possibility that he had offered to defray the expenses of a medical class if a woman doctor could be sent from America.

Early in 1869 Mrs. Thomas had written to a former missionary colleague, Mrs. J. T. Gracey, in Philadelphia: "Now I see no way of having this class of native girls properly instructed except by a lady, and you will see at once that a full-fledged missionary is what we want as soon as possible. Do you think the Woman's Union Missionary Society to which you belong would help us by sending out the Doctress if one should be found willing to come?"

Immediately Mrs. Gracey had inquired of members of the staff of the Philadelphia Women's Medical College if they could recommend some graduate of suitable Christian character and professional acquirements who might consider going. The name of Miss Clara Swain of Castile, New York, a student about to receive her medical degree, was suggested. Mrs. Thomas had written to Miss Swain that very night. Would she accept an appointment by the Union Missionary Society to go to India? Miss Swain had replied favorably, but had asked for three months to make her final decision. Meanwhile, the Woman's Foreign Missionary Society of the Methodist Episcopal Church, her own denomination, had been formed.

Mrs. Butler was aware of these developments. She had ascertained also that Dr. Swain, if she decided to accept the appointment, would prefer to go under Methodist auspices. It was with fear and trembling but with an audacious faith and courage that, at a meeting called on September 9, Mrs. Butler rose to address the women.

"Ladies, I believe it is not enough for us to send one missionary to India. Our sisters there need teachers, yes, but they also need doctors." Simply she explained the situation, ending with the astounding suggestion, "Ladies, I move that we send two missionaries to India instead of one. I propose to you also the name of Dr. Clara Swain."

There were gasps of amazement, disbelief, consternation.

Rules of order were forgotten as exclamations erupted like "Amens!" in a fervent Methodist class meeting.

"Oh, but we couldn't!"

"It would mean raising at least a thousand more dollars!"

"Hard enough to get the money to send one—but *two!*"

"But they do need doctors. How wonderful if we could!"

"What a pity—one of our own Methodist women—not to send her ourselves!"

"But of course—out of the question...."

A figure suddenly emerged out of the confusion of buzzing tongues and bobbing bonnets, a well-dressed woman of distinguished bearing.

"Madam President."

The pounding gavel finally succeeded in restoring order. "I recognize Mrs. Edward Porter."

"Sisters." Mrs. Porter's voice was firm and clear. She spoke simply, quite unaware that her words would be remembered and often quoted during the next hundred years. "Shall we lose Miss Thoburn and Dr. Swain just because we have not the means in sight to send them? *No*. Rather let the Methodist women of Boston walk the streets in calico gowns and save the expense of more costly apparel! But let us send these missionaries to our sisters across the seas!"

Murmurs of approval swept the room. Bonnets began bobbing again. Mrs. Porter sank to her seat amid a wave of applause which slowly gathered momentum, swelling and surging as if stirred by an invisible wind. Again disorder reigned, but it was a disorder of unity rather than confusion.

"Hear, hear!" "She's right!" "What more do we need?" "Question, question!"

When order was finally restored, the vote was taken. There was no dissenting voice. The first woman doctor would be sent to India, and it would be the women of Methodism, walking the streets of Boston in calico gowns if need be, who would send her.

2

Seeing the puny child of the 1830s, sheltered and pampered by nine older brothers and sisters, one would never have guessed that she would grow up to pursue a profession at that time almost taboo to women, certainly not that she would brave the rigors of an exotic foreign culture which demanded an excess of pioneer courage and physical stamina.

Yet even in these early years, Clara Swain exhibited some of the qualities which later shaped her remarkable career. Singleness of purpose and a strong will to fulfill it, however, appeared as faults rather than virtues in a spoiled youngest child. She wanted everything she saw and thought she ought to have it. But her mother could be firm as well as loving. Once when the small Clara had shown excessive rudeness, Clarissa Swain, displaying a grief which her daughter never forgot, sternly impressed on her the necessity of controlling herself if she expected to be loved by others.

"I will," promised the six-year-old Clara earnestly, "I *will* be a good girl. I'll ask God not to let me be naughty again."

This early religious awareness, nurtured by a devout family, soon became the dominant motivation of her life. When she was eight and her sister Ann, six years older, joined the Methodist Church, Clara was impressed and troubled.

"Why am I not a Christian, too?" she asked her mother. "I want to be good."

Before she was ten, under the influence of a powerful sermon, she passed through the emotional upheaval deemed necessary for even an innocent child's "conversion" and gained a faith and direction of purpose which were to become increasingly vital throughout her life.

Not that all her problems of temperament were solved! Child of the fun-loving, Irish John Swain as well as of the quiet and devout, New England-born Clarissa, she worried constantly about the conflict of fun and sobriety in her own nature until her mother assured her, "Be yourself, child, as God wants you to be. It's the duty of a Christian to be joyous, and you can please him in your play as well as at church."

There were evidences also in those early years of the reverence and concern for life which were later to inspire her choice

[13]

of a profession. Her love for animals led her to pat every dog she met, and she and her sister Hattie, two years older, were always bringing home stray cats. Once, seeing a lame chicken, she wrapped it in her apron, took it home, bandaged its legs neatly, and nursed it to health with great devotion.

"And she probably used splints!" one of her cousins observed years later.

She was soon showing an equal concern for the ills of people. When her beloved "Aunt Post," her mother's sister Elizabeth, broke her ankle while Clara, perhaps fifteen, was visiting her in Michigan, the girl stayed and cared for her almost a year, even at that age proving herself a careful and competent nurse. No sooner had she returned home than the local minister, Mr. Hurlbut, fell ill with typhoid and she was called to assist in his care. In spite of the reluctance of her family, for typhoid was a deadly scourge, Clara insisted on going. There followed anxious and harrowing days. One child after another fell ill. Two of them died, as well as the father. For many weeks afterward Clara remained with the widow and her other children, caring for them. Aside from sad experience and grueling self-discipline, the weeks yielded little compensation except a book, in which she wrote, "This is the first Bible I ever owned. It was presented to me by Rev. and Mrs. Hurlbut."

But such episodes were merely incidental to her primary purpose, getting all the education possible and making use of it. Her thirst for knowledge was insatiable. Throughout childhood she would borrow books and read them over and over. The summer of 1855 found her, now twenty-one years of age, teaching a few private pupils in the village. The following summer she went to live with some cousins in Pike and attended school there. Then John Swain's sister in Canandaigua, knowing Clara's passion for self-improvement, invited her to come there for a year of study. This enabled her to get a position in the primary department of one of the public schools, where she taught for nearly five years, meanwhile working as actively in the church as in the school. The impact of her Christian witness was strong and constant.

"We noticed that you always went to prayer meeting," one of the boys in her Sunday school class told her, "so we thought we would go and see what was in it."

But teaching did not completely satisfy. The inattention of children less avid for learning than herself was irritating as well as disappointing. Surely there must be some work in which she could use her full powers and render greater service! She waited more or less patiently for God's leading. Then suddenly there came a letter from a close friend, a woman physician.

"You know that I have not long to live," the letter said in brief. "My greatest regret is that I must give up my work. In spite of the prejudice against us, I know from rich experience that the woman doctor can render a unique service. My dear, why don't *you* fit yourself for such work as I have to lay down?"

The idea broke like a flash of light—until she considered its implications. So many more years of training? And she was already nearing thirty. She had never been strong physically. Could she endure the rigors of long hours, extreme nervous tension, exacting disciplines, even the repugnance of animal and human dissection? Then, even if she finished training satisfactorily, could she face the opposition that was sure to follow? It was little more than ten years since Dr. Elizabeth Blackwell, setting up an office in New York City, had been insulted and jeered at in the street, ostracized by fellow physicians, bombarded with threatening anonymous letters, heard even members of her own sex remark in horror, "I would rather die than have a woman doctor!" Clara knew herself to be a woman of independence and courage but also one deeply sensitive of spirit. Could she face such antagonism and remain calmly resolute of purpose? As the months passed and uncertainty became growing conviction, she knew that there was only one answer to all these questions. *Yes, if it was what God wanted her to do.*

But—was it? How could she be sure? Then suddenly a door was opened. A position was offered her in the Castile Sanatorium working under the capable Dr. Cordelia A. Greene. Gladly she gave up teaching and entered a course of training. Dr. Greene was thorough in her instruction, sympathetic, encouraging. They became fast friends. During three years of study and practice in the sanatorium Clara became assured that her strength of will was sufficient to overcome all obstacles and difficulties that the medical profession might present, even to a woman. She applied with confidence for admission to the Woman's Medical College in Philadelphia, now fifteen years old, and began her training in medicine in 1865, when she was already thirty-one years of age.

Born out of necessity because no medical college in the country would accept woman students (after Elizabeth Blackwell even little Geneva had refused to admit another!), the college had had a stormy but doggedly valiant growth. Obstacles had been tremendous. Hospitals had refused admission to its students even as observers and to its graduates to treat patients. Pharmacists refused to fill their prescriptions. Crowds of street loafers had gathered to jeer at Hannah Longshore, one of the college's first two graduates, when she dared to open an office in Philadelphia. There were few clinical facilities. It was not until 1868, when Clara had been for three years a student, that Dr. Ann Preston, the other of its first two graduates and now its dean, was able to arrange with the Philadelphia Hospital at Blockley for a group of students to attend clinics in its amphitheater.

Nevertheless, Clara Swain was able to obtain what was at that time a thorough and first-class medical education. Medicine had made great progress since Elizabeth Blackwell in 1849 had qualified for her doctor's degree in just two terms of four months each. The Woman's Medical College now offered a four-year course. Its staff, which included many distinguished and dedicated men, compared favorably with that of any medical school in the country. Dr. Ann Preston was a pioneer in science as well as women's rights. Her dissertation had been a prophetic anticipation of psychosomatic medicine. As professor of physiology and one of Clara's teachers, she imparted as much of her own radiant pioneer vigor as knowledge of bones and muscles. The college was as much an adventure in social reform as a training school. Clara reveled in the whole learning experience. She took keen delight in its smallest details, the revelations of a drop of blood seen through a microscope, strolls through the park after class hours on the way to her boarding place, the intimate talks with her instructors. And she felt a fierce joy in being part of this struggle of a small but determined group of men and women to establish the right of a woman to study and practice medicine.

It was a spiritual as well as a mental and physical experience, for the central purpose of the college was to train for service. Where the need was greatest, it was emphasized, there a woman doctor should work. Since in those days only the most serious and courageous women were likely to apply for admission, the result was a student body of high ability and moral commitment.

Like most of her fellow students, Clara was dedicated to a career of service rather than of personal reward or distinction.

But it was not until her last year that she began to ask seriously, "Where is this place of greatest need which God wants me to fill?" A series of sermons by some of the celebrated preachers of the day goaded her to deep concern and soul-searching. "What do ye more than others?" demanded Dr. Willett in November, 1868. "One thing thou lackest," Dr. McGowan admonished his congregation, Clara Swain among them. Bishop Simpson's Christmas sermon, she noted, "filled my heart with peace and good will to all men." But with a restless concern for them also! And as her spring graduation drew nearer and with it the necessity for decision, she became more and more restless and concerned.

"A wonderful sermon!" she noted when she heard Phillips Brooks preach on Malachi 4:2. "But unto you that fear my name shall the Sun of Righteousness arise with healing in his wings; and ye shall go forth leaping like calves from the stall."

"Healing . . . go forth. . . ." How she longed to do just that! But what? Where? How?

Then suddenly another door opened, revealing a breathtaking, frightening vista. She wanted to heal? Very well, here was a condition of greater need than she had ever dreamed of. She was ready to go forth? Fine. How about a strange country halfway around the world where no woman doctor had ever gone?

Clara Swain read the letter from Mrs. Gracey with a whirling head and pounding heart. India! The very word conjured up exciting but dismaying images: hideous idols, throbbing heat, blinding color, snakes, dust, beds of nails, surging masses, incredible beauty, incredible human need. It was hard to focus her eyes on the bold, clear handwriting.

"Your name was suggested to me by your professors as one most competent, most conscientious, and most dedicated to Christian service."

As Clara Swain read on her heart still pounded, but with excitement rather than dismay. Names which had been familiar to her through many years of church attendance leaped at her from the pages: Butlers . . . Bareilly . . . Humphrey . . . Naini Tal . . . the Methodist Orphanage. . . . She needed few descriptive words to picture the crying needs of Indian women. She could see vividly the little class of girls and Mrs. Thomas, eager but painfully limited in knowledge, trying to teach them the fundamentals of physiology and hygiene. If only they could have a woman doctor! And the Woman's Union Foreign Missionary Society was willing to send one if a volunteer could be found. It was asking *her*, Clara Swain. . . .

Then, as the implications of the words smote her, again the excitement was sharpened by dismay and terror. Leave family, friends, travel for weeks over heaving, sickening waters to a land filled with nameless mysteries and dangers, to be gone for no one knew how many years, perhaps forever? Become the first woman missionary doctor ever to go out to a foreign land? It was this last which frightened her the most. Here she was not yet graduated from medical school! What audacity to think herself capable of such a serious and sacred responsibility! Yet even while her mind whirled with such fears and uncertainties, she knew what her answer must be. If she could prove to herself beyond a doubt that this was what God wanted her to do, nothing on earth would keep her from accepting.

"Give me three months to think and pray about it," she wrote back. "Then I will give you my answer."

At the end of the three months she accepted the appointment to Bareilly by the Woman's Union Foreign Missionary Society. But during that time her own Methodist women had organized, and she preferred to go out under their auspices. The Union Society generously waived all claim.

Cheerfully, Clara Swain set about her preparations, answering to all demurs of family and friends, "It is God's call. I must go." Nevertheless, she was vastly relieved and heartened when she discovered that another woman missionary, Isabella Thoburn, was to travel with her.

A farewell meeting was held for her in Boston on October 14, but she had no chance then to meet Miss Thoburn, who had been honored at her farewell the week before. Another mass meeting was held in the old Bedford Street Church in New York, where the building was crowded to the doors. Even the stairs were occupied and the aisles filled. There was an equally loyal but in many cases tearful group gathered to bid the two women Godspeed when they sailed for Liverpool on the *Nevada* on November 3, 1869.

The two young missionaries were instantly attracted to each other, each recognizing in the other the same intensity of purpose and deep spiritual commitment. Yet even on shipboard Clara found little opportunity at first to establish intimacy with her shipmate. Both were too seasick, to the disgust of the captain, who remarked that if the voyage were two or three days longer he would be tempted to throw some of his passengers overboard. The letter announcing their arrival was delayed, so there was no one to meet them in Liverpool, and they had to manage their baggage themselves. To Clara the thought of opening her two trunks and six boxes was not pleasant, and the brusqueness of the inspector caused her heart to sink.

"What's in this one?" he demanded, pointing to one of the trunks.

"It contains nothing except my own personal belongings," she replied politely.

He lifted the lid, pawed roughly through the contents. Then suddenly an expression of horror crossed his face. "Blimey, what's this!"

"What—oh, you mean my skeleton. I'm a doctor," explained Clara composedly. "Of course I have to carry some of my tools with me."

Hastily the inspector jammed the articles into the trunk and closed the lid. His face was as pale as if he had seen a ghost, as in a way he had. "All right, lady. I guess you can go through."

In London they were entertained by Mrs. Kelly, a sister of Mrs. Butler. Since there was no steamer for Alexandria for ten days, they enjoyed a heyday of sightseeing, visiting the Tower, the Museum, the Crystal Palace, Parliament, and City Chapel Road, renewing their vows at the grave of Wesley. Clara purchased a steamer chair and rug. On Monday the twenty-eighth they sailed for Alexandria.

The voyage continued to be rough. In the Bay of Biscay waves washed over the deck and broke the skylight. Water poured into their cabin, and everything on the floor was soaked, but fortunately they had taken most of the things out of their trunks and stored them in vacant berths. The small ship rolled and tumbled. But the sunsets were magnificent, "worth the whole journey," exulted Isabella Thoburn. Leaving the boat at Alexandria, they crossed country by rail to Suez, and here, watching men plowing with cows and camels dragging a long curved stick, they had their first preview of the poverty of India.

Arriving at Suez at seven in the morning, they were instantly surrounded by demanding coolies and spent an hour defending their baggage before they finally managed to reach an English hotel. Here, to their relief, they met two young women sent out to India by the United Presbyterian Board, and together they chartered a boat to take them down the amazing Suez Canal, which had just been opened on November 17. Everywhere people were discussing whether it would be a success or not. Most thought it doubtful. Back at Suez they boarded the steamer *Krishna* and started the last lap of their journey to India.

At last the two had opportunity for long and intimate conversation, and they laid the foundations of a lifelong friendship. Now just under thirty, Isabella Thoburn was going to India as the result of a letter written by her brother, James M. Thoburn, who had been for ten years a missionary there.

"It's an odd story," she said, laughing. "You'd never believe it, but I'm here today because a vulture happened to drop a feather."

Her brother, it seemed, had pitched his itinerant's tent in a mango orchard and gone to walk among the trees. A vulture had built her nest in the top of one of them and had dropped a quill. Picking it up, James had made a pen out of the quill and gone into his tent to see if it would work. He had written a letter to his sister, describing mission work in the villages, where he had found a few scattered Christian converts. But there was no education at all, he had written, for the girls in the families. What they needed desperately was a school where the most promising ones could be gathered together and taught.

"How would you like to come and take charge of such a school if we decide to make the attempt?" he had broached, half jokingly.

"I'm sure he was dumbfounded when I wrote by the next steamer that I would come. That was three years ago, and they've just got around to finding a way for me to go."

Hopefully, fearfully, the two women discussed the adventure to which they were journeying, wondering if they would be able to fulfill the expectations of the infant society which had sent them. Little did they realize that one of them would found the first college for women and the other the first women's hospital in all of Asia!

India! Seen from the railway carriages after leaving the bewildering confusion of Bombay, it was still only fragments viewed from a distance, a vast kaleidoscope of changing shapes and colors. But the railway line was under construction, and a break through central India made it necessary to travel a week or more by bullock train. Now suddenly, as they bumped at a snail's pace along narrow dirt roads, it became close and real, its red dust smarting in their eyes and seeping into their bonnets and long dresses, its brown thatched huts close enough to observe in every crude detail, its odors of spices and burning cow dung and human sweat and jasmine blossoms heady in their nostrils.

In Nagpur they were met by James Thoburn, but, since they were detained there a week waiting for their baggage, he had to leave them to attend the Annual Conference in Bareilly. They left Nagpur on January 17 in a delightful *dak gari,* a horse-drawn vehicle. All went well until one of the horses lay down in the road and the men tried vainly for an hour to get him up. Then they left the women alone while they went back three miles for another pair of horses. When darkness fell the two women took scant comfort from the fires glowing all about them in the jungle, built to keep tigers away from the village huts. But they made themselves as comfortable as possible with blankets and shawls, closed the doors, and lay down to sleep. They reached the government rest house at Jubbulpore toward night of the next day, just in time to miss the train. While waiting, they absorbed more unfamiliar details: big, painted, ornamented houses; men making ornaments for noses, ears, ankles, and toes; lead rings being pounded into shape for anklets; workmen beating brass into plates and drinking vessels.

They traveled by rail to Cawnpore, then took another *dak gari.* This time the horses were more tractable. On the road to Bareilly, 180 miles, there was only one rest house. The women managed to secure bread and tea by making signs. At the Ganges they left the *dak gari* and were carried across the river in small *dholis* on men's shoulders. It was five in the morning when they reached Bareilly and received a warm welcome from the other missionaries. At the Annual Conference then in session Isabella Thoburn and Clara would receive their appointments, one to Lucknow, the other to Bareilly.

But Dr. Clara did not wait for her appointment before starting work. When she came out of her room that morning, she found a large company of Indian Christian women and girls eagerly waiting to greet the "Doctor Miss Sahiba" and to ask her help. With the aid of another missionary she was able to understand their words of welcome and discover what she could do to help them. Though her own medicines had not arrived, she procured some simple remedies from Mrs. Thomas, who had been trying with her limited knowledge to conduct a dispensary. Clara Swain had fourteen patients that first day!

3

Thirteen years before, in 1857, the brave new Methodist mission in Bareilly had been reduced to dust and ashes. It was the time of the Sepoy Rebellion, and all foreigners in north India were in danger. Bareilly, site of a large British cantonment, was an obvious target of the rebels.

At first William Butler refused to leave, but when news came that Delhi had revolted with a resultant massacre of most Europeans, he fled with his family one night to the hill station of Naini Tal. With no carriages or palanquins available and Mrs. Butler in frail health, they turned string cots upside down, tied ropes to the corners, and made makeshift hammocks in which she and the children were borne on the shoulders of coolies. It was a hazardous trip of many days, the trail passing through malarial and beast-infested jungle, where once even their bearers deserted them. Many times they came close to death. But at last they saw the sun shining on the green slopes and clear blue lake of their mountain haven and arrived in Naini Tal just in time to hear the English church bell ringing.

The small group of Christians left behind in Bareilly was not so fortunate. As Joel Janvier, Butler's faithful interpreter and assistant, was preaching on the text, "Fear not, little flock," sepoys rushed in, and the tiny congregation was forced to flee for their lives. One, a devout Anglo-Indian named Maria Bolst, failed to escape and became the mission's first martyr. The house was burned, with all the Butlers' books and possessions.

The Butlers were among the few missionaries who survived the mutiny in that part of India. With eighty-six English refugees they defended themselves in the hills for months. A price of 500 rupees was placed on Butler's head. But his courage remained undaunted.

"All is lost," he wrote home with philosophic candor, "save life and the grace of God. On account of my Mission I am depressed. It is crippled. But shall we give it up because heaven and hell have risen up against us? Nay. Greater is He that is for us than all that can be against us!"

At last, after months of anxiety, near starvation, bouts of jungle fever, and the birth of a little daughter to Mrs. Butler, the storm abated. News came that Delhi had been recaptured by the British. Leaving his two boys but taking his wife and the new baby, William Butler set off for the royal city. It was December and bitterly cold in the mountains. Wild beasts abounded. As they tented one night, the milch goat, brought along for the baby and tied to the tent rope, was carried off by a tiger. At another point they had to cross a fierce mountain torrent on a rope bridge, pronounced unsafe, 80 feet above the waters. Mr. Butler walked, but his wife with the baby was carried in a sort of hammock called a "dandy" by the natives, whose toes clung skillfully to the swaying ropes.

"A strong, sure-footed set of fellows," she wrote later, "with the smallest possible quantity of clothing on them, and I can testify that they carry ladies with the greatest care."

After three weeks they reached Delhi. Arriving at the great Kashmiri Gate at night, William Butler knocked and was challenged by the sentry. "Friends," he announced clearly, giving the day's password. The gate swung open, and the Butlers, first travelers to reach the city after the siege, ended their long journey.

Later, in the Diwan-i-Khass, the famed Hall of Audience in the Red Fort, they were among the crowds who came to see the Mogul princes brought to trial. Mrs. Butler wore the priceless cashmere shawl which her husband, trying to augment her scant wardrobe, had bought in the bazaar for only 25 rupees and which was destined to outlast a century. One day during the long trials they became tired of standing and, seeing the fabulous Crystal Throne, they went and sat down upon it. It was while sitting there that an inspiration came to William Butler. Immediately he took a notebook from his pocket and began a letter to the church officials back home.

"We can never reach the mutineers of Bareilly, but what is to become of the orphans of these men? Shall they perish? Or shall we take them and rear them for Christ and His church? I beg

[23]

you, send me money for the support of these children!"

Almost at the same hour as the massacre in Bareilly two new recruits for the mission, J. L. Humphrey and Ralph Pierce, with their wives, were attending their farewell meeting in Boston. It was fitting that when the two new couples finally arrived in India, William Butler chose to meet them in the beautiful pavilion of the Taj Mahal. Under the marble dome of this symbol of supreme beauty they joined in singing the Doxology.

"I have them at last!" exulted William Butler. "Thank the Church for having sent them. Little did Shah Jahan (King of the World) imagine when he built this that the missionaries of God's Messiah would find a friendly shelter in the enclosure, or sing, as we do now with glowing hearts, our Doxology over his very dust!"

Humphrey and his wife entered Bareilly to start their work in February, 1859. In July he baptized the first convert, a Muslim, Zahur-ul-Haqq. A new site was chosen for the mission and buildings erected. Here the first Methodist printing press was set up, later to be removed to Lucknow. William Butler's dream of an orphanage for children of mutiny victims came to fulfillment, forerunner of the vast network of schools which were to become such a vital organ of the mission enterprise. The boys' orphanage was opened immediately in Bareilly with twelve boys. By 1860 its number had increased to sixty. The girls' orphanage, started in Lucknow in 1858, was soon moved to Bareilly.

When Clara Swain arrived in 1870, she was plunged immediately into this surging tide of history in the making. She saw the ruins of the house where William Butler had started his work, about a mile from the present compound; the round building with its pointed tiled roof and circling arched verandah which had housed the first printing press; Kashmiri Kothi, the Indian mansion which had been put at the disposal of the mission by the British government, where the Humphreys and Butlers had first lived after the mutiny; the spot where Maria Bolst had been hastily buried by a friendly native at the foot of Mrs. Butler's hedge of roses.

"India is far more beautiful than I expected," Clara wrote home. She might have added, "And far more ugly."

It was a land of hyperboles, of colors so sharp and bright that they hurt one's eyes, crimson of poinsettias, orange of saffron robes and marigolds, rainbow hues of saris and huge, intricately wound turbans. Yet never had she seen such dull grays and browns and wan yellows. And no wonder, with the meager Christmas rains past a month ago, and little more to be expected until June! Yet there was something beautiful about the dust, even while it clogged the pores and choked the throat. It rose in a golden haze from the feet of cows and goats and sheep and bare-foot children, turned glossy leaves a shimmering silver, and created the most breathtaking sunsets.

It was spring when she arrived, if India could be said to have spring. The peach trees, the strawberry vines, the mangoes were in bloom. Used to the limited diet of a snowbound winter, she savored the sweetness of guavas, oranges, limes, and *pumelos* ("something like an orange," she wrote, "which looks like a pumpkin growing on a tree"). The mission garden provided fresh peas, string beans, lettuce, cabbage, and beets. There was an abundance of rice, mutton, fowl, goat meat, and occasionally beef or fish. Mr. Thomas, the missionary now in charge, kept cows, so there was milk for tea and coffee, and the cook made a fresh pat of butter every morning. If Clara had pictured herself living on rice and curry in a mud and thatch hut, she was happily disappointed.

"The two mission houses and grounds are very pretty and pleasant," she assured her relatives in her first letter. "The houses are one story high, built chiefly of sun-dried bricks, plastered over and whitewashed. They have tile roofs and wide verandahs. The floors are brick covered with coarse matting over which are spread cotton floor-cloths stamped in neat pat-terns. There is a fireplace in my room, for here in north India the nights are cool in winter. On the mantelpiece stands my favorite vase filled with beautiful roses and sweet jasmine. The *mali*, gardener, brings me fresh flowers every other morning."

But the mission compound, comfortable and familiar though she found much of its routine, was no Western island. The life of the Eastern city, with its population of 125,000, teemed all about and through it. It flowed past its gates in an endless stream of pony carts, rickshas, bullock carts, gaudy palanquins, *dholis* carried on men's shoulders, elephants, an occasional camel heavily burdened, barefooted and equally burdened pedestrians, handcarts, cows, monkeys, goats, holy men in saffron robes or scant loincloths, beggars. It assaulted her ears with drumbeats, the raucous cries of hawkers, the hoarse morning cacophony of crows. Its pungent smells of hot spices, sweating bodies, jasmine garlands, cow-dung fires, open drains, sweet incense, stung her nostrils. And every day, all day, its disease, poverty, appalling needs both spiritual and physical, challenged her skills, exhausted her energy, tore at her heartstrings. It was frustrating at first to work with only the simple remedies which Mrs. Thomas could supply. Would her own equipment never come?

From that first day there was no lack of patients. The girls' orphanage was in daily need of her services. One of north India's frequent famines had brought in many homeless waifs. Every morning a little group of them came to her room, accompanied by a teacher or older girl, gathering around her to kiss her hand, pull at her long skirts, make silent appeal with their huge eyes and thin little bodies. Tenderly she treated them for fevers, colds, sore eyes, abscesses, worms, and other ailments, rejoicing as the good care and food in the orphanage, as well as her medicines, caused the eyes to brighten, the cheeks to fill out, and many of the symptoms of ill health to disappear. The children were never in a hurry to leave.

The families of servants and the many Christian workers on the compound also became her special care, as well as the families in a Christian *mohalla*, village, where lived many of the converts made in the thirteen years since William Butler had established the Methodist mission in Bareilly. Deprived of former means of support and often ostracized by friends and families, these converts would have been destitute without some assistance from the mission. To provide employment for them, Mr. Thomas in 1868 had opened an "Industrial Establishment," forerunner of many such enterprises in mission work, where the people were taught to make cabinet furniture, work with iron and brass, and weave carpets, cotton cloth, table mats, and towels. When Clara arrived there were forty-six families in this Christian community, with ninety-six persons employed in such crafts. She would never forget the first time she was called to visit a patient in the village.

"I'll go with you," offered Mrs. Thomas, always her adviser and interpreter.

Merely leaving the compound and crossing the road, Clara entered a new world. The brown clusters of mud and thatch huts glimpsed from railroad carriage and bullock cart ceased to be picturesque landscape, became a way of life she had not dreamed existed. She found the patient, an elderly woman, lying on a cot of woven rope with no mattress, no sheet, shaking with malarial chills. A pile of glowing coals and hot ashes had been placed on the dirt floor under the bed to keep her warm. "A good idea," thought Clara with a growing respect for the simple wisdom which through unnumbered centuries had fashioned its own pattern for survival.

She administered a good dose of quinine, gave the daughter-in-law directions for bathing the patient with cool water if the fever returned, and made a mental note to send the *chaprassi*, errand boy, with a blanket. Looking about, she observed the appalling dearth of objects in the one small room.

"You mean"— she expressed her shock as they walked back through the narrow lanes—"it was all there? They have nothing else—nothing at all?"

"That's right," said Mrs. Thomas. "A string bed, a drinking vessel, a large brass plate, an iron plate on which they bake bread, and a vessel to cook rice and vegetables—that's all most of these poor families own."

"But—how terrible! How do they live!"

"Cheerfully, philosophically," replied the older missionary, "and with an amazing dignity and courage." Her eyes twinkled. "I suppose it does have its advantages. If you have to move, it's easy. You just bundle your goods together, put them on the bed, place the bed on the head of a man or woman, and start off, all the family following."

"Yes," agreed Clara, remembering ruefully her own mountains of baggage, much of which had not yet arrived.

"At last," she wrote home joyously on the eighteenth of February, "my boxes containing library, medicines, charts, yes, and skeleton, are here!" The trunk had gone by mistake to the Punjab, but at last it arrived also. Now she could really apply her skills to the desperate needs she saw all about her!

The news spread quickly that a lady doctor had come from America and would visit in the homes of the city, also that any sick person could come to the mission house and receive medicine free of charge. Patients soon came, with ailments real or fancied, coughs and fevers being the chief complaints. For

[27]

Bareilly was in an area rife with malaria, perhaps nine out of ten of its people suffering at one time or another from its ravages.

In accordance with custom, many Indian gentlemen called to pay their respects. Some expressed appreciation for her having come. A few invited her to visit in their homes.

"Just now I hear you have arrived," said one such visitor, a strict and wealthy Brahmin, using painfully correct English. "Pleased I am with this idea of a lady doctor in our midst. Possible it is that from this great good may result."

A few days later the man's small son came, saying that his father had sent him to make his salaams, and would the Doctor Miss Sahiba please come and visit the boy's sick mother?

Dr. Clara was both elated and apprehensive. Suppose the woman was too sick to be helped! Failure at this point might jeopardize her reputation among Hindu patients for years to come. She went, Mrs. Thomas accompanying, breathing a prayer for divine aid.

The boy led them through narrow, winding streets to an imposing house set in a walled enclosure, its façade ornately decorated with Hindu gods and goddesses. They passed through a small apartment used as a stable for a horse and cows, entering by a doorway into a square open court on two sides of which were verandahs, with sleeping rooms back of them. One of these verandahs with its apartments was occupied by servants; the other led to the family's sitting and dining room. It was Clara's first glimpse of a well-to-do Indian home, and it was all she could do to keep from staring. The room was luxurious compared with the huts of the *mohalla*. A thick cotton rug lay on the floor. There were three chairs and a small table. The Hindu gentleman received them graciously, seated them, then brought his wife and introduced her, telling her to shake hands. Then he brought forward a chair and motioned to her to be seated.

"An unusual honor," Mrs. Thomas told Clara later, "for a woman to sit on a chair in the presence of her husband. Only a mother of sons would be allowed such a privilege. And did you notice? She sat with face uncovered and showed no embarrassment!"

Dr. Clara's concern was instantly aroused. She could hardly wait to test her skills on the fragile, wan little creature half buried beneath lavish silks and jewelry. But she was already

[28]

learning that India could not be hurried. First the guests must be offered *pan*, a little three-cornered leaf packet containing a bit of tobacco, a morsel of lime, and fragments of betel nut, cardamon, and other spices. Then they must be served many varieties of food—fruits, coconut, sweets, spicy mixtures—all on large banana leaves, since it would defile the family dishes to be touched by Christians. It seemed an interminable time before the two women found themselves alone in an inner room with the patient.

Even then there was more waiting. The little wife, starved for variety in her luxurious but monotonous life, burst into a torrent of questions. She fingered the fabric of their dresses, lifted their long skirts to examine their shoes, stockings, and several petticoats, fingered their white collars and fichus, felt the texture of their unoiled coils of hair, all with a frank and unabashed curiosity. Patiently Mrs. Thomas answered the questions in Hindustani, explaining to Clara, "She's asking me all about our dress, our customs, our religion."

Seated uncomfortably on a mat on the floor, Dr. Clara tried to contain her impatience. At last the woman's gestures indicated that the conversation had turned to her own complaints. She pointed to her head, pressed her delicate ringed hands to her chest. With Mrs. Thomas as interpreter Clara was able to ask the necessary questions and, finally, to give a careful examination. To her relief she found that the illness was not too serious and would yield to proper treatment.

"The best medicine," she whispered as they left the inner apartment, "would be something to give her more interest in life, something to do."

Mrs. Thomas nodded. While making their salaams to the grateful host, she suggested that it might be helpful if his wife could learn to read and, perhaps, be taught needlework. He agreed, and it was arranged that someone would come from the mission to teach her.

"You see," said Mrs. Thomas earnestly as the two women jogged slowly home in a tonga, "why it's so *very* important that India should have women doctors? That poor little wife has probably not been out of the house a half-dozen times, and then in a tightly curtained palanquin! They would no more think of letting a male doctor into that zenana apartment than of—of cooking beef for dinner! And her husband is one of the more liberal Brahmins, with a government office. Do you realize what you've done, my dear? We've been trying for ten years, in vain, to make friends with women like that!"

Visits to other homes soon followed. One of Dr. Clara's first cases was the wife of a deputy collector. Her success with these patients caused her fame to spread about the city. When after a time she was called to the house of Lachman Narain, one of the most strict and orthodox Hindus, her reputation was assured. At the end of the first six weeks her notebook recorded 108 patients.

"Miss Swain is a grand success," Mrs. Thomas wrote home to America, "and we are only afraid that she will work herself to death. She has lost only three patients in all her practice, and those were children to whom she was called in the last extremity."

But the treatment of patients, important though it was, constituted only a small part of her responsibility. She had come also to give training to young Indian women in medicine.

Mrs. Thomas, who with her limited knowledge and facilities had tried to give some of her orphanage girls instruction in physiology and hygiene, was not the only missionary to vision the possibilities of such medical education for women. J. L. Humphrey, one of the two missionaries who had joined Butler in 1858, had been an even earlier pioneer. Traveling over the mountains to his first mission station, he had been sharply impressed with the need for some knowledge of medicine. When on furlough in 1863 he had studied medicine for a year in Albany, all the time necessary at that period to qualify for a medical degree, and, returning to Naini Tal, had taken charge of three dispensaries and a hospital. Then an old friend, Pundit Nand Kishore, a concerned and progressive Indian, had suggested to Humphrey that he train some native women in midwifery and diseases of women and children, and he had assumed the responsibility for some of the expense. Humphrey seized on the idea with alacrity, but the civil surgeons whom he consulted advised against it. Native women, in their opinion, "had not sufficient ability to grasp the subject, nor sufficient stamina and strength of character to practice with success."

Humphrey persisted, gaining the approval of his Methodist Annual Conference, also that of Sir William Muir, the Governor, who took the view that it was "of course an experiment, but worth trying."

The first class was opened in 1869, at just about the time a little group of women were holding their momentous meeting in Boston. It included ten women and six men, three of the former from the girls' orphanage in Bareilly. The female department of the government hospital in Naini Tal was placed under Dr. Humphrey's supervision to make possible the medical practice needed. The course was to extend through two hill seasons, from May to November.

"He's proving it can be done." Mrs. Thomas eagerly discussed the possibilities with Dr. Clara. "And I'm sure our girls are the equal, mentally, of those in Dr. Humphrey's class. I've been preparing them two years for your coming."

Clara began her medical class on the first day of March with fourteen girls from the orphanage and three married students. Several of them understood English well enough to act as her interpreters, and she was rapidly acquiring enough simple Hindustani to make communication not too difficult. She met with them every morning at six in one of the schoolrooms of the orphanage and spent one or two hours teaching them, beginning with the rudiments of anatomy, physiology, and *materia medica*. She found the girls eager to learn and intellectually keen, sometimes bafflingly so, as when she introduced her skeleton to give practical instruction in anatomy. The reaction of the English customs officer had been no more unpredictable.

"Oh, Miss Sahiba!" exclaimed one of the girls. "How will this woman rise in the resurrection with her flesh in America and her bones in India?"

Immediately Dr. Clara began grounding her class in practical experience. She appointed two members each week to look after the sick girls in the orphanage and to accompany her on her calls to the Christian village, occasionally into the homes of the city. As the calls increased, her days became more and more crowded. But each one brought new challenge, new sense of achievement, new glimpses of beauty as well as of ugliness, and she rose to each with a new anticipation.

"Just in front of our mission bungalow," she wrote home one day, "is a pretty little summer house, in shape like the Temple of Jupiter in Rome but of more perishable material, covered with trailing vines. We take our early breakfast, a cup of tea and a slice of toast, here every morning before going to work, then we have a late breakfast when the morning work is over."

"It was cool and pleasant this morning," she continued, "and after teaching my class and attending to the patients who had come to the bungalow, I drove to the city to visit some patients in their homes. Mrs. Thomas and one of my class girls went with me. After driving quite a distance through the main bazaar we turned into a narrow crooked street and came to the house where my patient lives. No wonder there is sickness in such unsanitary surroundings! The woman is very ill, a pathetic little person with one child, a little boy about three. But her willingness to submit to treatment and take the medicines prescribed for her makes her case more hopeful than many that come under our care.

"Next we visited a high-caste Hindu family consisting of a man and his wife and five married sons. The mother is a chronic invalid, and no wonder, trying to keep her five daughters-in-law in submission! Each of them has her separate apartment and cooks for herself and her husband. The mother has taken a fancy to me. Today she asked if I would marry a Hindu gentleman and said she would find me a husband. She thinks I'm not too bad looking and cannot see why I did not marry in my own country. Some of the young women are learning to read and sing hymns, but the mother is not willing for them to learn anything that would disturb their faith. In spite of her bigotry, she has some admirable qualities.

"On the way home we called at a house to see a young Mohammedan woman who has gradually been growing deaf. I found she had had a severe attack of earache a year ago and had applied some medicine on cotton to both ears. Examination showed a little ball of cotton encrusted with wax against the drum of each ear. The trouble was soon removed, and she was terribly grateful. They are very poor but insisted on our taking *pan* and sweetmeats."

Cool and pleasant, had she said? With the first of April the hot season burst like a blast from a gigantic furnace, the thermometer soaring to 105, 110, even occasionally to 120° Fahrenheit! Grass shriveled and turned an ugly yellow-gray. The parched earth cracked. Palm leaves crackled with a false sound of rain. The hot winds blowing from midmorning till late afternoon ground dust into pores, gritted the teeth, reddened the eyes, turned the hair to pale stiff bristles which resisted both comb and brush. Clara had harder work now discovering fresh beauty in India, but it was there: the delicate gold fretwork of gulmohur blossoms against a peacock-blue sky; the tangy sweetness of a perfect ripe mango; yes, even the shrill, fluty notes of the koels, splitting the predawn peace with their noisy crescendos, growing louder and louder as the weather grew hotter and hotter.

The bungalow was kept fairly comfortable. Fragrant grass mats fitted into the open doors on the side from which the wind came, and kept constantly wet, brought magical relief; and the great swaying punkahs, huge rectangles of cloth hung with ropes to the high ceilings and kept in flapping motion by patiently squatting peons, made the hottest hours bearable.

She soon learned the techniques of coping with the heat, rising very early and doing most of the day's work before the late-morning breakfast, after which she slipped into a dressing gown, rested, wrote letters, and prepared her lesson for medical class; bathing again, putting on fresh clothes which became sodden before the many hooks and eyes could be fastened; braving the still-intense heat of late afternoon to treat more waiting patients; driving into the city in the evening with Mrs. Thomas to visit more patients in their homes; only occasionally finding time for a brief cooling respite by driving through the cantonment or out into the country.

For these were the months of terrible and ever-increasing sickness, for cholera and smallpox, for opththalmia and other eye troubles caused by dust and heat and glare. Of these latter it seemed there would never be an end.

"Yesterday," she wrote home, "a woman was led into my room by her ayah. She had opththalmia, and both eyes were so swollen she could not open them. After two hours of treatment I sent her home rejoicing, both eyes open and the pain nearly gone." The days were not long enough to treat all the patients who came, to say nothing of those she had to visit in their homes. All her original doubts as to whether Indian women, especially those of caste, would come to the mission house had long since been removed. Patients crowded the verandahs, overflowed the small room which was all she had to use for consultation and examinations. Oh, for more space to work, a place where patients who needed longer and more intensive care could be kept and treated! Soon an even more daring possibility was finding expression in thought if not in words. *Oh, for a hospital!*

It was one of her new Indian friends, an intelligent and liberal government official, who did put the idea into words. "Some sort of home for the sick is just what we need," he said to her. "Native ladies would not hesitate to go to a hospital if it was superintended by a lady physician, and I am anxious that the first one should be in Bareilly."

By now Dr. Clara was visiting regularly in fifteen zenana homes. She found it necessary to make trips into the city nearly every day, both morning and evening. She was acquiring new knowledge herself, almost as fast as the girls in her medical class, who were already becoming proficient in diagnosis and treatment of simple ailments and in compounding and dispensing medicines. For she also had much to learn: how to diagnose the diseases peculiar to the climate and country; how to treat them, always keeping in mind the mode of life, which was often unfavorable to recovery; most of all, how to communicate. Oh, for some easier, faster way to learn the language!

It was during this first hot season that she was initiated into the splendor of Indian royalty, for in April Sir William Muir, Lieutenant Governor of the North West Provinces, visited Bareilly on his way to Naini Tal, seat of the British government in the hot season. He held a *durbar*, reception, for all the native chiefs of the Rohilkund District, and Lady Muir invited Mrs. Thomas and Dr. Swain to sit on the dais. Clara found the colorful scene almost blinding in its splendor. The delicately tinted turbans, the gold-embroidered robes of satin and velvet, royal purple, bright blue, green, and scarlet, of the imposing Hindu and Mohammedan dignitaries struck her speechless. Most impressive of all was the Nawab of Rampore, whose official seat was only forty miles from Bareilly. He arrived in a golden carriage drawn by fine horses and outriders, followed by a retinue of horsemen, state officials, and servants, a brilliant procession. Each of these dignitaries was presented in turn to Sir William, after which the Governor gave his official address. To Clara's surprise, her name was mentioned.

Said Sir William, "The women of Bareilly and adjoining towns in their time of need will now have the advantage of a woman physician who can enter their homes. I hope you will make use of the generous and skillful services of Dr. Clara Swain."

The next day both the Governor and the Nawab paid a visit to the mission. They inspected the orphanage and, to Clara's mingled delight and dismay, Sir William asked to visit a session of the medical class. Outwardly composed but inwardly quaking, for the girls had had only a few weeks' training, she conducted her usual class in anatomy and questioned them on the bones and muscles of the body. To her immense pride and relief they gave prompt and intelligent answers. Sir William, always interested in projects for human betterment, was delighted. Even the Nawab, noted for his violent opposition to Christianity, appeared impressed.

"I did not know that girls could learn so much," he was heard to admit grudgingly. To the amazement of all the missionaries, on his return to his tent he sent 1,000 rupees as a gift to the orphanage!

The coming of the rains in June brought relief from the heat if not from the demands on time and strength. The scorched lawns turned a beautiful emerald. Freshly washed leaves shone and glistened. Rain would fall for a few hours in torrents, then the sun would come out, hot as in May, filling the air with steam as from a boiling teakettle and sapping one's energy until, as Dr. Clara expressed it, "one feels that even a grasshopper is a burden." One day as she was coming home from the city she was caught in a sudden rainstorm. The carriage box soon filled with water, and she found herself in an impromptu foot bath, shoes, stockings, limbs, skirt, all plunged in a brimming, swirling tub. It was a warm day, but the thorough wetting resulted in an attack of rheumatism.

No time, however, to pamper her own little ailments! For the rains were worse breeders of disease even than the heat. The narrow lanes of the village and many of the town streets became running streams or stagnant pools, their unsanitary ditches and floating waste ideal spawning ground for mosquitoes and flies. Fevers flared afresh. Those ugly little parasites known as scabies burrowed under soft brown skins. Guinea worms from infected wells needled their way into water-soaked limbs and hips, to be carefully wound out, inch by painstaking inch, lest they break off and even more painful infection set in. And children, always the hapless victims of the "eye-fly season," developed gummed and sore and running eyes by the scores.

September, with its cessation of the rains, brought some relief, but with her practice steadily increasing, there was no diminution of patients. When her first year in India ended, her records showed that she had treated 70 families, visited in 250 homes of the city, prescribed for 1,225 patients at the mission house. Yet in spite of her much-acclaimed success, frustrations were far greater than triumphs. She was ministering to a few physical needs, yes, but how about the spiritual? Though she had tried to express in halting words as well as actions the love of God which was the motivation of all her work, what response had there been except polite attention, amused or stolid forbearance, an occasional wistful rejoinder like that of the patient who had said, "I wish there could be only one religion in India. Then we could all eat together without breaking our caste."

And the frustrations of her medical work! Long ago her morning clinics had outgrown the size of her living quarters. The homes of the sick were all too often destitute of the comforts needed for their recovery. What she needed, what she *must* have, was a hospital! Her eyes turned yearningly toward a fine open tract of land adjoining the mission compound.

"The Nawab's," she was told. "All that land, at least forty acres, belongs to that estate with its mansion."

What a place to build a hospital! At last she voiced the hope, timidly.

"Would—would he sell a little of it, do you think?"

"The Nawab? Sell his land to Christians! Not a chance!"

But as Dr. Clara continued to eye the empty space, the yearning changed to speculation, and the speculation to determination. Forty acres! If she could have only one of them!

4

January brought roses and other flowers in bloom, golden fruit on the orange and lemon trees, and the Annual Conference of the Methodist India Mission. That year of 1871 it met in Lucknow. For Dr. Clara Swain, in India now just a year, it was like a homecoming. Especially rewarding was her reunion with Isabella Thoburn. With keen delight she listened to the story of her friend's achievements in the educational field, saw the one-room house in the bazaar where, on April 18, 1870, Miss Thoburn had opened her school at sunrise.

"Not much of a beginning," she confessed. "Only six little

girls, and in the sight and dust of all the passers-by. The grandson of Joel Janvier stood guard outside, fearing opposition from the crowds, but we had no need of his stout bamboo stick. A few weeks later we moved into a better place, a vacant room in Dr. Waugh's bungalow, and from there to the rented house where we are now."

Then the two young women shared their secret ambitions, Clara for a piece of the Nawab's land to build her hospital, Isabella for a much bigger building for her school. Together they peered through the gate of a magnificent estate which had once been the house of the treasurer of the last king of Oudh and which now, Isabella had learned, was up for sale.

"Lal Bagh, it's called," she sighed. "Ruby Garden. And it's just what we need. But of course it's much too grand a place. I wouldn't dare ask the women in America for that much money. But one can dream!"

Little did either of them realize that before the year was out both of their dreams would be realized. Learning that Lal Bagh was to be sold for only one-fifth of its value because of the reduced circumstances of its owner, Isabella Thoburn was to borrow the money, drive up with her brother in a wagon with fourteen bags each containing 1,000 rupees, and take possession in the name of the Woman's Foreign Missionary Society. The Cincinnati branch of the society was delighted to pay the $7,000 which purchased this splendid property, a veritable palace, with its 9 acres of ground, to become in turn through the years the Lal Bagh Girls' School, the Lal Bagh Girls' High School, the Lucknow Woman's College, and, in 1903, Isabella Thoburn College.

Dr. Clara returned to Bareilly as unexpectant as her friend of what the year would bring. The hot season came again with all its added burdens and discomforts, but she accepted it with far more equanimity and felt a bit of condescending pity for those Westerners who deemed it necessary at the 100 degree mercury to scuttle off to the mountains. She was far too busy even to think of it.

Her zenana visits were constantly increasing. They followed much the same pattern, whether in a Hindu or a Mohammedan home. The gentleman of the house received them and did the honors. At first the woman sat on a mat in the corner, face covered, while her husband remained in the room. But after a few visits, when her husband left she would sit on a chair or stool, uncover her face, and talk freely. Though she still took along a companion on her visits, Dr. Clara could now make herself fairly well understood in Hindustani.

She always took pains to explain to the husband the details of Western medicine and customs relating to health. It would be much simpler, she told them, if their women could come to the mission house in the same manner that Indian men went to the government hospitals. She would promise that there would be no embarrassment, no breaking of caste, no danger of a man being present. And occasionally a Hindu or Mohammedan gentleman would break through the rigid shell of centuries and bring his wife to the dispensary, always, of course, in a tightly closed palanquin or curtained carriage. Once there, he would pace the verandah like a lion, constantly on the watch for an approaching stray male, fearful, even though the blinds were closed, lest someone might get a glimpse of his woman through an accidental crack.

The women were by no means so cautious. Once inside, they would roam eagerly from room to room, fingering the unfamiliar objects curiously and asking many questions.

Dr. Clara longed with all her vigorous and impatient concern to push back the curtains imprisoning the delicate little hothouse flowers in their palanquins and carriages, to pull away the muffling scarves which kept the self-effacing Hindu wives from lifting their faces to the sunlight and breathing purer air. Most of all she yearned to lift away the stifling *burkhas*, those cover-all tents of heavy white cotton in which Mohammedan women enveloped themselves from top of head to ankles every time they ventured out of their courtyards. Whenever she went through the bazaar and saw them, pathetic little figures like children in Halloween costume, she was consumed with helpless pity and frustration. No wonder Indian women were such ready victims of tuberculosis and other unhealthy humors and miasmas!

Yet, harnessing her own sweating body into tight stays on a May morning when the temperature gave promise of climbing to 110°, pulling on her ankle-length, long-sleeved dress over voluminous petticoats, and fastening a frilly lace collar high about her neck, she grinned at herself with wry humor in the glass.

"Slaves to custom, all of us!" she admitted sheepishly.

In June her problems of space were eased a little. A small house in the compound built for an Indian pastor but no longer used was put in order for patients brought in from the out-stations. The three tiny rooms seemed at first like a palace.

"What do you think!" she wrote home. "Who should come in this morning to occupy the first room but 'Abraham and Sarah'!"

Abraham was a converted Jew, a merchant who on one of his trips from Damascus had heard the Gospel preached in India and had accepted Christianity. Sarah, his wife, now a Bible woman, was the daughter of an Indian minister, formerly a Hindu. She was ill with fever. What a blessing to have a place for her to stay, so she need not be sent away!

The larger facilities increased rather than lessened Clara's work load, and by midsummer she was feeling the strain of the long months of continuous and grueling routine. A request came for her to go to the mountain station of Almora to care for one of the missionaries who had come there in search of health, and it offered a possible relief. ·

"You must go," insisted her friends. "He needs you, and you need a vacation."

"But—my patients need me too. How can I possibly desert them?"

"The girls in your class will conduct the dispensary. They're growing more efficient every day."

She yielded reluctantly, for she was desperately tired. The trip itself was no holiday. She left on the tenth of August, taking one of her servants with her for the first thirty miles; then sent him back with the conveyance and trusted herself to the native guides, traveling all night in a *dholi* carried by four men at a time, changing bearers every eight miles. She negotiated the next sixty miles with the aid of thirty-five men and three horses. It took thirty-one hours to reach the foot of the mountains. There she found fresh men sent down by the mission at Naini Tal, with a letter telling her how to proceed. At Naini Tal she received a hearty welcome from the missionaries. Here she was detained two days by heavy rains, reveling in the wonderful scenery of this nearly nine-thousand-foot elevation, its 122 varieties of ferns, its trees covered with mosses of every shade of green.

Twenty-four miles more! She mounted another conveyance, a contraption like a chair with a canopy, and a pole on each side with a sort of harness at each end fitting over men's shoulders. It took four men to carry it. Another carried her tin trunk on his back, a sixth her roll of bedding on his head, and a seventh carried her satchel. The first day they traveled twelve miles and at evening reached a government rest house, a long bungalow with a dozen Indian huts near it. A fire was already kindled, and soon her bedding was spread out to dry. Presently a cook arrived with a roasted chicken and hot potatoes. She lay down to sleep, unable to cast off a feeling of fear and desolation. Here she was, completely alone with these strange hill men, honest and reliable though they were, the only white person within a day's journey! Starting at seven the next morning, she was so overpowered by the magnificent scenery that she soon forgot all fear. Even the sheer drop beside the narrow footpath failed to shatter her awe-inspired delight, though it was somewhat shaken when a cow just ahead of them fell over the precipice. They reached the second rest house at noon and found lunch waiting. At Almora she found the missionary, Mr. Elliot, prostrated with tuberculosis. He lived only two weeks, during which time she nursed him faithfully. The following two weeks became a real vacation, a time of physical and spiritual renewal.

"Just imagine," she wrote her family in an ecstasy of exaltation, "a dozen mountains of silver reaching to the heavens, piercing the gold and crimson clouds of an eastern sky, glistening in rays of sun. Some are cone-shaped, some like pyramids, but all shaped with majestic grandeur. No wonder the Hindus bow and worship!"

She returned to Bareilly in September to plunge with renewed strength into a work which was becoming increasingly demanding. Within days the three rooms were overflowing with patients and as inadequate as the single room had once been. The mountains had stretched her vision and strengthened her determination as well as her energy. She was no longer fearful of attempting the impossible.

"We need a hospital," she announced boldly. "And the best place for it is next door on the Nawab's estate."

"But—that's impossible. They say a Mohammedan ruler never sells landed property that belongs to his inheritance!"

"He hates Christianity. He's even made a boast that no Christian would ever dare enter the gates of his city of Rampore!"

In spite of all objections Clara continued to insist stubbornly and to anyone who would listen, "We *must* have a hospital. And I want it on the Nawab's estate."

One of the people who heard her was the Commissioner of

Bareilly, Mr. Drummond, who had shown great interest in the medical work. The Nawab was coming to Bareilly soon on business, and the Commissioner promised to speak to him about the possibility of purchase and find out if a request could be made.

"All we would need is one acre," Clara told him eagerly.

Late in September she learned that the Nawab had invited representatives from the mission to visit his city, saying that he would arrange for their journey if he knew what day they were coming. Clara was jubilant.

On the morning of October 3 the party set out, Mr. and Mrs. Thomas, Clara, and an Indian Christian, a convert from Islam, who understood royal etiquette. The Nawab, through his prime minister, had made all the arrangements. A fine carriage was sent to convey them the forty miles to Rampore, with twenty-four horses, so that at each of the six stages of the journey there were four fresh horses. The carriage was an ancient but magnificent conveyance, adorned with much gold and crimson and equipped with coachmen, two grooms, and an outrider. As they approached the city, three cavalrymen rode out to meet them and escorted them to their lodgings, a house just outside the city maintained for European travelers. Here they found waiting a large troop of bustling servants, a huge breakfast of twenty-four dishes—fish, flesh, fowl, eggs, vegetables—and Mr. and Mrs. Parker, who had come from Moradabad to join them. After breakfast, which Clara barely tasted, all knelt in prayer, asking the Father who had led them this far to still guide them as they came to the crucial moments of their mission.

"Please, God," breathed Clara silently, "unbend his heart. Let him give us just an acre! It's not for us, but for the women and children who need it so much."

Presently the Nawab sent a messenger saying that he would not be able to see them that day since he was engaged in special prayers. But he provided numerous features for their day's entertainment: two music boxes, a band of trained athletes, a cast of players who performed a clever burlesque on English officials, which showed remarkable keenness of imitation and appreciation of the foibles and defects of human beings. After a dinner so sumptuous that they lost count of all the dishes, two carriages were sent to take them for an evening drive to a country palace set in the midst of a magnificent garden containing a lake of clear fresh water.

Clara could hardly bear the suspense. The spiced delicacies might have been sawdust. Was the Nawab prolonging their hopes, feeding them all these sweet preliminaries, merely to dash them, like an executioner stuffing his victims before the hanging?

The next morning early the carriages were sent again. Now surely they would be taken to the Nawab! But, no, they were driven to several more palaces and gardens and given more exhibitions of grandeur. Finally, however, the main palace loomed before them. As they entered the gates, five royal elephants, gaily painted and bedecked, saluted smartly by lifting their trunks and touching their foreheads. And at last they were escorted into the royal presence of His Highness Mahomed Kallub Ali Khan, Bahadur, Nawab of Rampore.

With great trepidation they mounted the steps. The ruler received them graciously and motioned them to seats at his right, Mrs. Thomas first in a chair with gorgeously embroidered upholstery, Clara next, then Mrs. Parker and the gentlemen, then the prime minister and his chief magistrates. His Highness smoked his hookah, meanwhile conversing pleasantly about matters of a general nature. Finally the prime minister approached the royal seat, spoke in a low tone to the Nawab, and when he nodded bowed to Mr. Thomas. "You may speak. His Highness will now listen to your request."

Clara's heart almost stopped beating. She tried to lean forward far enough to scan the features under the resplendent headdress, but the dark profile was enigmatic. Only an acre! she prayed silently. Surely he can spare that!

Mr. Thomas rose and cleared his throat. He began his speech, which he had been carefully preparing for a week in his best Hindustani. If His Highness pleased, the mission would like to secure by legal process, on whatever terms His Highness might choose, a small portion of the estate adjoining the mission premises in Bareilly, for the purpose of building a hospital for women and children. For some months now Miss Dr. Swain, the woman physician from America, had been rendering service with excellent results but very poor facilities. It was possible that some news of her work might have reached the exalted ears of His Highness. If they could only buy a very small portion—

Before he could finish, the Nawab gestured him to silence. "No, no, the land is not for sale."

Clara's heart sank. She was almost too numb with disappointment to absorb what followed.

"But I *give* it to you. Take it, take it." The Nawab waved his hand. "Take the whole estate. I give it with pleasure for such a noble purpose."

Clara slowly emerged from numbness, all her senses prickling. Had she heard aright? Her Hindustani was still badly deficient. Then she saw the faces of her friends, startled but joyful, heard Mr. Thomas, obviously at a loss for words, stammering his gratitude.

Again the Nawab stopped him. "There are two merits in this gift," he continued, "one for myself and one for you, Sahib Thomas, for taking so much interest in this charitable work for the women of my country."

The missionary again sought for expressions of gratitude. "Then we may have permission to found the first hospital for women in all India in His Highness' name?"

The Nawab bowed. "As you think proper, so do." His general, he added, would come to Bareilly on Monday to make out the papers and put them in formal possession. Almost at once he rose, bowed, and left the room. "I shall be glad," announced the prime minister, "to show our honored guests some of the rooms of the palace."

They trailed after him through several sumptuous apartments, murmured admiration of the elaborate carvings, the priceless Persian carpets, the beautiful furniture. But, though the women were disappointed not to be taken to the women's apartments, all could hardly wait until they were out of the palace, finished with the panoply of officialdom, carriages, footmen, elephants, and were back in the guest house.

"Think of it! It's too good to be true!"

"Forty whole acres of land—! And a house!"

"Not just a house, a mansion—you might even call it a *palace!*"

"It's because of you, Dr. Swain, of course. Everybody for forty miles around has heard of the wonderful work you are doing."

"It's the work of God," said Clara quietly. "Only He could have brought such a miracle to pass. He has given it in answer to prayer. Let us thank Him!"

5

This was December, 1871. As soon as the transfer of papers was completed, the new owners examined their property. The estate consisted of 42 acres of land with two good wells, an extensive garden, and a fine old *kothi*, mansion, badly in need of repairs. Undoubtedly the Nawab expected them to use this for a hospital, but its style was unsuitable for use by Indian ladies with their ideas of seclusion. However, Clara saw immediately that it could be used very well until other buildings could be provided.

"Some of the gentlemen of the city were pleased also," she wrote home on December 22, "and they promised assistance. So I resolved to circulate a paper stating our plans and asking for contributions. I shall be able to report to Conference next month that we already have seven hundred rupees!"

The *kothi* was immediately repaired, and on the first day of January, 1872, Clara moved into it with Miss Sparkes, who was head of the education department of the orphanage. It was fashioned of brick and oriental in architecture, a big, rectangular, two-storied building, with two projecting rectangles in front, a broad flight of stairs between them leading to the second story. There were many arches and wide verandahs, an impressive semicircular tower at one end, at the other a substantial wing flanked by a staircase, and, to crown all, a beautiful flat roof surrounded by a parapet.

Clara and Miss Sparkes occupied the upper story, and for the present one of the lower rooms was set aside for a dispensary. Others were used by various servants and Indian helpers. It was a luxurious building, which Dr. Butler immediately dubbed "The King's Palace."

But for Clara it was only a stepping stone. At the Annual Conference held in Moradabad later in January she was ready to present a building plan for a dispensary, worked out with the assistance of a native architect. It would contain six rooms: a clinic room where patients would be received and prescribed for, an operating room back of it, an office in the right wing, a room in the opposite wing designed for a lecture room when she should have another medical class, and two small bathrooms. Feeling sure that the Woman's Foreign Missionary Society in America would respond to the need financially, she laid the plans before the Conference building committee, which approved them. In subsequent weeks arrangements were completed, and by May she was able to write home that the dispensary building was actually under way. Mr. Judd, who with his wife was now in charge of the orphanage, was supervising the work.

"From my window I can see quite a little army of men, women, and children, all very busy in their own estimation, though I can see that now and then some of them linger over their loads or sit down behind a pile of boards to take a whiff from the hookah. They call their hookah smoking 'taking a drink' from the pipe."

But the building program was by no means her sole occupation during these hot spring months of 1872. All through March she spent two to three hours each day with her class of medical students, in preparation for presenting them for examination as fourth-grade doctors. On April 10, thirteen of her class passed their final examinations in the presence of two civil surgeons and the Rev. Dr. Johnson of their own mission. They acquitted themselves well and were granted certificates for practice in all ordinary diseases. One went to Moradabad to practice medicine, another to Almora, where her husband had charge of the commissariat in the leprosy colony. Eleven of them left the orphanage to marry. Five remained in the compound, since their husbands were students in the new theological seminary which had been opened on April 1, with Dr. D. W. Thomas as its first principal. To these Clara hoped to give further instruction in hospital work. Rebecca, one of Dr. Humphrey's class who had come to her at the close of last year's rainy season, was now her assistant in the dispensary.

"My third year in India!" Clara wrote with much satisfaction on June 10. "The weather has been very hot for the past six weeks, hotter than I have known it. My patients sometimes send me food and sweetmeats, and one has just sent me a jar of mangoes pickled in mustard oil, mango preserves, and other delicacies. Another native friend lately sent me a milch buffalo. I already had a cow sent by an old patient, and I had also bought one, so now we have quite a dairy. Our cream is churned in a bottle and worked over with a spoon, which makes it very good."

Work on the dispensary proceeded at what seemed to Clara a crawling pace. Her plans for the adjoining hospital were completed and its building sanctioned by the Woman's Society, as well as approved by the Conference in India. But being in India, she tried to cultivate the patience which was inherent in a country of ambling cows, jogging bullock carts, human beasts of burden, and a people constantly and courageously battling the hazards of heat or cold, droughts, floods, disease, insufficient food, a poverty which it was impossible to make her comfortable friends and relatives back home understand. She did not often try. Most of her letters were bright, cheery, filled with interesting, homely details, like the one dated on December 22.

"Miss Sparkes and I are giving the Christmas dinner this year. There are three missionary families here, the Scotts, the Judds, and us. One of my patients has sent me two fine turkeys, and a Mohammedan friend has sent three chickens for our *Bara Din* (Great Day), as they call it. We also have peas, lettuce, cauliflower, and other vegetables, and such delicious oranges! Our trees are loaded.

"Three men work in our garden. The *mali*, head gardener, gets about $2.50, the other two, say, $1.75 a month. They also have fruits and vegetables, probably take some to sell. Right now it is the season for custard apples and guavas.

"It's a lovely country to live in after you get used to it, perfect for six months after the rainy season. We are just beginning to have a fire in our grate in the evening. The sunshine is still so bright it's painful to the eyes.

"The dispensary building is going up gradually. I am directing it now. The hospital buildings will be begun soon after Conference, which meets here in Bareilly January 16th. We shall entertain all the ladies of the W.F.M.S. and two missionary families."

It was another May, with the thermometer soaring again to 120°, when the new dispensary was ready for dedication. The attending dignitaries sweated in long coats and turbans, Prince Alberts and high collars and flowing ties, long mutton-leg sleeves, voluminous skirts, tight waists, and neck ruffs. Sweltering on the platform under the leafy *pandal* built for the occasion, Clara's joyful thanksgivings were tainted by a slight envy of the lesser but more comfortable guests thronging the compound in scant loincloths, blouseless saris, or, if youth permitted, devoid of all encumbrance.

But the new dispensary compensated for all discomfort. Daz-

[46]

zling in its fresh color wash, the tiled roofs of its projecting front and side porches supported by sturdy square posts interspersed with graceful columns, it was a dream fulfilled.

"It's strong enough and fine enough to last a hundred years!" she exulted, little knowing that she was speaking prophecy.

It was put to immediate and satisfying use. Opened each morning except Sunday at six, within a month it was some days serving as many as sixty patients. Two of her medical class were valuable assistants, Emma Baker, who had married a theological student, and Jane Paul. Rebecca, who had come to her from Dr. Humphrey's class and had been for some time her loyal fellow worker, rounded out the medical team. Of course, Indian Bible women were also in constant attendance, and on the back of each prescription—written in three languages, Hindi, Persian, and Roman-Urdu—was a helpful scripture text.

But the fulfilled dream was immediately replaced by another. Impatiently Clara watched the slow progress of the adjoining hospital buildings, often wishing she could instill some of her own driving energy into the plodding bullocks dragging loads of brick or pulling the heavy wheel along the narrow circular channel of the cement mixer; into the creeping procession of men and women, boys and girls, with their enormous headloads of dirt, bricks, crushed rock, bamboo stagings, window frames; into the squatting figures patiently pounding out bits of rock by hand. Yet, noting the lean bodies, the protruding rib cages, the unmistakable evidences of ill health and undernourishment, she was as often constrained to bid them not to hurry, to please get out of the hot sun into the shade of the big mango tree and rest.

The plan for the hospital was to build as much as was needed now and no more, using Indian modes of architecture as far as possible, so the patients would feel at home. It would be like an Eastern *sarai*, inn, only with greater conveniences and comforts. A piece of ground 250 by 175 feet was enclosed by an 8-foot wall. At the front of the enclosure stood the dispensary building. At the right of the dispensary within the enclosure was a row of dormitories one story high, extending nearly the whole length of the wall and across the end. Opposite the dispensary was another row, more commodious, for patients needing larger rooms. Other accommodations would be built as needed. A front verandah extended the whole length of the buildings, with another at the back which would serve as kitchens. The rooms were 12 by 14 feet. In the center of the enclosure was a fine large well, where each modern Rebecca could come and draw water for herself, using her own bucket and rope as was the custom of caste people. Later there would be roses, bougainvillea, and other shrubbery.

"At last!" rejoiced Clara when the new hospital was finally ready for use on January 1, 1874. It was the beginning not only of a new year but of a new era, for the institution then opened was the first hospital for women in all of Asia.

Her fears lest Mohammedan and high-caste Hindu women would not come for in-patient treatment were unfounded. The rooms were soon occupied by Hindus, Mohammedans, and Indian Christians, all in separate apartments. Nor did the patients come alone! A poor woman would bring her child and sometimes her mother-in-law or a widowed sister. It would be a disgrace for a high-caste woman to come with such a humble entourage, so her husband would accompany her, bringing not only their family and several servants, but a yoke of oxen, a horse and conveyance, a goat, their food and cooking utensils, and often articles of furniture. No attempt was made to limit the number of people or their accoutrements, for it was felt that exposure of the whole family to a Christian environment was of the utmost value. Since each patient supplied her own food and it was cooked on the verandah space adjoining her room, the additional numbers caused the hospital no expense. The immediate and eager response of all classes to the new service was unmistakable proof of the benefits a zenana hospital and dispensary could render.

Each morning the compound became a showcase of motley vehicles and dress: bullock carts bringing a whole family with most of their possessions; *ekkas*, carefully covered with canopies and draped with cotton curtains; perhaps a pretentious *rath* drawn by beautiful white oxen; a palanquin or two; little *dholis*, like string cots, so small that it was a puzzle how a woman could sit in them, though often Clara saw not only a woman emerging but two or three children as well. Other women would come on foot, sometimes leading an old or a blind person. There was an even greater diversity of dress: Hindu women in bright silk or dingy cotton saris; Mohammedan women wrapped from crown to ankles in *burkhas;* both Hindus and Mohammedans in *chadars,* a sort of sheet worn over the head, thrown over the shoulder and pulled closely about the face; neatly clad, white-robed Christian women; the orphanage girls in their gingham skirts and white *chadars*.

Often the Indian women had their *dholis* brought into the dispensary room and remained in them while being examined and treated, with one curtain thrown aside while they received their prescriptions. One morning there came a Mohammedan lady in a conveyance so large and imposing that it could not be brought into the room. Unwilling to expose his young and pretty wife to the dangers of male scrutiny, the husband was much perplexed, for there were several men on the road in front of the building. Clara assured him that an umbrella was quite sufficient to protect her from spying eyes, but he was not satisfied until *two* umbrellas were brought and held over her.

So shy were many of the patients that at first, even with her increasing mastery of the language, Clara found it difficult to examine them. They refused to let her feel their pulses or look at their tongues. But, like the women she visited in the zenanas, they soon lost their shyness.

She soon had to make many visits to patients in their homes. In fact, looking back over the year 1874, she found there were fifty new families on her list, representing all castes, all levels of wealth and poverty. Occasionally those in moderate circumstances would offer her a fee for each visit, but most of them were not able. A few sweets on a leaf, a coin worth less than a penny, perhaps a few oranges were the usual offerings. Sometimes in a wealthier home she would receive a substantial fee for a first visit, the husband evidently feeling that one gold mohur ought to insure for his family permanent help. All the fees were used to defray medical expenses.

Always she attempted to combine her medical service with education and evangelism. Three members of the first medical class now worked with her as Bible women, Nellie Bain, Libbie Husk, and Harriet Richardson, all of them married to theological students. Harriet's courtship was unique. Joshua Soule, one of the Indian students, came to Miss Sparkes, who had charge of the orphanage, saying that he wanted an educated wife but one of light skin and attractive appearance. A few of the older girls were together in the compound, and Miss Sparkes pointed out one or two whose marriage arrangements had not been made, but the young theolog found none of them to his taste. Just then Harriet crossed the compound and joined the group.

"There!" exclaimed Mr. Soule. "That is the girl I will marry."

He was more than satisfied when he heard the girl's name and attainments. Miss Sparkes told him he could come in the afternoon for his answer. When consulted, Harriet was agreeable to the arrangement, so that afternoon the future husband and wife were introduced.

The visitors found it hard to persuade Hindu women to learn to read. They said their religion forbade it. When Clara tried to persuade one patient, the woman said, "When I was quite young I began to learn, and after a few days my brother died. Our priest and all our friends said it was because I was learning to read, so I stopped and have never dared to begin again."

A few days later as Clara was passing her house, the woman called her in. She was in great trouble. Weeping, she explained that her husband was making arrangements to take another wife. Would the Miss Sahiba go to the magistrate and get him to forbid her husband to do it, for they were very poor?

Though this was impossible, Clara promised to talk to the husband and ask him to wait for a while. "If you will consent to learn," she said to the woman, "we will come often to see you, and bring you books to read, and you will learn to keep the house tidy. When your husband finds you are eager to improve and can talk with him intelligently, he will be pleased, and perhaps he will care more for you."

"*Achchha,* good! I will learn!" exclaimed the woman with new hope. "When will you send someone to teach me?"

She was a keen and zealous pupil, always ready to display her new book knowledge and astonishing Clara and the Bible women by the swift improvement in appearance of both her house and person. Her husband also became interested in her progress and had the walls and courtyard of the house whitewashed and the floor laid with brick. He soon abandoned the idea of taking another wife.

Another pupil-patient, become so expert in reading that she was studying the Old Testament in Hindi, said one day, "Before I began to learn I used to go from house to house to hear my neighbors talk and see their jewels, but now I have no time for that. I hurry to get my work done, and if any of the neighbors come in to talk I feel impatient for them to go. The stories in my book are better than any they can tell."

Her home, formerly untidy, showed the change in her mental condition. Now it was spotless. Her husband, an educated man, had believed his wife (all women, in fact) incapable of anything beyond cooking and attending to the servants. Now his affection and pride were a joy to see.

One day a bright-faced little woman came to the dispensary closely concealed in her covered conveyance. After she received her medicine she inquired which road led to the railroad station. Startled, Clara asked why she wished to know.

Eyes sparkling, the woman laughingly replied, "It will be a long time, perhaps, before my husband will let me come out again, and I am determined to see the railroad carriages and the engines and things that the English people talk about. I will bribe my servants, and my husband will never know about it."

Then there was the Bengali patient who stayed for some days in the hospital. "May I not come and stay awhile every year," she asked Clara wistfully, "even if I am not sick? I like to go out in the garden and go to your bungalow. I am not afraid to go out here, but if I should walk out at home my neighbors would think badly of me. I do not care to see fine houses or anything that man has made. I love the trees and flowers and the pretty green fields."

Later when Clara visited this woman in her home, she found it clean and orderly. There were pots of rare geraniums in the courtyard, which she cherished more carefully than her jewels. While this woman was in the hospital, her husband, an educated, cultured member of the liberal Hindu Brahmo Samaj, came to visit her. Clara and other Christians were able to talk with him about religion. He was accustomed to spend much time in prayer, and each morning he arose early and drove out to a mango grove to pray.

The art of healing, Clara was beginning to discover, had other tools than pills and potions and scalpels, even than pure water and fresh air and sanitation. A book could be one of them. Or a friendly talk with another woman who showed genuine concern. Or just a walk in a garden.

6

"Come with me for a morning," Clara wrote home on March 17, 1875. "First we will visit the hospital patients. In the first room at the right as we enter we find a Mohammedan woman who has been here some weeks. She has been very ill, but Allah has heard her prayers and now she is almost well enough to go home. In the next room is a poor woman from a village brought in in low condition. She is a native Christian, too ill to be benefited, but we can give her nourishing food and care. Next is a young Eurasian girl deceived by the brother of the woman with whom she lived. Her mistress brought her here for her confinement. She is a leper, but goes about everywhere.

"There are two Hindu women in the next room. They come from the country. One is a bright young widow who has come with her sister-in-law who is under treatment. This woman's fingers are covered with jewels, which is remarkable for a widow, but they may have been put on just for this occasion. The next patient is a lovely Christian woman from Cawnpore, the daughter of a native minister. She is well educated but delicate.

"Now we will visit the European ward. In one room is a woman from Burma, in the next, one from Naini Tal. The third room is occupied by a lady from Allahabad, the wife of a civil engineer.

"Now we come to our Bible woman, Mrs. Sheahy. It was such a trial when her eyesight began to fail. A surgeon from the Bengal infantry has just performed a successful cataract operation.

"Now let us go to the dispensary. See, here is our clinic room and back of it the operating room; this is the office, and the room corresponding to it in the opposite wing is the lecture room.

"The crowd here this morning is mostly from the city, but I see a few villagers. See how patiently they wait, attentive to the Bible reading. Rebecca is a great help to me here. She prescribes for the more simple cases, and the more serious ones will wait to be examined and treated on my return from the city. The people are never in a hurry.

"Now our carriage is at the door. The half-mile drive through the bazaar is interesting. We pass through a large gateway and turn to the right through a lane hardly wide enough for our carriage. Our first call is on a Mohammedan woman too ill to come to the dispensary. Her house is not as neat as some of our Hindu patients'. Her husband is a mechanic earning four or five annas, perhaps ten cents a day. 'Have you taken the medicine as I directed?' I ask. 'Yes, Miss Sahiba, I took the powders as you told me, and I ate the papers too.' We must not let her see us smile. 'I am glad you took the powders, but it is not necessary to eat the papers. How about the fever?' 'My fever came on as usual, but not so strong.' We give her some more powders.

"Across the street is another patient, the wife of a wealthy Hindu banker, ill with an incurable disease. She is resigned to her fate but begs me to come often. 'It is a comfort to talk with someone who knows how I suffer.' Her husband is kind, but she has never had a child, and he has taken a second wife. However, his first wife is the one he loves.

"Now we go to another part of the city, into a low-caste home. This boy is recovering from smallpox. We were not called early enough, as happens so often. His condition is serious. He will never be able to wait on himself.

"Now we walk back to the entrance of the lane where we left the carriage. We stop to see a little Mohammedan girl with typhoid fever. See, she's just a mere skeleton, but, oh, so determined to live! She's well married, and her people are anxious for her recovery. She needs better care and air, but her family will not bring her to the hospital.

"Here is another case nearby, a young married woman seriously ill, but I hope she will recover for the sake of her child, so precious, her first-born son. She's low caste. I love to tell them that God loves them just as much as he does a Brahmin.

"One more visit. Here there are several in the family suffering from an epidemic. It's a pity we don't have time to stop to answer their many questions. But it's now ten-thirty, and we must go home to breakfast. Then there will be all the dispensary patients to attend to. All this time they will have been waiting so patiently!"

Clara had never been strong physically, and by the end of her fifth year the arduous pace had begun to take its toll. These were days long before missionaries gained an annual reprieve in the hill stations from both the enervating heat and the year's intensive activity. Though she was due for a furlough at the end of five years, there was no other doctor to take her place, and she could not think of leaving. Even though often physically unfit for work, she continued the grueling daily round: medical classes, hospital rounds, dispensary, calls, more dispensary, brief siesta, more calls, more hospital rounds, occasionally more calls at night. Her duties were not only medical. They included supervision of all zenana work, both educational and religious.

During her sixth year she treated 1,929 patients, gave out just a few less than 5,000 prescriptions. Forty homes in the city were visited twice each week. There were more high-caste patients than formerly, also more paying patients. Fees during the year amounted to $566.

"My best year in India," she summed it up with gratitude.

But early in 1876 news came that the Society in America was sending a replacement, and in March she sailed home for her first furlough, arriving in time to attend the seventh annual meeting of the Woman's Foreign Missionary Society in Washington. Though her health was so frail that she was able to be present at only one or two meetings, it was reported that "every hand was extended to give her a kindly greeting; every heart beat with gratitude as they looked upon her face."

Dr. Lucille H. Green—"Lovely Lucille," as her friends liked to call her—sailed for India on January 1, 1876, reaching Bareilly in March. A graduate of the Woman's Medical College in Philadelphia, she was young but mature in character and culture. With the help of the faithful Rebecca Gowan and Bertha Sigler, she was able to continue the medical work without interruption. Bertha was one of Clara's greatest joys and triumphs. Brought to the orphanage a wild, screaming, frightened little creature of six, she had finally been subdued and put in school. Each year she had improved, becoming one of the brightest and most eager pupils. During her last year in India Clara had placed her in the dispensary, where she had learned to write neat and accurate prescriptions.

Dr. Lucille's radiant devotion was an ingredient of her "loveliness."

"It is early morning, fresh and sweet," she enthused in her first year's report. "The skies have forgotten all about the rain last year, and surely are brighter and bluer than the skies at home. We enter the dispensary and receive the graceful salutation of the country from my two assistants and several already seated on the floor, whom I recognize as Christians no less by their clean white clothes than by their bright faces. My first patient is the wife of a rich merchant. Her skirt is of crimson silk, with a pretty pattern of glistening leaves; a rich purple *chadar* is thrown gracefully across her chest and shoulders; a tiny round cap fits closely, and from its edge falls a long full silk garment which covers her entirely. She enters the room closely veiled, but finding only women here, throws aside her covering, revealing a bright face, and talks with freedom.

"The next one is a Mohammedan woman, her dress consisting of pants full at the waist and fitting closely at the ankles. A veil completes her costume. Next is a mother with two weak and puny children. The branch that she carries is to prevent me from exorcising an 'evil spirit into them.' Fresh from an American hospital, one's first impulse is to order eggs, milk, and meat for them, but a glance at their dress and closely shaven heads tells us they are Hindus. I must call my wits to aid me in securing a substitute.

"The next woman walks in with a half-defiant air, evidently determined to find out if I know anything. Without a word she reaches out her hand and expects me with my finger on her pulse to 'tell her all things she ever did,' but I have learned not to feel the pulse of such inquiring individuals.

"It seems strange that so few of these women know their age, but the majority when asked spread out their hands in a helpless way: 'How should I know?' or 'The news has not yet reached me.'

"I hear the tinkling of bells outside, and in a moment more the clanking of anklets and jewelry as two more zenana women enter. Do you notice how much cleaner they are and how much more jewelry, how much larger and fuller their veils? These are insignia of wealth and rank. Then come some hill women, tall and peculiar in appearance, their dress always of dark blue, full pants with a tunic of silk. And here is a Mohammedan gentleman with his wife and child. You may offer her a seat, but she will not take it while her lord remains standing, neither will she speak in his presence. If he will step outside a moment, she will talk freely, and you will quite lose your heart over her pretty, fresh young face, lustrous dark eyes, and winning expression."

During her service at Bareilly Dr. Lucille lost her heart over more than patients, for in 1877 she was married to the Reverend

Mr. Cheney and moved to Naini Tal, where she converted one of the closets in her house into a little dispensary and received patients there. A year later she contracted cholera and became the first medical missionary of her church to die in service. Her successor in Bareilly was another woman doctor married to a missionary, Mrs. Julia Lore McGrew, for Clara Swain was still too ill to return to her post.

Mrs. McGrew, a graduate in medicine of the University of Michigan in 1873, had been working with Mrs. Parker in the Methodist mission in Moradabad. From the beginning her work in Bareilly was beset with difficulties. Early in the rainy season the mission premises were flooded, deluging the orphanage and destroying much property. The floods were followed with sickness, diarrhoea and dysentery. Then in August cholera appeared among the orphanage girls, continuing for three weeks, during which nine out of the sixteen girls died. But the orphanage was soon filled again with famine victims, accounting for forty-eight of the sixty-one patients she treated that first year in the hospital. One of her helpers, Bertha, died of tuberculosis. But the work went on despite all difficulties, and the following year she had thirty-three new medical students, treated over 2,000 patients in the dispensary and seventy-eight in the hospital, visited in eighty-nine homes and gave over 4,600 prescriptions.

Meanwhile Clara Swain was impatiently marking time at her home in Castile, New York. Though her strength was not fully restored even after three years, she was determined to go back in spite of the concern of friends and relatives.

"I must respond to the tremendous need," she told one of them. "I would rather go back even if it means dying on the field."

She sailed alone, leaving New York on September 27, 1879, and reaching Port Said on the twelfth day from Liverpool. This time the ship rode through the Suez Canal, taking two days for the ninety-mile trip at six miles an hour. On one bright moonlit night it anchored in the lake not far from where it was said the Israelites had crossed.

Arriving in Bombay thirty-nine days after leaving New York, she found a telegram of welcome from Isabella Thoburn, and a few days later she met her friend in Lucknow. After joyfully embracing the newcomer, one of Miss Thoburn's associates, an

Indian woman, fled to another room, where Miss Thoburn found her crying.

"Oh, Miss Sahiba," she wept, "do you not see how Miss Swain has changed? If you go to America, I am afraid you will come back looking as she does!"

"The great cry is, 'How thin you have grown!'" wrote Clara to her friends back home. "I never dreamed so many people were interested in the amount of flesh that covers my bones. I tell them that I am the same. It is only the house I live in that has grown smaller and taken on a look of age and dilapidation, but the tenant within is stronger and wiser and better fitted to work among them.

"It's so good to be back! This is my country, the land to which my Father has called me; these are my people, these simple-hearted people living in their mud huts, with clothing hardly enough to cover their nakedness, with the spark of immortality imparted to them by the Divine Being buried so deep under their superstition and idolatry. I must, *must* help them!"

It was even more blessedly exciting to be back in Bareilly and, once the McGrews had left for their new appointment in Cawnpore, to occupy her own house and plunge into the work again. There were changes. A new church had been built near the seminary across the road from the hospital compound, commodious and beautiful in its fresh color wash, even though its fine tower was still empty of clock and bell. For ten years the mission had suffered for lack of a good place of worship, and with the others she rejoiced in the addition.

She worked through the winter with renewed energy, but with the hot season, which came early, her strength was soon exhausted, and she was forced to take a few weeks' rest in Naini Tal, a holiday which ended in tragedy.

She was getting ready to return to the plains when on September 16 the rains started, continuing for two days with increasing violence. On the second night she awoke about one, so uneasy that she got up and lighted a lamp; then, finding nothing wrong, left it lighted and went back to bed. A few minutes later the window in her room burst open, letting in a rush of water and shale which extinguished the lamp and plunged the room into darkness. Managing to wade and grope her way to the door, she found it stuck fast from the jar of the crash and the rush of shale, but after a terrifying struggle she got it open, fumbled her way through the living room and out the front door.

Here wind and rain almost swept her off her feet, but by hugging the wall she managed to reach the next apartment. There Mrs. Mudge was trying to rescue her child from the rushing water and had only one lamp. In the next room Miss Layton and Miss Sparkes, who had also come to the hills for a rest, were trying to salvage their things and could not help her. However, Mrs. Thomas in the room beyond was able to give her a lamp, and Clara rushed back to her rooms. Water was running out of the front door in a small river, some of her things floating with it. She caught what she could, then pushed her way in to see what else she could rescue. It was little enough. Most of her personal possessions were buried under shale and water. Fortunately, she had put her watch in its case on the mantel near the head of her bed, and she rescued it gratefully.

But this was only the beginning. Men came to help them all down the hill to the mission house where the Bucks were living. Here Mrs. Buck gave them dry garments; but just as they were beginning to feel a little comfortable, news came that this house also was in danger and the Bucks must pack everything possible. All set to work pulling up carpets, packing Mr. Buck's library, piling articles into baskets, until suddenly water began pouring into the house and the whole group hurried down the hill to the mission chapel, where they found many of the Indian Christians gathered. Huddled together on the verandah, the missionaries wondered what they would do if the water came there, for the chapel was not far below the mission house. By now it was daylight, and at least they need not cope with darkness.

"The assembly room over by the lake," suggested Clara, always the clear-headed one in an emergency. "That will be as safe a place as any."

Even as she spoke she looked up toward the hill back of the sanatorium and noticed trees shaking. In another instant down came the hill, demolishing everything in its path, a large hotel, a department store, and the assembly rooms. Within two minutes not a trace of any building could be seen. The missionaries stared in horror. They had just seen thousands of dollars' worth of mission property in the finest locality in Naini Tal—three houses, a schoolhouse, a large building occupied by Indian Christians, and a number of servants' houses—wiped out of existence! And the human toll, both Indians and Europeans, what must that be! But there was no time to think of losses, human or material.

"Get out!" shouted Mr. Thomas above the confusion. "Everybody leave, *now!*"

They all started down the road, cut so deeply into gorges that they were often wading waist-deep in water. Finally they reached the outlet of the lake, but here they were told the bridge was in danger, so they could go no further. They took shelter in a house near the European hospital, where they spent the night. But there was no rest for Clara, for she worked ceaselessly helping other doctors minister to the wounded and dying being brought into the yard.

In the morning Sir Henry Ramsay, the Commissioner of the district, sent word that the missionaries could occupy a cottage of his on the other side of the lake. Gladly they took possession and soon had most of the Indian Christians, those who had survived, gathered with them in safety. Two hundred and fifty Indians and fifty Europeans had been buried with the ruined buildings. Gratefully, but with little sense of satisfaction, the missionaries surveyed their remnants of possessions salvaged from the debris. Clara did no complaining because the roads prevented her leaving on the day intended. Even the loss of her valuable instruments, her box of medicines, the beautiful leather medical case which she had bought in Boston, brought only fleeting regret. She was glad enough to be alive.

And, when the time came, she was glad to be back on the plains, where there were no hills to fall. But there had been disastrous floods here also, for the Ganges had risen and swept away thousands of homes, demolished hundreds of villages. It would be weeks before the trains could run.

"Poor India!" she reflected. "One calamity after another! Famine and fever scourge, then cholera, and now flood!"

During her absence the faithful Rebecca had taken full charge of the work, with a new helper, Miss Yerbury, who, besides assisting in hospital and dispensary, gave morning Bible lessons to patients waiting for prescriptions. Her health renewed in spite of the harrowing experience, Clara met the constantly accelerating demands of the medical work with her usual zest and courage. During that year of 1880 the hospital and dispensary treated just under 6,000 patients. In addition she made her usual visits in homes, traveling on an average at least six miles a day.

The years of her second term passed swiftly, with a kaleidoscopic shifting of colors and moods and seasons: heat and cold, greens and browns and crimsons, frustrations and triumphs, disease, healing, death, and renewal of life. Her letters reflected all of them.

"January, 1882. There is cholera in the city, and smallpox. I have been exposed to both many times. Am living in our house again. The last cold season I lived in the hospital. The house has been whitewashed inside and out and with new mattings and clean floor cloths we are very bright and nice. In addition to medical work we have been building and repairing all winter and have had fifty and sixty persons at work. The masons receive 12½ cents a day and coolies 3½ cents, others 6 cents. . . . A missionary ought to know all trades, have engineering ability, be a good financier and accountant. One of our missionaries said to me, 'If you had been a man, you would have made a general.' 'No, indeed,' I replied, 'I would have been an engineer.' "

"June 24th. The rains have begun, all fresh and green. The mangoes are in their glory. I bought 100 this morning for 50 cents. Peaches are abundant."

"Feb. 22nd. There is such a great need for more missionaries. All of us are overworked. This is the coldest weather ever known in Bareilly."

"March 15th. We just housecleaned, shall be clean for about two weeks. At the end of that time spider webs, dust, and insects innumerable will accumulate, and the doors, windows, and curtains will be so soiled that a stranger might wonder if there were a housekeeper on the premises. We all go out to our work early in the morning and come back about eleven; by that time we are too tired to care how things look."

"December 28th. A little boy of two who had been a patient of mine since he was a few months old was brought to the hospital and after a few hours he died. The last of five children! Poor mother, with her hopeless lamentations! After she had gone home I went to see her and tried to comfort her with a story of heaven."

"January 18th, 1884. We need two doctors, but I must work alone another year. We are having a cold winter with frost. The days are much like late autumn days in America just before the snow comes. No rain since early in September. But such a beautiful evening glow all over the world!"

"February 13th. Last month I came near being killed. I was out in the country, about 100 miles away, visiting the family of the Nawab. Coming back I rode an elephant. My native assistant and I mounted and just as we were passing out of the yard the driver said we must lower our heads or get hurt. The yard was enclosed by a high wall and had a gate fifteen feet high with a beam across the top. I thought my head was as low as I could get it, but the beam caught me under the chin. My assistant screamed, and the driver backed the elephant, but my head was black and sore for some days. One of the governors of north India was killed in this way."

"December 29th, 1884. The patients in the hospital at present are of the most needy class. One is a beggar whose only home is a little hut on the shore of the Ganges. Sufficient food will in itself be a luxury, but clean rooms, comfortable beds, kindly ministrations, mean a new world. She and her husband were professional beggars. When he died, she had gone her rounds led by her eight-year-old boy. One morning she appeared before me with twin babies in her arms, saying she had come to give me her babies. I saw she was blind. 'If I take your babies, you must stay and nurse them for me,' I told her. 'I will treat your eyes and give you your food for taking care of them for me.' I asked her if she would give me the other boy. 'Oh, no,' she said, 'he has to lead me about.' 'But if I cure your eyes you will not need him to lead you.' She consented, and I gave her a room. At first she would disappear for a few days to visit her old friends by the river, but she became more contented, and now the sight of one eye is partially restored. I told her of the boys' orphanage at Shahjahanpore and of the widows' home there where they would care for her baby boys until they were old enough to go into the orphanage, and she has consented to go."

"January. Rebecca Gowan, who has served so faithfully in the dispensary for ten years, came back very ill, and she has died. How I shall miss her!"

7

In March, 1885, Clara Swain took a journey which was destined to change her life.

The preceding month an Indian gentleman, secretary of the

Rajah of Khetri in Rajputana, had asked her if she would make a professional visit to the Rajah's wife if she should be summoned. He was assessing the ability and success of several woman doctors and taking his report to the Rajah.

"What should I tell him?" she asked her fellow workers worriedly. "I don't see how I could possibly leave, with the work growing so fast."

"But think of the opportunity," they urged her warmly. "A whole kingdom into which no Christian missionary has ever gone! You *must* go!"

"Anyway, there's no likelihood of my being chosen."

Clara had agreed to spend a month in Khetri if desired, then promptly dismissed the matter from her mind. By this time there were several other woman doctors in north India.

The first of March she received a telegram from the secretary asking her to be ready to leave in about ten days, the secretary himself arriving soon after. She was to take with her an English-speaking nurse, her cook, and other servants necessary to her comfort, sparing no expense. Learning that there were no Europeans nearer the palace than the railroad station, seventy-two miles away, Clara also took along a teacher friend as a companion. There were seven in her party beside their escort.

By no means the least important of her entourage was her devoted and clever *khansama*, cook, Mathru Masih. His European meals were the envy of the whole compound, and he could turn out the most succulent curries and pilaus that Clara had ever tasted. Such a treasure was he that when leaving for America on furlough she had loaned him to her best friend, Isabella Thoburn, in Lucknow. But his loyalty had been firm, and he had been waiting for her in Bareilly, all smiles and with a lavish platter of her favorite curry, on her return.

At the end of the railroad they found elaborate facilities for their transportation the rest of the way. There were a camel chariot drawn by four lordly and disdainful beasts, two palanquins carried by seventeen men each, two riding horses, and a unique vehicle called a *rath*, a favorite conveyance of noble Indian women. It had four wheels, a little covered section in the rear with tasseled curtains, and a driver's seat in front with an extension of the curtain fastened to two diagonal poles. It was drawn by two beautiful white oxen. Accompanying the grand procession were more than one hundred servants.

The luxury was deceptive. The chariot had no pliable springs, and in the palanquins they were swung dizzily as in a hammock and bumped and shaken until their teeth chattered. The first twenty miles in chariot and palanquins were long enough to make the Westerners hail camp with pleasure. A tent awaited them, together with a good breakfast prepared by Mathru Masih. After resting until midafternoon, they started on the next stage of their journey, arriving in the early morning at Koth, a large Muslim city in the state of Khetri, where the Rajah had a rest house.

A richly caparisoned elephant arrived to take them on a tour of the city. They climbed the ladder, gingerly entered the howdah, hung on for dear life while the animal rose to his front legs, then with a mighty lunge and heave reared to a dizzying height. With the mahout sitting behind the flapping ears and guiding the elephant with his feet or an occasional endearing word, the sightseeing party rocked and jolted through the ancient Rajput city. News of their mission spread, for on returning to the rest house Clara found a large crowd waiting to be given medicines.

It was three in the afternoon when they started the last forty miles of their journey, changing several times from chariot to palanquin to elephant. There was only one mishap. Mathru Masih fell asleep on his horse and in the darkness slipped off without waking. Sometime later it was noticed that the horse was riderless, and one of the men went back and found him, still asleep, lying in the desert sand. But, alert and refreshed, he was ready to cook breakfast when they arrived in Khetri, where a luxurious tent was waiting for them.

Since her visit to the Nawab of Rampore Clara had felt little awe of royalty. She went without trepidation when summoned to the palace that afternoon at four. Miss Pannell, her companion, was far more nervous.

"But—how will we know what to do? Suppose we make mistakes!"

"Suppose we do, what matter? They're people, just like us, and they need what we have to give."

The Rajah, an attractive, well-educated gentleman, received them in his palace, showed them his excellent art collection and library, then took them to the Rani's palace. Clara's heart immediately went out to the tiny, beautiful, but frail-appearing young woman with the smiling lips and big dark eyes. Face uncovered, the Rani rose and extended her hand to receive them, leading Clara to a chair at her right. The Rajah seated himself at her left, while fourteen of the court women, almost as beautifully dressed as the Rani, stood behind, seven on each side, ready for service. It was a formal call, and the visitors soon took their leave, Clara to return for a professional visit the next morning.

It was about two weeks later, when the little Rani had begun to show marked improvement, that the secretary approached Clara with an astounding suggestion.

"His Highness proposes that the Dr. Miss Sahiba remain permanently in his realm as physician to the women of the palace. He begs to inform her that all possible arrangements will be made for her comfort. If she will stay, her name will remain always on the palace register, and the family will regard her as their own as long as she shall live."

Clara was stricken speechless. Finally she recovered sufficiently to tell the secretary that she appreciated the kind invitation and would consider the matter. Then followed days of the most intensive prayer and heart-searching which she had ever experienced. Where could she be of the greatest service? Where was she most needed? What did God want her to do?

Bareilly? Her heart was there: the hospital built from her own flesh and blood, hundreds—thousands—of patients who needed her. Or—did they? Not her, just a woman doctor, and any one of the many now in India could fill her place. While here in Khetri, a huge area comprising hundreds of square miles, thousands of people, where no missionary or Christian worker had ever lived—! Her head swam, a bewildering battleground of pros and cons. Yet as days passed and the possibilities for mission work became more and more apparent, she moved slowly toward decision.

"If I do agree to stay," she asked bluntly, "may Miss Pannell remain with me, and may we be allowed to work as Christian women?"

Permission was freely granted, and Clara became convinced that she was called by God to this new field of service. After signing a contract to remain for at least two years, she returned to Bareilly in late April and stayed for a month settling her affairs. One of the acts she most regretted was having to dismiss her *khansama*, Mathru, but she sent him and his increasing family once more to Isabella Thoburn in Lucknow, where he was to remain in faithful service for fifteen years.

Again a doctor from Moradabad, Dr. Mary Christiancy, was appointed to fill her place in Bareilly, and in late May Clara and Miss Pannell repeated the strange journey by rail, camel chariot, palanquin, *rath*, and elephant, this time with a train of carts and beasts of burden carrying most of their possessions. The glaring heat of the desert pursued them into their first dwelling in Khetri, a fine house but as yet without doors and windows.

"Birds, squirrels, and lizards have full liberty," recorded Clara, "but we do not mind them unless they make too much noise and get into our food."

The house was soon repaired and remodeled so it was not only habitable but luxurious.

"We are living in a tomb," Clara told her friends back home. "The person for whom it was built was cremated by the Ganges. It's in a garden and is very artistic with porches and pillars, carved, and a domed roof. It's built of stone and has a stone floor. Formerly it had no partitions, but it has been divided to make two small side rooms for pantry and storeroom. The rest we have made into three rooms by curtains in the arches. The walls are frescoed, each room a different tint. The dome is sky blue, shading down from a rosy flush to meet white walls, as delicate as porcelain."

The house was formally christened on July 18, when, to Clara's dismay, the Rajah requested that she celebrate her fiftieth birthday, American fashion, by giving a party. She could not politely refuse.

"A success," she described the occasion. "Our sitting room upstairs has white walls paneled in blue, and white lace curtains at the doors were looped with blue ribbons. Thin white floor cloth was spread over the blue and orange striped carpet with the colors showing through. We borrowed a white marble stand from the secretary, wreathed it with myrtle and put on it the cake, which I had made and frosted myself.

"About four the Rajah and his suite came, with the prime minister and his principal men. It was a happy occasion, he said, that my fiftieth birthday should occur in Khetri. After he had gone the Rani arrived, accompanied by the chief officers of the state, who remained below while she and her ladies came upstairs. 'You are to me in the place of a mother,' she said with a charming smile. We distributed *pan*, the Rani's wrapped in gold leaf, the others' in silver. She fastened a beautiful necklace on my neck. Throughout the royal visits the state band played outside. Afterward Miss Pannell and I sat down to enjoy a quiet cup of tea and a slice of the cake."

But such social events were the least of their activities. Within a month after her arrival Clara had opened a dispensary for women and children of the city and surrounding villages and was carrying on a busy practice in the palace. She soon asked the Rajah's permission to open a school for girls, and he not only gave his consent but promised to use his influence to induce his people to send their daughters, giving each one a pound of wheat flour every morning to encourage their attendance, the equivalent of a day's wages, also a new skirt and head covering, so they could come in clean clothes. An extra pound of flour was given each Saturday to those who had not been absent through the week. Soon Miss Pannell was teaching eighteen bright little girls, as well as the Rani and some of the court ladies. Religious books in Hindi were being distributed, and it was not long before more than thirty persons were singing Christian hymns, some of them proving very popular. They could sing their religion to people, it seemed, when they could not talk about it openly.

"Your songs are purer than ours," the Rani commented. "I like them better."

But she herself had much to teach her Western friends in the way of religious devotion. Once Clara watched her prepare for her daily worship. The room in which the bath water was heated was washed as well as the one in which the little Rani was to bathe, which she always did before prayer time. She put on a clean yellow sari, letting her hair fall loose. When ready, she entered a large brass cabinet in which were all the articles required for worship, and there she sat, without having taken food, until three in the afternoon, saying prayers over and over and bathing in wine a little image of Krishna. After pouring about a teaspoonful of wine over the tiny image, she would drink it. Clara was finally able to persuade her to take a glass of milk before going to prayers, since she needed more strength for the ceremony.

It required strength also to wear some of her royal garments. One of her state dresses, of a delicate yellow, had a skirt so heavy Clara could hardly lift it, cut in small gores and 70 yards wide, trimmed around the bottom with silver lace a quarter of a yard in width. A jacket of the thinnest gauze, with a veil of the same material and pearls on head, neck, and arms, completed the costume. No one was supposed to sit in her presence until invited or go into her apartments without permission.

"We have made several mistakes," confessed Clara cheerfully, "but the Rani overlooks them."

A state visit in November to Jaipur, a hundred miles away, introduced her to all the lavishness of Rajput royalty when on display. The caravan contained three hundred soldiers, a brass band, a thousand men. It took a hundred men to carry the flagstaff alone, unjointed, in one piece. There was a palanquin for the Rani, one for her sister-in-law, one for the little princess, and two for Clara and Miss Pannell. It took seventy-five men to carry them. There were three elephants, one for the Rajah, one for the princess and her attendants, and one for Clara and her companion when they wanted to change from the palanquins. There were over two hundred camels and as many horses. Seventeen ox carts carried the tents and provisions. Ten other conveyances, covered with white cloth and drawn by white oxen, contained the women attendants of the Rani and the twelve schoolgirls who were going with the expedition. Six camels drew the three gun carriages for saluting as they entered the towns on the way. There was also a treasury cart. The crimson sashes and gay red, yellow, pink, and green turbans worn by all the men added to the dazzling extravaganza. It took five days to make the trip, traveling twenty to thirty miles a day, stopping at night for the camels to be unloaded, tents put up, beds made, food cooked. Now and then an unruly camel would run away and throw off his load. A few chairs were broken, and Clara's cook grieved over his quilt which was torn by a biting camel.

All this splendor, Clara reflected, beside the nakedness, rags, mud huts, and squalid poverty through which they journeyed? Yet the Rajah was an enlightened and much-loved ruler, honestly trying to improve the condition of his people according to the standards of his cultural tradition. If he could only become a Christian! Yet—she honestly had to ask the question—were the millionaires of her own Christian country, whose mansions overlooked the slums and ghettos of great cities, any better? She relieved her uneasy conscience by giving advice and medicines wherever possible in the villages they passed through. In one she gave a little Hindi Gospel to a villager, but when they returned a month later he brought it back, saying he was afraid to keep it.

And in Jaipur, that splendid pink city with its seven-storied palace, its famous observatory, its delicately beautiful Hall of the Winds, Clara experienced the high hour of the whole journey. Not the magnificent *durbar*, reception, for the Viceroy with all its floral decorations and illuminations, but the visit she had with his wife, Lady Dufferin!

The interest of Her Excellency in medical work for the women of India was already well known. It had a curious origin. In 1881 Miss Beilby, an English missionary who had a hospital and dispensary in Lucknow, had been called by the Rajah of Punna to treat his wife. Just before returning to England Miss Beilby had called again at the palace.

"You are going to England," the Rani had told her earnestly. "I want you to tell the Queen what the women in India suffer when they are sick." Then she had dictated a message to the Queen. "Write it small, Doctor Miss Sahiba, for I want you to put it into a locket, and you are to wear this locket around your neck until you see our Great Queen and give it to her yourself. You are not to send it through another."

Word had reached the Queen about the message, and Miss Beilby had been summoned. The Queen had listened with sympathy. She had not known the needs were so great. Before Lord Dufferin had left for India she had called Lady Dufferin and told her, "Do what you can to relieve this suffering."

Arriving in India in 1883, Lady Dufferin had taken the charge seriously. She had written to the wives of all the governors and lieutenant governors of the principalities and provinces and consulted the heads of the medical service and of missionary institutions inquiring what the needs were and how they could be met.

The meeting between the Viceroy's wife and the world's first woman missionary doctor was a historic one. It was a meeting of kindred minds and pioneer spirits. Each had much to learn from the other. Clara spoke long and earnestly of her own experiences and made some pertinent suggestions about what might be done. The Countess was most impressed, and together they outlined a plan which was to mark an important milestone in Indian progress.

"It is her idea," Clara recorded enthusiastically, "to form a national association with a central committee and a central fund, with branches all over India managed locally to promote female medical tuition and medical relief, and the establishment of hospitals for women all over the country, and to raise subscriptions for this object."

That very year, 1885, the Viceroy's wife initiated the Countess of Dufferin Fund, together with the organization by the Viceroy of the National Medical Association for supplying Female Aid to the Women of India.

8

Clara returned to Khetri with renewed hope and assurance. She was but a small and isolated unit, to be sure, but now she felt an integral part of a great forward movement penetrating into all parts of the country.

During the next three years she followed the developments with eagerness: the growth of the fund to seven lakhs of rupees, the opening of major medical colleges to Indian women, the establishment of several Dufferin hospitals. But not for thirty years, with the founding of the Lady Hardinge Medical College in Delhi, would Lady Dufferin's ambition to start a model government-recognized training school for women in medicine be realized. Meanwhile, however, the Ludhiana Christian Medical School for women, founded by Dr. Edith Brown in 1894, would graduate many excellent licensed medical practitioners.

Clara's own achievement during these years was by no means insignificant. In the Administration Report of the Khetri State for 1886 the Rajah wrote: "I cannot look back with greater pleasure or satisfaction on anything I have done than on the facilities introduced by me for rendering medical aid to the female portion of my subjects. . . . I have employed a very competent European lady doctor, Miss Swain, M.D., to attend on Her Highness, the Rani Sahiba, and, feeling it my duty to place her advice and assistance within the reach of all my subjects, have established a regular dispensary for women, opened June 1st, 1885, at the expense of the state, and a room in the palace building appropriated to it until a more convenient and suitable one could be provided."

Under Section 12, Schools, he gave this report: "I am glad to say that the people of my state are beginning to evince greater interest in the education of their children. I engaged a competent European lady, Miss P. E. Pannell, as mistress, and the Khetri Girls' School was opened by Her Highness in April, 1885, in the teeth of opposition from the orthodox portion of the community. As was expected, at first every effort to teach these girls was frowned upon and considered absurd by their relatives and friends. This feeling, however, gradually gave place to trust and confidence, and the school is now showing some return for all the time and patience spent upon it. . . . Great pains have been taken to teach truthfulness, honesty, and love for one another."

Because of the illness of one of her sisters, Clara returned to America in 1888, but in spite of her own poor health her native country could not hold her. As she landed in Bombay in December, 1889, the first sight meeting her eyes was two happy faces from Khetri, one belonging to her old and trusted servant, the other to a servant of the Rajah sent to make arrangements for her journey.

"I felt irresponsible at once," she confessed happily.

Back in Khetri with Miss Pannell in January, she found her house in order, curtains up and carpets down, a warm welcome, and many people suffering from influenza and smallpox. She vaccinated herself and set to work immediately. During her absence another little princess had been born. This necessitated close attendance at the palace, for the baby was delicate, and gave Clara renewed opportunity for Bible study with the Rani. A Sunday service was held in her apartments, at which women of the court and their attendants were present, yet, though the meetings increased in attendance and interest, Clara felt that the results were meager. Then, just when she became most discouraged, there would come a ray of light, as when the wife of one of the men who attended the meetings came to her and said, "My husband is much better since he began to come to your meetings. He treats me better and does not get angry at little things as he used to."

Or as when the Rani asked her to speak to a large group of women sitting on the floor of her apartment.

"Tell them how wrong it is to destroy the girl babies born to them," she urged.

Clara did so earnestly, yet understandingly, knowing how the terrible expense to the poor of marrying off a girl contributed to the inhuman custom. "A girl takes," was a common saying, "but a boy brings."

"In the case of poor families in the state," the Rani told Clara, "the Rajah gives money toward the marriage expense hoping the custom of infanticide will be done away."

The greatest event in Khetri during Clara's second term there happened in January, 1893. Not for a hundred years had a son been born in the royal family. All the heirs to the throne had been adopted. But now a son was born, and all through February and March the celebrations continued. On trips to Agra and other cities there were days set aside for feeding the poor in gratitude to God for his gift of the little prince. And when the Rani came riding into Khetri there was a huge demonstration. Fifty-one guns were fired in salute, the streets were lined with infantry and cavalry, bands played. Costly gifts of gold and silver vessels, jewels, money, and beautiful garments of rich material kept arriving.

"The little prince is a fine baby," Clara wrote her family. "He gives no trouble. I bathe and dress him and look after him almost as if he belonged to me. They call him Moti Raj, the Pearl of the Kingdom."

But it was the older little *Bai*, Princess, who was her greatest joy. Sensitive, intelligent, the child responded to her teaching like a flower to sunlight.

"What are you learning, Bai?" asked the Rajah one day.

"The Bible, Father."

The Rajah frowned. "Do you read about Jesus Christ?"

"Yes. Some."

"Are you going to be a Christian?"

"I am not a Christian," the child replied, "but the Bible is a good book, and I like to read it."

That evening His Highness came again to the women's apartments. "Do not read the Bible any more, Bai. I do not wish you to read it."

The little princess began to cry. "Father, do not hinder me from reading the Bible."

The Rani was present and said, "That Bible is a very good book. I read it myself sometimes when I am in trouble, and I get great comfort from it. Let Bai read it. It will do her no harm."

The Rajah was silent for several moments. "Well, Bai," he said finally, "you may read the book, but do not read much about Jesus Christ."

The Rani with her quiet insistence had her way about many

things. When she also persisted in reading the New Testament and seemed much interested in it, the Rajah looked anxious but said nothing. When the little Moti Raj was a few months old, His Highness wanted her to part with him and let him be removed to the men's quarters.

"He will never be brave," he objected, "if he remains in the zenana."

But a year later Clara recorded, "The Rani gained her point about the little prince. He is still with her."

There were both excitement and consternation in the palace when the older Bai approached marriageable age. The Rani sent messengers and a Brahmin woman to a native state to negotiate for the marriage of the princess to the son of the Rajah of Shahpuri. There was much traveling back and forth before the matter was settled. The first inquiry was about the girl's looks, was she a beauty or just plain? And what about her disposition, had she her mother's temper or her father's? Could she read, and was she really clever? Once these points proved satisfactory, then came the real business. How much was the Rajah willing to spend on the wedding? What dowry? In jewels or money? The answers were given. The Rajah of Khetri would spend 110,000 rupees, both in money and in jewels.

Then the Rajah of Khetri presented his requests. He wished for his daughter a yearly income of 10,000 rupees and did not want the marriage to take place until she entered her fourteenth year. She was now twelve. The prince, eighteen, had had a good English education, and, to Clara's relief, his family belonged to the Arya Samaj, a Hindu reformist sect which did not believe in idol worship. The little princess, sincere in her desire to serve God, would not find the adjustment too hard to make. Finally the arrangements were all completed.

The time had come also, Clara sensed, to make new plans for her own life. For nearly ten years she had given unstintingly of herself to the Rajah, his family and people, and in return the royal household had made her one of themselves. They had surrounded her with comforts, taken her on all their journeys—to Agra, to Jaipur, to Mount Abu, to Allahabad, to Calcutta, to cool resorts in the mountains. They had treated her to *durbars*, excursions, and tiger hunts; cooled her drinks with ice brought from Rewari, seventy-two miles away. They had built her a new house, four years in the building, all of stone on a rock higher even than the palace, with rooms of mansion size, arched and paneled and tinted in many colors, and a verandah that overlooked the whole city of 6,000 souls. Their children had called her Nani, Grandmother. They would have been glad for her, indeed they expected her, to stay here the rest of her life. But, though she was just turned sixty, her strength was failing, and she knew it was time to go.

"Oh, no!" wailed the Rani when she suggested returning to America. "At least not until Baby is five years old!"

Clara shook her head. "I cannot stay as long as that."

"Then you must stay two years more; then I will give you leave to go for six months."

"I will stay one more year," Clara decided.

She went with them to Agra in December when they selected jewels and clothing for the coming wedding. She saw trays brought in bearing jewels worth thousands of rupees, necklaces, bangles, head ornaments, jewels for the hands and feet, toes, and ankles. Out of the collection the Rani chose emeralds, pearls, and diamonds, all to be purchased by the state. The parents' personal gift to the bride was a necklace and bracelets set with pearls and diamonds—beautiful, but, oh, so heavy!—and to the groom an emerald necklace worth 3,000 rupees. Clara was often asked to model them, "just to see how they look on a white person." In all, 20,000 rupees worth of jewels were to be given, besides a quantity of clothing, silverware, and other objects. The wedding would cost at least 100,000 rupees.

"Just two days before the ceremony," Clara wrote home on January 28. "The guests are arriving. The Rani's sister came Saturday with 400 attendants, three elephants, and 200 camels. The Rajah of Secor has sent 100 fine horses, and will arrive today with 1,000 people, 300 camels, oxen, tents, horses, carriages, and elephants. The Maharajah of Jodhpur will arrive the day after the wedding as the Rajah and his suite cannot go out to meet him in proper style before that time. He will stay in our house while we move back into the old one.

"On Wednesday, the day of the ceremony, the Rajah and his men will go out to receive the groom and his father's family. The people of Khetri will go out about a mile, and the returning procession will number 6,000 people on elephants, camels, and horses. Yellow is the color of joy and gladness, and the palace gates are trimmed with red, green, and yellow cloth. All the roads are repaired.

"My little princess is sad at the thought of leaving. She cries a great deal, and the Rajah sheds tears with her. She was only 2½ when I came here ten years ago."

The ceremonies lasted a week, with a visiting assembly of nearly 8,000, who brought with them 2,000 horses, 1,900 camels, 12 elephants, 78 pairs of bullocks with conveyances. All were fed by the state. Besides the guests, many thousands came in from the countryside to witness the grand parade. When the two processions met about two miles from the city a cannon was fired. The groom alighted from his horse and mounted an elephant. As he rode on, a golden umbrella was held over him, and golden fans were waved to keep the flies away.

Clara suffered with the little princess while she sat for three hours, face covered, under a red canopy beside the groom while the priest read pages and pages of Sanscrit which no one but other priests could understand. The air was heavy with the smells of burning *ghi*, of marigolds and jasmine and roses. Later the couple sat on a beautiful silver bedstead with a green and purple mattress and pillows of rich velvet, one of the wedding gifts, while the rajahs and other dignitaries came and presented their gifts of money in gold and silver in bags of clean white cloth, each containing 2,000 rupees. The bride sat veiled while her husband received the gifts.

There were great heaps of clothing, sixty suits for the bride, full large skirts trimmed with gold lace, and scores of fine silk *chadars*, veils; shawls, turbans, hundreds of finely woven cloths. There were carved boxes of all shapes and sizes, trunks of wood and leather, cooking utensils, lamps. Presently the zenana women retired, and the Rajah came in, followed by his royal guests, then by lesser nobility. After viewing the scene for some moments, he formed them all into a procession, and they marched around the huge display of presents. When they went out, he asked Clara to watch the jewels and her companion to guard the silver, to avoid danger of theft.

It was all over at last, and little Bai, not yet thirteen, departed for her new home with her mountains of new possessions, a list of them, a hundred servants, and many tears. For Clara it was the beginning of the end. In the months that followed, every day, every act assumed a fresh clarity and pertinence. "The last time I shall reach out my hands and lift my face to feel the first cooling rains.... Next June I'll be eating oatmeal for breakfast instead of this delicious curry of mangoes and cucumbers cooked in butter with spices and eaten on rice...."

In spite of her declining strength she worked with an almost superhuman zeal, as if in the few weeks left she must try to heal all the ills of India. Every patient became of supreme importance ... the little girl who had been stolen from her home for the sake of her jewels and thrown into a well, but crawling into a crevice had escaped being killed by the stones thrown in after her. Fortunately she had only a few flesh wounds and a body badly shaken.... The boy brought from a distant village with severe softening of the bones. She could not persuade him to change his diet, for his family would rather see him die than taste meat or eggs.... The tiny girl screaming with pain because her nose had been pierced to have her marriage jewel inserted....

"Please take a vacation in the hills and get a little stronger before going to America," urged the Rajah. But Clara told him she thought her native climate would be the best tonic.

"You must remain in America no more than a year," he admonished her. "Then you must come back to us."

Clara smiled. "I am getting old enough to go to heaven before many years."

"But India is just as near heaven as America. You can go to heaven from here."

Her eyes misted so that when he had gone she had to wipe and wipe her glasses.

She sailed from Bombay in March, 1896, believing she would never return to India.

9

Meanwhile, the hospital which Clara Swain had founded and which was in time to bear her name kept pace with the banyan trees she had planted, putting down fresh shoots and continually rerooting itself in new soil.

Dr. Mary Christiancy, who took her place at Bareilly, was also a graduate of the Philadelphia Woman's Medical College, which from its inception had stressed the foreign-mission field as the place of greatest need for women doctors. At the end of one of her first speeches as dean, to the class of 1875, Rachel Bodley had asked for two volunteers for the mission field, one to relieve Clara Swain during her first furlough, the other to take the place of Dr. Mary Seelye, missionary to Calcutta, who had recently died. Nearly ten years later she received a letter across the top of which she wrote, "After Many Days."

"My dear Professor Bodley," wrote Mary Christiancy, "I received a letter yesterday confirming my appointment to India. I expect to sail on the 20th of September. Since the day I heard you give us the message from Dr. Seelye's closed lips and folded hands, I have felt this must be my work, though I did not want to do it. Now I feel differently and am glad to be counted worthy to carry the message."

Dr. Christiancy left a good government position in Washington to go to India. Sent out by the New England branch of the Woman's Foreign Missionary Society, she went first to Moradabad but was soon transferred to Bareilly. In spite of the disruption caused by the change in personnel, during her first year she treated over 10,000 patients.

"When these women come to the dispensary," she said in one of her reports, "and say, 'I have been walking since long before daylight to come to you for medicine,' or, 'Having heard of you, I have come twenty, forty, fifty miles to show my child,' then I feel that our medical work is a blessing, and I long for the day when we can have an itinerant service."

During her six years in Bareilly Dr. Christiancy found time to do some itinerating herself with Dr. and Mrs. Hoskins, traveling for several weeks through a part of the country never before visited by a missionary, many of the people never having seen a white face. But they were not afraid and came in crowds when they learned there were doctors dispensing medicines.

"Our fame preceded us," she reported in 1880. We never had a lack of patients. The fact that nearly everybody was suffering from malaria, and that the nearest dispensary was thirty-five miles away, sufficiently explained our welcome." When that same year they set up a clinic at the spring festival in Brindaban, one of the holy cities of Hinduism, their medicine so attracted the people that they would not even look at the god Krishna, passing by in all the glory of his war chariot. That year she reported over 12,000 patients in the dispensary.

In her philosophy of Christian missions, Mary Christiancy, like Clara Swain, was many years ahead of prevalent conceptions.

"Do people ever get any good from staying here?" she was asked by a devoted missionary as they walked through the hospital one morning. Good! Dr. Mary looked at the questioner in amazement. Didn't it matter that the life of a mother was saved, or that a child was restored to health? The popular idea that medical work should serve merely as a bait to draw people, or that a medical missionary was a pioneer to open the way for the Christian preacher seemed to her inconceivable. Medical work, she constantly emphasized, was a factor, not an incident, an end as well as a means.

"The command is," she summed up tersely, " 'Heal the sick *and* preach the Gospel.' "

Though she carried on classes in both nursing and midwifery, she was constantly hampered by lack of helpers. At no time did she have more than three, an assistant she had trained herself, a compounder, and a Bible reader.

"Our medical treatment is all wrong," was her appraisal when she was forced to return home in 1892 because of illness. "We place doctors too far apart. In all India there is not a better zenana hospital than ours in Bareilly. It has a fine location, good air, and adequate buildings. Yet the doctor in charge must often send away patients in need of surgical treatment because she has no one to help her perform the operation. Experienced surgeons should be chosen rather than recent graduates, and there should be two doctors to every station."

Her successor, Dr. Mary Bryan, though a surgeon, had even greater difficulties. At first she had to act as doctor, compounder, assistant, and nurse for sixty to eighty dispensary patients and some nine or ten in the hospital. And it was not only frustrating but grimly hazardous, she discovered, to attempt to operate and at the same time administer chloroform. Nevertheless, in her first nine months she managed to treat over 7,000 women and children. And before her first year was over she had acquired a nurse, Bella, an assistant, Mary Singh, and a compounder, Harriet Subh.

Many of her patients came from a distance. One Indian pastor's family arrived late at night after traveling all day in an ox cart with three very sick children, one with hemorrhage of the lungs. No help had been available in their village. Dr. Bryan fought grimly and successfully for their lives. Another woman was carried four miles on a charpoy after giving birth to one of a pair of twins, in the hope that her life might be saved by hastening the birth of the other. Strangely enough, the husband and relatives begged that the woman's life might be saved even if the child, a boy, must be sacrificed. In spite of complications, Dr. Bryan had the joy of sending both mother and son home well.

Equally frustrating with the lack of proper assistance was the dearth of funds. Though she was instructed by the Conference to start a training class in nursing and elementary medicine and five girls applied for admission, there was no money to implement the project.

But Dr. Dart, later Mrs. Dease, who succeeded Dr. Bryan, was able to report in 1898 that eighteen young women were being prepared for future medical work. And in spite of limitations in staff and finance, during her five years of service the work continued to grow. Each year more treatments were given in the dispensary, more visits made in the zenanas, more patients received into the hospital. With famine as well as poverty swelling the girls' orphanage to as many as three hundred in the year 1900, it could easily have consumed all her time giving service without ever leaving the compound. In 1900 she reported 17,000 treatments.

Under the direction of Dr. Margaret Lewis the work of the Zenana Mission Hospital continued to increase. So hard pressed was the new missionary from Chicago, who arrived in 1901, that she found little time for learning the language. Within a year the number of in-patients doubled. The larger hospital rooms were turned into wards. Twenty-four new beds were added. Annual visits in homes approached 700. A training class was instituted for the wives of men studying in the theological school, many of whom would be sent on circuits far from medical aid. There was a bout with plague, which sent half the city's population into temporary exile. Yet during her first three years her only helpers were a medical assistant, a pupil nurse, and a compounder. No wonder that with the exhausting, year-round labor exacted from these early successors of Clara Swain, no one of them was able to complete more than a single term of service!

With the coming of Dr. Esther Gimson, however, in 1904, there began a new era, for, with time out for furloughs, Dr. Gimson was to direct the activities of the hospital for more than twenty years. During the first two of them she and Dr. Lewis worked together, performing what often seemed like miracles in the apology of an operating room, with its plaster and cement floor constantly throwing up dust, its tiled roof with a ceiling cloth stretched below, giving only partial protection from dirt, its single small window facing north. Though cases often had to be refused because of lack of an aseptic room, many serious operations, the most difficult of them obstetrical, were successfully performed. One old Mohammedan woman, blinded by cataract for more than a year, was sent home seeing, both physically and spiritually. A schoolgirl, after months of treatment in a government hospital, was sent to them as incurable, to have her leg amputated, and they sent her home perfectly well, her leg saved. A similar case with a diseased hand, sent with the idea that amputation was the only resort, was discharged with both hands strong and healthy. In a city whose population was now approaching 200,000, the hospital founded over thirty years before was slowly assuming a place of dignity among buildings and institutions far more hoary and ancient: the walls of the old fort built by Bans Deo about 1550, Bareilly College founded in 1837, the temple of Devi with its magnificent tank known as Talab Chaudhary, its history far predating Mogul times.

Amid all this wealth of tradition, an institution counting only fifty years seemed little more than infantile, yet in 1906 Indian Methodism prepared to celebrate its Jubilee with all the pomp and ceremony of a maharajah's *durbar*. Bareilly, birthplace of the mission with the arrival of the Butlers in 1856, was naturally chosen as the site of the celebration. Preparations for the December event began as early as May. Carpenters were engaged. Hundreds of articles of camping and housekeeping equipment were ordered or made on the premises: bamboo beds, *morhas* (stools) of coarse reed and rope, tin mugs, *gharras* (earthen water jars), *matkas* (large earthen casks), *nands* (large earthen vessels), *surahis* (earthen water pitchers), tables, commodes, washstands, mattresses, straw mats.

For three months before the occasion the compound was in a turmoil of repairing, housecleaning, rearrangement. Three hundred and thirty grass huts were built. Sixty ox carts were requisitioned to bring in straw for tents and huts. Tents were brought from neighboring mission stations and pitched in the open space between hospital and mission houses. A huge *shamiana*, a bamboo and thatch canopy, was erected to provide an outdoor tabernacle. By the first of December, when many of the guests began to arrive, the compound began to resemble a huge military camp.

A key figure amid all this bustle and confusion was a tall, white-clad and turbaned, dignified but extremely efficient Indian charged with the task of providing food for the four or five hundred people who would be entertained on the compound. For after the death of Isabella Thoburn in June, 1901, Clara Swain's faithful *khansama*, Mathru Masih, had returned from Lucknow to Bareilly, to again assume culinary charge of the hospital bungalow. Flitting about his heels during all the excitement was one of his twelve children, an eight-year-old boy named Nizam, whose bright, curious eyes and winning smile, as well as nimble bare feet, were in constant motion. He carried messages, ran errands, balanced trays and jugs and bundles and bedrolls on his mop of curly hair, poked his small inquisitive nose into tent and tabernacle, made himself a friend and favorite of the guests, both foreign and Indian. If the hospital could be said to have a mascot, symbol of its lively involvement and concern, it would have been Nizam Masih. It was a relationship which was to endure with increasing interest and loyalty during the next sixty and more years.

The procession of carts began moving on December 18. All the bungalows and tents were ready for the influx. The Nawab of Rampore had granted the use of one of his large mansions near the mission, ideal for the housing of guests and the reception of the opening day. A big *durbar* at Agra for a state visit of the Amir of Afghanistan, which commanded all hackney carriages within a radius of 200 miles, raised momentary consternation. How convey all the guests from the station! But some of the leading citizens of Bareilly gave the use of their private carriages for the days of arrival and departure.

"How different from our reception fifty years ago!" marveled Mrs. Butler as she rode in sumptuous comfort beside her daughter Clementina.

Sixty-eight people came from America for the Jubilee. Besides Mrs. Butler, her daughter, and her son John, among the most notable were Bishop (Isabella's brother James) and Mrs. Thoburn, Bishop and Mrs. Foss, and—most significant for the Bareilly hospital—Clara Swain herself.

Her presence here still seemed incredible, for she had thought never to return again. Yet once she landed in Bombay the ten years of absence dropped away. She might be returning from a short furlough. This was home—these crowded streets with their absurd medley of traffic, their jumble of color and motion and clamor, yes, even these gaunt, whining beggars thrusting their poor stumps of fingers through the windows of the train, the openings of her carriage—not the chaste, cold, proper world of a town in upper New York State.

She looked with envy at the new young missionaries who had come with her on the trip, eyes bursting with wonder, a bit of shock, but eager, determined, dedicated. To have another thirty-five years to give this sick, tumultuous, hungry, yet heartbreakingly beautiful country, to see what would happen to it in the twenties, the thirties, perhaps even the forties!

She marveled at the smooth efficiency which met them at the boat, handled their baggage, whisked them away to a comfortable mission rest house, put them on a train, supplied their every need. What a contrast to that first wild trip in trains, *dak garis*, bullock carts, and *dholis!* Who could have imagined that the little group of eight women meeting in Tremont Church less than forty years ago could have grown to such a huge, self-sufficient, effective organization!

For by this year of 1906 the Woman's Foreign Missionary Society had become a body of tremendous size and significance. Operating through ten branches in the United States—New England, New York, Philadelphia, Cincinnati, Northwestern, Des Moines, Minneapolis, Topeka, Pacific, and Columbia River—it had budgeted for its expenditures of the coming year the impressive sum of $612,282. Its assets in buildings and equipment amounted to $1,358,282. Since its inception it had sent out over three hundred woman missionaries to fourteen different countries, a hundred of them to India alone, twenty-five with medical degrees. Shades of male officialdom, which had decried the ability of women to both raise and administer their own funds! They had indeed "sent Miss A. to India, obtained bills of exchange, taken care of her on her voyage, provided a home for her when she arrived at her destination, and so forth." Not one Miss A. but three hundred of her!

Clara Swain arrived in Bombay on December 20, and on the twenty-fourth she attended a dinner party at Mrs. Parker's in Moradabad. On the twenty-seventh she was in Bareilly, being entertained on the familiar old compound, greeting friends, making new ones, marveling at the many changes. The old "palace," the first hospital building, was gone, having been declared unsafe in 1905, and was replaced by a new bungalow. How immense the banyans had grown, which she herself had planted! And what a glory was the mango grove whose seedlings she had placed in the ground just twenty-two years ago! A good income it must bring for the hospital and dispensary!

"Mathru, old friend!" Her eyes misted at the sight of the aging, familiar face, the faithful hands raised and folded together in *namaste*.

"Doctor Miss Sahiba!"

"And is this fine straight boy your son?"

"One of my nine sons, Miss Sahiba. This is Nizam."

The young eyes looked curiously into hers, frankly appraising the fine thin features, the heavy brows with severity belied by smiling lips, the white hair drawn back in two wings and pugged behind, the austere black dress. Sixty years later Nizam Masih was to describe the experience in great detail and enjoy a unique and proud distinction, the only person still associated with the hospital who had ever seen its founder.

The mood of the Jubilee was one of awe and solemnity, not of jubilation. Here in Bareilly fifty years ago Mrs. Butler and a tiny handful of Christians had lived and labored and suffered, fled into the night for their very lives. Here Methodism in India had buried its first martyr. Now 3,000 people, fruits of that blood-nourished soil, marched in long procession around the compound and assembled in the *shamiana*. As Mrs. Butler, old, frail, stooped, was led to the platform on the arm of her son John, with one voice the throng broke into the beloved hymn, *"Isa Masih ki Jai"* (Victory to Jesus Christ)!

It was an impressive service. A blind woman was led forward who had come all the way from The Central Provinces. She was one of the orphan children taken in by Mrs. Butler after the mutiny, and she threw herself on her knees, attempting to kiss the feet of the woman who had been more to her than mother. A Tibetan boy was brought in by Dr. Martha Sheldon, who had established a mission dispensary on the pass leading to the forbidden country, the first convert of this land to which Christians had long hoped to take the Gospel.

Among the thousands of Christians living during the Jubilee in the little grass tents was one group which was of particular interest to Dr. Clara, a band of former Hindu fakirs, religious mendicants who had spent their time doing penance as they sat among little fires or practiced severe austerities to show loyalty to their special god. Now, having found a greater loyalty, they sang almost continuously to the accompaniment of their *tablas* and cymbals, not *"Ram, Ram,"* but *"Jai, Jai, Jai, Isa Masih ki Jai!"*

That night the huge reception was held in the palace of the Nawab of Rampore. All the splendor of feudal India had been placed at the service of the foreign God and his followers, once so feared and despised. Treading the rich carpets, sipping from the royal goblets, accepting silver-wrapped sweets from servants in long white robes, ornate turbans, and crimson sashes, Clara Swain relived that first visit to the Nawab's palace over thirty-five years ago, its trembling hope, its terrible suspense, its triumph.

"Palace of healing," she thought, "that's what he gave us." A pity that all the palaces of India could not be turned into schools and hospitals!

She left Bareilly with both joy and regret. The work, like the banyans and the mangoes, had grown far beyond expectation. But she knew this was indeed the last time.

A letter of welcome and an invitation from the little Prince of Khetri and his sisters took her to Ajmer. Both the Rajah and the Rani were now dead. Here the prince visited her, now a fine lad of fourteen, tall and manly, dressed in an English riding suit and a handsome turban. Though he did not remember her, he had her photo holding a baby who he had been told was himself. As they sat together, she asked if she might drop his title and call him by his name, Jai Singh, as it made her boy seem so far away to address him as Rajah Sahib. He seemed pleased.

She talked to him about his childhood, told him many interesting stories about himself and his mother. He read a page of English to her, and she found that he spoke it well. His guardian told her that the prince was a noble youth and they hoped to keep him so, for in four years he would become Rajah in his father's place.

The two princesses visited her, and she was much pleased with both of them. The elder had grown into a beautiful queenly woman, much like her mother. Dr. Clara spent some weeks as her guest in Bombay. She found to her delight that the Bai Sahiba still

[83]

enjoyed reading the Bible, especially the Sermon on the Mount, and was devoting her life to the good of her people.

She remained in India for eighteen months, sailing home in March, 1908. Dr. Cordelia Greene, who had established the sanatorium in Castile, had been succeeded by her niece, Dr. Mary Greene, who had arranged that Dr. Swain and her lifelong friend, Mrs. Hoskins, should occupy rooms in her beautiful cottage, Brookside, opposite the sanatorium ground. Through the years Clara Swain had sent letters home to Dr. Greene, and now Dr. Mary urged that these be collected and published in a little book. Clara Swain made vehement objection. "But—I have done nothing—!"

"Nothing? You call it nothing to be the first woman missionary doctor in the world, one of the first two missionaries sent out by the Society, to act as medical adviser in a rajah's palace, to found the first hospital for women in all of Asia?"

Dr. Swain at last consented, and the letters were published under the title, *A Glimpse of India*.

She spent her last years in quiet and serenity, taking her meals in the sanatorium, participating in the morning and evening prayer services. But after the last trip to India she grew steadily weaker and died early on Christmas morning in 1910.

There are few relics of her person today in the hospital which bears her name: a picture on the wall of the old dispensary, now the administration building; a Victorian sofa beautifully carved and upholstered in a faded flower pattern; a bed and chair of the same style and vintage; a lone copy of the book containing her letters. But there is no need of relics to keep her memory alive. Her memorials are human beings—doctors, nurses, patients—who after a hundred years are still giving and receiving more abundant life.

10

One of the few living links between Clara Swain and recent hospital personnel was that wide-eyed, eight-year-old boy, Nizam Masih.

"If you could give one of your sons to serve in the hospital," said Dr. Esther Gimson to Mathru when it came time for him to retire, "your family could stay on the hospital compound."

The six older sons were already married and working. The two youngest were too small to work, so Nizam, then studying in the third class, was chosen. He started in 1913 as an errand boy. Medical superintendents, doctors, nurses would come and go, but for the next half century and more Nizam would continue to serve the hospital with all his remarkable pride, loyalty, wit, and common sense.

Except for one brief period! One day during World War I he was sent on an errand to the railroad station. He did not return. For days the doctor was beside herself with worry. Then came a letter addressed to the doctor and to Nizam's parents. It contained an answer to the message he had been sent to deliver at the station, also to the mystery of his disappearance. There had been a recruiting officer at the station. Whether through the latter's compulsive or persuasive powers or his own spirit of adventure, Nizam had joined the army. He was in Bombay, on his way to France. He returned some years later minus his boyish naïveté, but plus much worldly wisdom and considerable skill as the driver of a Model T. It was rumored that in acquiring said skill he had wrecked a car and been confined to quarters for a month.

The episode marked his graduation from the role of errand boy. When Dr. Gimson's brother sent a car for hospital use, Nizam started working as a cleaner, taking immense pride in keeping it washed and polished. In 1923 he got his driver's license and served in that capacity *ad infinitum*. But his services to the hospital included far more than motor driving. Though his English was by no means perfect, he used it with sublime confidence and often served as interpreter between Western doctors and villagers, as on one occasion when a medical team from the hospital was making a trip into the villages.

"*Mere pet men mitha, mitha dard sa uthe hai*," one patient detailed her symptoms, "*aur pet se gardan men akar ruk jae hai.*"

The doctor could not understand what the patient was trying to say. She called the nurses, and even they failed to convey the woman's ailment. Finally Nizam was called. Immediately he understood the difficulty. The doctor was puzzled by the word *mitha*. "She says," he translated, "start my pain in stomach and, going very slow and very sweet (*mitha*), come to my neck."

The doctor at once understood. "See," she said, "it took Nizam to get it across to me."

On another occasion the hospital milkman brought some *khees* (coagulated milk in the udders of newly calved cows or buffaloes) to the doctor. It is a custom in India to give such milk free to friends and relatives. The doctor, not understanding why he had brought her so much milk when she had not ordered it, scolded him soundly. The poor milkman did not know how to explain. Nizam arrived during the commotion.

"See, Nizam, I'm asking this milkman to take back these ten *seers* of milk. I did not order it, and I'm not going to buy it."

"Nizam," explained the unhappy vendor, "this is *khees*, and I want to present it to Miss Sahiba for her patients and school-girls."

Nizam turned to the doctor. "Last night, Miss Sahiba, two buffalo giving boys, he brings first milk as gift to you."

Smiling, the doctor accepted the gift.

Once his confident versatility almost got him into trouble. In the early days all medicines containing poisons had to be secured through the Collectorate, and someone from the hospital had to sign for them. When Nizam was sent one day for such medicines and was given a paper, he signed, "Nizam Masih, M.D." Presently a policeman from the Collectorate came to the hospital requesting to see Nizam Masih, M.D.

"Nizam!" scolded Dr. Gimson. "You know very well you have no business to put an M.D. after your name."

Nizam ran to the car, got his driver's license, and displayed it triumphantly. "Why are you angry with me, Dr. Miss Sahiba? See, here is my license. It say right here what I am, M.D., Motor Driver."

Dr. Gimson laughed heartily. "So that's it. Well, next time, Nizam, you put the M.D. inside parentheses."

But there were times when the "M.D." stood for more than "Motor Driver." Once, driving in a village, he met a man whose heel was painfully swollen. Having often seen such abscesses treated, Nizam told him to foment it with hot water and salt, whereupon the abscess soon opened and discharged, and the man obtained relief from pain. Not having any materials for dressings, Nizam asked him to come to the hospital, and gave him his name on a piece of paper. The man came.

"Please tell me where I can find this doctor," he begged, showing the paper.

"That's no doctor," laughed those who read it. "He's only a motor driver."

"*Achchha,* good," replied the villager. "For you he may be motor driver. For me he is very good doctor."

When the medical superintendent heard of the incident, she was pleased and gave Nizam a package of sterilized bandages and Mercurochrome to take with him. Later he was given a standard medicine box with remedies for headache, itch, and other simple ailments. And his services as a public relations man were often of greater value than his driving. Many villagers, even city dwellers, were afraid of operations. Nizam took it upon himself to talk to them, listen to their fears, explain why an operation was necessary, and calm their worries.

But this was not all. In accompanying the mission team to the villages he often translated for the doctors when they preached and gave religious instruction. Often he would be left with the car when other members of the team were busy calling on patients. Returning, they would find him talking and gesticulating with vigor, a group of enthralled villagers gathered around him. He was telling them "Jesus stories," he would explain to the interested missionaries. These stories would usually begin, "Jesus said," then resolve into eloquent tales combining Old and New Testament events in highly dramatic sequence with slight personal editing, but always stern and emphatic emphasis on the moral involved. His fame as a preacher spread. When Bishop Pickett in Delhi heard of it, he gave Nizam a local preacher's license, waiving the necessity of an examination.

"We owe everything to the hospital," Nizam kept telling the five sons and five daughters who came to him through the years. "Be proud that your grandfather and father have served it faithfully, and see that you also are ready to serve it if you are needed."

Nizam was not the only one of the service staff whose contribution to the hospital was to span a lifetime. There was Kallan, for instance, who began work as a house servant during the regime of Dr. Gimson. Though a simple, uneducated man, for sheer goodness and Christian devotion he could not be surpassed. Later when his eyesight failed he had to be taken off house duty, but he was so insistent that he still must work for the hospital that he was first transferred to the student dining room, then given the job of night watchman at the hospital gate. When unable to perform that task successfully, he was given an assistant and still permitted to hold his post.

"I want to die working for the hospital," he maintained, but his wish was not quite realized. Becoming so weak that he could not travel to the gate, he finally was to die at home.

Then there was Dulari, ranking far above most of the other sweeper women in ability and intelligence. When an ayah was needed in the missionary bungalow, it was suggested that Dulari be given the position. The amazement and pure joy that overspread her plain features when she learned that she was to be promoted from sweeper's work! She became a comfort to all in the house, always dependable, winning a place in the hearts of the long succession of missionaries whom she served.

During Dr. Gimson's twenty years progress was made in many areas. In 1905 nurses' training was started with a class of four, the beginning of the school of nursing which was to become such an important feature of the institution. "If possible," specified Dr. Gimson, "every girl should be a middle passed, should understand English, and be without domestic encumbrance." But of this class one died, one was married before completing training, one was dismissed, leaving only one to graduate. However, with her in this first graduating class of 1908 were four others admitted in 1906. They had passed in anatomy, hygiene, *materia medica*, surgical nursing, and anesthesia.

Dr. Gimson labored often alone and under great difficulties. It was recorded of her in 1908: "Neither day nor night has she thought of herself, never refusing a call. In addition to this heavy work, she has had to pass through another rainy season without a dry spot large enough to keep her instruments from being ruined." Plague was very bad that year. The next year there was a terrible prevalence of malaria, and she was nearly four months without even an assistant. During October alone attendance in the dispensary reached 4,400. But she rejoiced over the new roof and exulted that "the hospital will now be good for twenty years!" And when the new roof was put on, a large window was installed in the operating room, which made surgery much easier by day, if not by night.

"One thing we see," she was glad to note, "is the increasing confidence of the people for obstetrical work. Formerly simply the abnormal cases were brought. This year only 13 of our 75 were abnormal. The other day a Mohammedan woman, living in the city, said that this place is known by many as 'God's Hospital.' "

The reports of subsequent years bore eloquent testimony to the courage and devotion of Esther Gimson.

1910 ... "Sick but did her work all the year. Others have feared she could not hold out until help reached her, but not a word of complaint."

1911 ... "Although tired to the point of breakdown, Dr. Gimson held on until the arrival of Dr. Kipp, whom the Northwestern branch sent to her relief."

1912 ... "Dr. Kipp transferred to Brindaban. Dr. Laybourne is helping Dr. Gimson, who asks for $10,000 to complete the hospital quadrangle, containing an up-to-date operating room, to be a memorial to Dr. Clara Swain."

1913 ... "Dr. Laybourne transferred to Baroda. Dr. Gimson alone again."

That year Dr. Gimson wrote: "The year a hard one, but we remember how good the Lord has been and what He has done. The hospital has been full all the year. Often we have had to ask patients from Bareilly to bring their own beds and have doubled the number of patients in the rooms. We cry for more room!"

1914 ... "Dr. Gimson alone. 1,761 in the hospital and 500 outcalls. Two nurses died of tuberculosis, due largely to lack of a suitable place for living."

1916 ... "The war has made it hard to get medicines; some we could not get at all; some are so high in price that we have had to substitute others; some, while expensive, we have had to have anyway, and so we have had a hard time to make ends meet."

1919 was the Jubilee of the Woman's Foreign Missionary Society. In the fifty years the organization had grown to a membership of 300,000. Over a thousand woman missionaries had been sent out, seventy-eight of them medical. But so great were the needs all over the world that only one could be spared for Bareilly.

"Outside the cities," wrote Dr. Gimson, "there is almost no medical work. The villagers have no conveyances to get to a doctor. Many die, many are left blind and deformed by native treatment. On one village trip a boy was brought to me who had been badly burned on chest, arm, and side; they had bound the arm down to the side to cover the entire burn, and it grew fast. Much eye trouble yields readily to treatment. When one is cured they bring many others, but what can one doctor do with village work when she is the only one in charge of a hospital visited each year by thousands? I am not complaining. I was never happier in my work, but the need is so great, and *one* can do so little!"

In 1920 Dr. Loal Huffman, substituting while Dr. Gimson was on furlough, was still struggling with a grueling schedule, doing major operations by lamplight, and sighing for a new hospital building. There were new responsibilities also, for that year Clara Swain Hospital (now bearing the name of its founder) was authorized to open a babies' home, and twenty-one babies were received during the year. The home was to continue under hospital supervision until Miss Olive Kennard took it over in 1922, serving until Miss Edna Bacon arrived in 1924. Later this was named the Warne Baby Fold in honor of Bishop Warne, because of his great love for children.

During Dr. Huffman's administration the nurses' training school became part of the North India Union, with a United Board of Examiners. A year was added to the course, making necessary more teachers and support. This mark of progress was a tribute to the work of Mrs. Bertha Shaw, its superintendent for many years.

Fresh from furlough, Dr. Gimson again assumed command, caring for the missionary staff, the orphanage girls, the students of the theological school and their families, the wee occupants of the Baby Fold, and the ever-flowing stream of patients. In her first year back there were 569 hospital patients, 8,089 out-patients, and a dispensary attendance of 23,670. But there was more exciting work, superintending the building of the new additions which were at last going up. Yet even with her splendid physique she could not stand up under the strain and twice during the year she was critically ill. The completion of the buildings, however, which added another wing to the hospital and raised its capacity to seventy beds, brought enough satisfaction to compensate for all difficulties.

Dr. Gimson's last term at Clara Swain was a mixture of triumph and sorrow. She received the coveted honor of the Kaiser-i-Hind on the King's birthday in recognition of her long and high-class service, one of England's most rare and prized awards. But the report of 1924 recorded: "The cup that our doctor has been called upon to drink has been a strange mixture of bitter and sweet, for in the space of a few short months she has donned both the bridal veil and the widow's weeds. Dr. Gimson-

Bare has the profound sympathy of all our Society, but more than that we accord her our admiration that she has found balm for her own wounds in heroically binding up those of others."

If the hospital suffered from a rapid turnover of doctors in the years following Dr. Gimson-Bare, there was compensation in the continuity of leadership in the department of nursing. Theresa Lorenz, arriving in 1926, qualified by five years of teaching, public health and administrative work, was to remain for more than twenty years. Tall, straight of posture, attractive, she was soon in command of both school and nursing services. Arriving the same year was Janette Crawford, associated for some time with the girls' school but later to become an invaluable member of the hospital staff.

Theresa Lorenz found some things in startling contrast to her previous life in Kansas and Ohio: an overabundance of mosquitoes, flies, snakes; huge monkeys boldly stealing cakes from the tea table or making off with the dough left by frightened women who had been kneading out of doors; a water supply dependent on a pair of "Gunga Dins" filling goatskins at a well; a big cooking vessel for sterilizing hospital instruments over a charcoal fire; no laboratory, no X-ray machine. But with only six months of language training she managed to teach some forty nursing students in their native tongue and supervise all work in the hospital, remaining on twenty-four-hour call for some years.

All hardships seemed as nothing when her first class of six girls graduated. It was a beautiful April day, with the *lou,* hot wind, not yet arrived. All the girls had come from wretchedly poor homes. There was Melvina, whose father, a retired mission worker, received less than four dollars a month to care for his family of four children. Cleo was not only poor, but her father failed to see the value of education for his girls and was always taking them out of school. Mercy's home was one not only of poverty but of extreme untidiness. It had been a real triumph for her to qualify for a profession where neatness and order were first essentials. Premi, an orphan dependent on the mission for many years, had become ill in the middle of her course and had had to spend time at the tuberculosis sanatorium at Tilaunia. Shevdatti had been a poor little starving waif taken in by a mission school. And Anna, who had come from a poor home in the mountains, had been the gayest and liveliest member of the class.

"Oh, boy!" she had exclaimed one day during a lecture period at Tilaunia. "This will be keen for school nursing!" For each of the nurses would serve at least one year as school nurse in one of the mission schools after graduation, and some of the special preparation for this work was received in a three-month affiliation with the sanatorium.

Part of the day's excitement was in having a picture taken of the hospital staff and student nurses, a difficult process merely to get them all together. Then the day after the first successful attempt the photographer came with news that during the night rats had broken his negative, so the process had to be started all over again.

But it was a beautiful commencement. The church was decorated with pansies, larkspur, jacaranda, and golden coreopsis and dharanta, blending perfectly with the class colors of purple and gold. It was a thrilling scene when the graduating class stood in their snow-white uniforms against a background of ferns and palms, between pure white lilies, and repeated the impressive Florence Nightingale pledge of service.

Visitors, even other missionaries, were amazed by the quality of work done amid almost primitive surroundings.

"But—don't you have electricity here? How can you possibly do these night confinement cases without it?"

"These gasoline lanterns give such a terrific heat on a summer night! How do you stand it?"

"Is that the only thing you have on which to boil water and sterilize instruments? I always thought those primus stoves were terribly slow!"

"Are these all your instruments? I was in a hospital at home once, and they had a whole room just for instruments, and its walls were lined with shelves, and every shelf was full of them."

The doctors and nurses would only laugh good-naturedly at these comments. The lack of modern conveniences was but a minor deficiency. The constant and far greater need was for more hands, more feet, more hours in the day to perform tasks which would have taxed the energies of a dozen professionals, to say nothing of a mere five.

The late twenties found Dr. Bertha Chase in charge of the hospital, with Dr. Massey, an L.M.P. (Licensed Medical Practitioner), as her assistant. Theresa Lorenz, the nursing superintendent, with her assistant Charlotte Westrup, and two staff nurses, Anna Singh and Miss James, completed the staff. Dr. Chase, springing from godly New Hampshire farming stock, working her way through high school, college, and medical school, was eminently suited to her task of serving an annual 700 in-patients, 16,000 out-patients, performing over 200 operations, and giving over 2,000 itinerary treatments. Small, smiling, unassuming in appearance, her long reddish-brown hair drawn into a discreet pug at the back of her very level head, she was a woman of quick and clear decisions, full of plans for improving working conditions in the hospital.

"I have a bright idea," she would preface a novel and often startling suggestion, like the one of asking fees from patients.

"But mission hospitals should give free service," was the shocked reaction. "We've always done so."

"Then it's time we stopped," was her calm rejoinder. Otherwise, she argued, they would never have enough money, even for bare necessities. And, besides, they were breeding a community of parasites. Many of their patients could afford to pay, some handsomely. It was better for others to pay what they could, if no more than a pice. As for those too poor to pay even that, of course none should be turned away. In spite of anguished protests and criticism, she had her way, laying the foundation for more traumatic changes ten years in the future.

Handicapped though she was by lack of equipment and sufficient trained personnel, Dr. Chase proved herself a brilliant doctor. She could remove tonsils, declared Theresa Lorenz, better than many skilled specialists. And she was given plenty of practice! Children were brought in from mission schools in large groups, all with bad tonsils. Once eighteen came from Pithoragarh, far up in the mountains, at that time five days' march on foot to the plains, then several hours' ride on the train to reach Bareilly. Under Dr. Chase's cheerful and expert direction they were whisked through the operating room with the speed and efficiency of an assembly line.

During her regime there was seldom enough bed space. Though it was called an eighty-bed hospital and there was room for that many, there were never more than seventy-two beds, and they were often full. But in India this was not a serious deficiency. Most villagers felt far more comfortable on the floor than in a high bed, and rush mats were always available. With only one doctor to meet all needs of medicine and surgery, to preside over operating room, dispensary, wards, and private rooms as well as be on constant call for house visits, it was no wonder that the health of doctor as well as patients was a major problem.

And even with the day's end her duties were not finished. In all mission hospitals the head doctor was expected to take care of all the business as well as the medical work. Watching Dr. Chase struggle far into the night with lists, invoices, bills, receipts, records, Theresa Lorenz fumed helplessly. The terms of too many doctors had been cut short because of broken health.

"It isn't right," she worried, first silently, then aloud. "There should be a nonmedical person to handle the accounts. You're a doctor, not an accountant."

"Try telling that to the powers that be," retorted Dr. Chase cheerfully.

"Thanks," replied Nurse Lorenz with the firm decision of the competent administrator. "I will do just that."

She approached the Women's Finance Committee of the North India Conference. They were almost as startled as by Dr. Chase's heretical suggestion of charging fees. But persistence won. They agreed to present the matter to Dr. Chitambar, India's first national bishop, in charge of their north India area. He presented it to his cabinet. By some miracle the innovation was accepted. As a temporary experiment Janette Crawford, a missionary teacher living in Bareilly, was appointed as "general assistant" at Clara Swain. She came to the new job with fear and trembling, for she knew nothing about hospital work, but during the trial year, the last of her first term, her interest and competence grew. Returning from furlough, she accepted the appointment as business manager of the hospital.

Her training for educational work was by no means lost, for part of her task, she soon realized, was to educate the public. "Are you a doctor?" visitors would ask. "No." "Are you a nurse?" "No." "Then what are you doing," their skeptical glances would imply, "in a hospital?" Seizing the opportunity, she would explain her duties. Sometimes visiting doctors would corner her and ask questions about her work. Presently other mission hospitals began employing business managers. Another *first* for Clara Swain!

It was not ill health, after all, which cut short Dr. Chase's service with the hospital, but romance. In the middle of her second term she married another missionary, and they took an appointment in Cawnpore. Her successor, the beloved Dr. Miriam Albertson, was called home after two years to care for her sick mother, but she later returned to spend a full term at Clara Swain, leaving as her great contribution to the hospital its first real laboratory. Heretofore, only minor tests had been possible, using a small microscope in the compounding room. With Miss Lorenz' co-operation Dr. Albertson set aside a room in the nurses' hostel, sent a nurse away for training, and in time a small but efficient laboratory was established.

But in spite of painstaking progress and innumerable persons helped, the decade of the thirties was one of much difficulty and frustration. Doctors came and went with distressing frequency. These were depression years in America. Missions were forced to retrench. While needs increased around the world, buildings grew shabby, few improvements were made, staff was depleted. Yet during this period the Clara Swain staff was strengthened, perhaps by these very difficulties, and prepared for the new era of progress to come in the next decade. It was augmented also by at least two competent Indian women whose loyal service would extend over more than thirty years.

Nurse Beatrice Brahmanand, arriving at the turn of the thirties, entered immediately into a round of activities which were to in-clude through the years a long period of service in the operating room, ward supervision, oversight of laundry, village work, and teaching. Coming in 1935, Mrs. Minnie Paul, a graduate in phar-macy and nursing from the Christian Medical College of Ludhi-ana, became a much-needed worker in pharmacy. She found a small hospital with no water supply, a minimum of electricity (only in the operating room and a few of the ward rooms), and a totally inadequate stock of medical supplies and equipment. There were few operations being performed, perhaps one a day, and open-drop anesthesia was still being used. There was a small delivery room with no fan. But she found a small staff of women courageously conducting every hospital activity with a deep reli-gious spirit and patients with such faith in them that they almost worshiped them as goddesses.

Minnie's marriage to Mr. Paul, a teacher in the boys' school, fulfilled a dream of her mother-in-law, Mrs. Ganeshi Paul, who had worked in the hospital for many years. As a child Ganeshi had been brought to the mission school for her education. Then there had been no compounders in the hospital and very few nurses. At the request of the doctor in charge, Ganeshi had left school and been trained as a compounder, working there until she was given in marriage to a student of the seminary. When they had gone to a village to work, she had lived in the hope that one of her children would grow up to serve her beloved hospital. When her one daughter, college-trained and dedicated, had chosen village work, the dream had been transferred to a future daughter-in-law.

"And now that desire is fulfilled in me," acknowledged Minnie gratefully.

Perhaps the greatest progress during the decade was in the school of nursing. A course for graduate nurses was introduced. The hospital became the teaching headquarters for a public health program. Another milestone was reached when it was recognized by the Punjab Nurses' Registration Council, and the nurses began to appear for Punjab examinations and went to Delhi for their practicals.

There were even a few material developments, such as a new ambulance. Heretofore the ambulance had been a stretcher placed across the rear doors of an old touring car, the patient's head projecting on one side and his feet on the other. The new one, a Ford V-8 on an ordinary-size chassis, had been rebuilt as a carry-all for a petty rajah to use hunting. They got it at a bargain. It had two long seats in the back to accommodate stretchers and plenty of space for equipment and passengers. When money became available, it would be equipped with cabinets for medicines and supplies.

Also with more money it could have made possible a far better rural extension program. They tried to make trips to villages perhaps twice a week, taking a doctor, a couple of nurses, a lab technician, a Bible reader, and of course Nizam, driver and man of many parts. But finances made such trips almost prohibitive. There was nothing in the budget for petrol or medicine, and the patients could afford to pay only a pice or two.

"We need so many things," wrote Mary Gordon, R.N., a missionary nurse sent out by the Northwestern branch in 1937. "For years we have had hopes for an electric pump, and our perennial want ad is for an X-ray machine! Even in these depression years someone might give it. What a pity that the Society's first medical work for women and children in Asia is so handicapped through lack of staff and good equipment!"

But winds of change stronger even than the hot *lou* were already stirring. As the world prepared for the convulsion of another world war, forces equally disruptive were undermining the foundations of primitive cultures, tearing down walls of old taboos and prejudices. In India the winds were blowing hot and strong. Women were taking their places beside men in the tumultuous struggle for independence. Soon there would no longer be the need or the demand for a hospital ministering solely to women. And the Indian governments were raising their standards for medical qualifications to a challenging and satisfying degree. Nurses, to be trained properly and become fully qualified, must soon receive their clinical training in a general, not a zenana hospital.

It was Dr. Mildred Burton who first recognized the need for change. After coming to India straight from medical school, she had served an internship in the large Presbyterian hospital at Miraj, where men as well as women were treated. Her sharp eyes observed that in India men were far more important than women and that it was much easier to obtain fees from men patients. Seeing the appalling needs at Clara Swain, she soon offered a remedy.

"Get a man doctor, so we can admit men patients," she suggested cannily. "Then we can get money for the million things we need."

"No!" was the shocked reaction. "Shades of Clara Swain! Heaven forbid!"

But gradually her persistent suggestions gained approval, for it was an idea whose time had come. The pioneer spirit which had created the first hospital for women in Asia was as vigorous as ever. The Woman's Foreign Missionary Society organized by eight intrepid women in 1869 and incorporated in 1939 in the new Woman's Division of Christian Service, an organization of more than a million members, prepared to meet the challenge of a changing social order.

The first opportunity came in 1939 when Dr. Mahler, an Austrian who, with his wife and ten-year-old son, had escaped the fate of millions of his fellow Jews and fled to India, made application to join the staff for a short term. He had been given work at a community hospital in the mountains which closed for three months during the winter, and he wanted work during that period. What to do? It was an opportune time, for another doctor was badly needed. Dr. Burton was on furlough. There were only two Indian woman doctors of L.M.P. grade in attendance. Should the experiment be given a three-months' trial?

"Yes." The decision was made, and the die was cast, the tradition of seventy years broken.

It was the task of Louise Landon, the missionary nurse in charge, to reconcile the diverse thinking of patients and doctor. In spite of Dr. Mahler's ignorance of the language and of the custom of seclusion of Indian women, he was well liked, and the experiment was a modest success. It prepared the way for the next step. For soon after, the Woman's Division and the Division of World Missions agreed to cooperate in the support of the hospital. It was to be reorganized under the direction of two young American doctors, Charles and Wilma Perrill, with Dr. Wilma in charge of the existing women's work and Dr. Charles initiating medical work for men.

Their arrival in Bareilly marked both the end and the beginning of an era.

PART TWO

Women and Men

1

It was as a child in India that Charles Perrill first got the idea of becoming a doctor. The son of missionary parents stationed in Ballia, United Provinces, on school vacations he traveled with his parents through the villages, studied Hindi, and learned the local dialect, Bhojpuri, and by the time he was twelve was thoroughly convinced that he wanted to be a missionary like his father.

Perhaps it was while watching Mrs. Ilahi Baksh at the small dispensary hospital at Rasra, the only Christian woman doctor in a large area, that his interest in medicine was aroused. Once, as he waited to have a wart cut off his finger, he sat and watched the swarm of patients, many of them women and children, was fascinated by her skill and patience, haunted by the thin racked bodies, the suffering faces turned eager, trusting, hopeful.

Then there was the time when he went hunting with his father and a guest who had come from the city to spend the Christmas holidays. By now the family had graduated to their second Model T, an improved version with real electric headlights. The first had come to grief following an encounter with a small herd of razorback pigs. The guest was a poor marksman. One of his bullets flew high, missed the *nil-gai* (blue antelope), penetrated a sugar patch 500 yards away, and struck a village lad in the thigh.

An angry crowd gathered, waved their bamboo poles, prepared to march the interlopers off to jail in Ballia, seven miles away. The wounded lad was squeezed, groaning with pain, into a small boxlike *dholi*. No, they would not think of carrying him on a string cot; those were used to take corpses to the river. Nor would they let Charles ride on a small pony cart which happened to come along the road.

It was dark when they reached the little civil hospital, where the assistant surgeon made a diagnosis. The police pronounced the case to be an accident, and Charles's father assumed the responsibility of the boy's treatment. In the months that followed, Charles often rode on his bicycle to visit the boy in the small hospital, keeping the vase on the window sill filled with fresh flowers. The next year, visiting him in his village, he found the boy smiling but a cripple, the injured leg five or six inches shorter than the other, and using a bamboo pole to get around. Charles gazed at the twisted foot in horror. Surely an expert doctor could have done better for such an injury! Later, in his medical textbooks, he was to recognize instantly a picture of this same deformity and read with grim fascination the steps that should have been taken. Still later, treating such fractures with stainless steel pins and the latest traction apparatus, he would thank God that he need settle for no less than perfect results.

But it may have been the rabies incident which really gave young Charles Perrill the idea of becoming a doctor. During his school vacation he went back with his father to visit his birthplace, Arrah, in Bihar, north India. In the school which his father had run as a young missionary, Charles went out to play soccer with the boys. A dog lying on the edge of the playing field suddenly jumped at him, foaming at the mouth, and bit his leg, then tried to attack other players, succeeding in biting another boy.

"Mad dog!" was the horrified cry, for rabies, a common curse of India, was a disease, once it took hold, from which no victim ever recovered.

Charles and the other boy were rushed to the civil surgeon, who washed out the wounds with fuming nitric acid. Then Mr. Perrill took the two of them, together with a jar containing the mad dog's brain, on a long wild drive to Kasauli in the Simla Hills, site of the Pasteur Institute. Here a kindly British doctor started them on injections, which after seven days he doubled in strength. Charles understood why when he saw the little pink ovals, Negri bodies, in the dog's brain cells under the microscope. Seeing the large pens full of rabbits and guinea pigs sacrificed to make the vaccine, he devoutly blessed Louis Pasteur and these doctors in India who had saved his life.

Added to all these experiences was the week he spent hanging around the Prince of Wales Medical College in Calcutta waiting for an operation on his knee, dislocated when playing basketball in the American school at Woodstock. One of the nursing sisters showed him the operating theaters, and through this and his own operation he gained a glimpse of all the possibilities of modern surgery for the India of tomorrow.

Whatever the motivation, by the end of his freshman year at

Antioch College in Ohio, Charles Perrill knew he must become a doctor and he transferred to Wesleyan University in Connecticut, which had a good premedical course. He did his medical training at Northwestern University, assisting in physiological chemistry under Dr. Farmer and Dr. A. C. Ivy, distinguishing himself by perfecting a metabolism machine using air instead of oxygen (designed for use in India, with its many large goiter cases), on which Northwestern took out a patent. One of these Portable Air-Using Metabolimeters was made and shipped to India.

"Information received from India indicates that the machine arrived in good condition," reported Charles in a paper describing the invention, "and that it should find a field of usefulness in an area where the cost of recharging a small oxygen tank is almost $10.

"The design of this machine is simple enough to permit the construction of duplicates in India, for the Indian tinsmith is often skilled in working with copper tubing and sheet metals. The materials in this apparatus cost $17 (in Chicago). This includes both the clockwork and the 6-volt motor, but not the cost of labor."

With this experiment in adapting expensive Western devices to the needs and resources of a poor country, Charles set for himself a pattern which was to shape his whole career. It was also to cause vast changes in Clara Swain Hospital.

Discovering after finishing his medical course that it would cost him only $10 plus the thesis, Charles also obtained a Master of Science degree, completing the work in two summer schools, including one at the University of Chicago.

As a medical student he was often called to speak on missions, and he went occasionally to the Board of Missions office to get lantern slides for use in his speeches. Here he met the Rev. H. G. Conger, head of the Visual Aids Department at the Chicago office of the Methodist Board of Missions.

"I have a daughter, Wilma," Conger told Charles, "who is about to graduate from Ohio Wesleyan. She wants to be a doctor."

Charles expressed his sympathy. *Tsk, tsk!* These hen medics!

"Maybe so," agreed Mr. Conger, "but her mind is made up. I say—maybe you'd be willing to show her through the medical school sometime?"

Charles grinned. "To see if she can really bear the sight of the cadavers?" He agreed with lukewarm enthusiasm, then forgot the incident.

Just before his first Christmas vacation Mr. Conger called and reminded him of his promise. Wilma was coming in from Ohio on a bus Friday night, arriving in Chicago at two in the morning. Charles was leaving for Kansas shortly, so the only time he could spare was at eight on Saturday morning. She would be there, agreed Conger. Charles was not pleased. Neither was Wilma. Reaching her home in Evanston at three in the morning, then having to be up at seven to go back to Chicago, just to meet a man!

They met . . . and kept meeting. Quite undaunted by the cadavers, Wilma persisted in her plans to become a doctor. Despite progress made in women's rights since the days of Elizabeth Blackwell and Clara Swain, most medical colleges still refused to accept women. Finally she was accepted conditionally at Northwestern, where four women were grudgingly admitted each year because of a stipulation in the 8-million-dollar grant from Mrs. Montgomery Ward.

"Why this prejudice?" Charles once asked the dean, Dr. Cutter.

Many times, he explained, money was wasted on women doctors who married and raised families and did not practice. Statistics, however, were to prove the dean wrong; and certainly Wilma herself, in spite of marriage and motherhood, was to have a much wider practice than Charles, in the actual number of patients treated.

A year ahead of her in medical school, he loaned her his notes, advised concerning microscope and textbooks; visited the Conger home in Evanston with its five lively children, where he was dubbed the "big stiff" because his only-child manners were so proper; had a date with Wilma every Saturday night over anatomy and physiology books; became more and more enamored of the slender, fair-haired girl who looked no older than a high school freshman and came barely to his shoulder; and got engaged to her before the year was out. They were married four years later, just a month before Wilma finished her internship and Charles his residency, and spent their honeymoon attending two missionary conferences, then returned to finish their residency and internship. Some years before, they had been accepted as missionaries, and now their appointment was made to a former women's hospital just now being opened to men doctors and patients, the Clara Swain Hospital in Bareilly, India.

Charles was a scavenger. He collected all kinds of cast-off equipment—old instruments, microscopes, operating tables—being discarded by the Wesley Hospital, which was moving into a new building, and they spent the summer packing. The draft caught him in San Francisco, where they were waiting for a ship, and his exit was delayed until he could be cleared by army headquarters.

"Where are you going, and what do you intend to do in India?" demanded the army officer. Charles told him.

"O.K.," came the reply. "If you're enough of an idiot to want to do that sort of thing, the army won't stop you."

These were still depression years. Funds for missionary enterprises, especially new ones, were at a minimum. Charles was warned that there was no obligation assumed except for his own personal support. There was even difficulty in providing shipment charges for the 3 tons of impedimenta which he had collected. He must understand that he was entirely on his own in starting the new venture. Charles understood and accepted the challenge.

2

The trip took two months, and it was December when they landed in Bombay. In spite of the changes which ten years had wrought in both himself and India, Charles was delighted to find he could still speak the language fluently. Putting the vast variety of his equipment through customs was a complicated process. He was glad some of it was listed as "junk," with only 5 per cent duty.

They were glad to leave the heat of Bombay behind, but as they traveled the thousand miles northward the air turned sharply cold. When they pulled into the Bareilly station at 4:30 in the morning, with the temperature below 40, the warmth of their rousing welcome was slightly tempered by their summer clothes. At the hospital all lights were on, and the student nurses sang them a song of welcome in English.

When daylight came they examined the scene of their future

work. The prospect was discouraging. There were the old white pillared out-patient building which Dr. Clara Swain had built in 1873, the long lines of brick buildings containing the eighty beds for patients, perhaps thirty of them in actual use. None of the buildings had been whitewashed for several years. There were the nurses' hostel, the bungalows for the women doctors and the nursing supervisors. The one reserved for them was more like a barn than a bungalow, with its big bare living room and its ceiling 19 feet high. The servants' quarters, teeming with children, goats, and chickens, were just behind their garden in the rear. *Their* garden? In days to come they sometimes wondered.

They arrived in Bareilly in time for the Methodist North India Annual Conference and were welcomed with enthusiasm. Funds being as yet nonexistent for the establishment of the new men's department, the men of the Conference responded in typical Methodist fashion. They took up an offering. Even the poor Indian preachers dipped into their nearly empty pockets, collecting what was for them a large sum, nearly a hundred dollars, and begged Dr. Charles to start the department immediately.

Two less eager and dedicated new recruits would have viewed the prospect with dampened enthusiasm. During previous years doctors and nurses had come and gone with disheartening regularity, with overwork, sickness, furloughs, and matrimony constantly depleting the ranks. But the remaining staff was loyal and expectant, eager to see both hope and faith translated into action.

And Charles Perrill was the man to do it. The more difficult the problem, the fewer the resources, the greater was the challenge to his remarkable ingenuity. His lean, long, gangling figure, never at rest, was soon the center of building operations, his slender surgeon's fingers as adept with hammer and saw as with scalpel. Knowing the Indian language and psychology, as willing to engage in manual labor as a coolie, exacting in his demands but pleasantly tactful in obtaining them, he was able to secure full cooperation, even a degree of speed, from his Indian workmen.

Taking a section of the old hospital for women, they first locked and bolted it securely, then opened an outside entrance where the male nurse, patients, and Dr. Charles himself could come and go without danger of disrupting the female traditions of the hospital. Twenty beds were then installed to form the beginnings of a men's ward. Next the 3 tons of equipment were unpacked, a process in which the whole neighborhood joyously participated. The decrepit operating tables and basin stands, the old suction-pressure machine, and the ailing instruments were tenderly reassembled and taken to Mr. Rossiter's garage a few blocks away. To Charles's surprise and delight he found there two excellent mechanics and a machine shop completely equipped with lathes and welding apparatus. With their help he soon had the beginnings of two fairly adequate operating rooms.

Lights were then the big problem. In the hospital they found a single circuit supplying only a few lights, the 220 D.C. voltage quite unsuitable for American electric motors or transfers.

It took several months to bring electricity to the hospital rooms, and even then ordinary lighting was not sufficient for operating. Here Rossiter again came across. He took an automobile headlight reflector, welded it to a long brass curtain rod, and mounted it with a little clutch to a wooden stand. The bulb was held in place by an ingenious spring and the light cord threaded down the curtain rod. A spotlight both flexible and brilliant, and a good bit lighter than some of the bulky streamlined products with a cannonball for a counterweight, so heavy that it took both a nurse and an intern to move them about! Next the two men constructed shadowless overhead operating lights made out of large aluminum wash basins beaten into exact parabolas and polished until they shone like reflecting telescope mirrors.

Then came a harder problem, running water. But it had to be solved. How the hospital had gotten along for seventy years with open wells, which with their bamboo sweeps, buckets, or earthen water jars were fearfully unsanitary, besides providing harborage for debris, frogs, cholera, typhoid, and who knew what else, it was hard to understand. Charles had brought with him a whole plumbing system, complete with a Meyer's pump and pressure tank. A new well pit was sunk. There was confusion for months while ditches were dug, holes knocked in walls, and about fifty faucets installed. But the new system was an unmitigated blessing. The hospital patients could drink directly from the faucet, while other neighbors on the compound still had to boil every drop they drank.

A room was set aside for Dr. Charles in the old dispensary building, and men were not long in coming. All the old chronic cases for miles around were soon queueing up outside the door, anxious to find out what the new Doctor Sahib could and would do for them—free.

His first surgical patient was a young preacher who came for repair of a hernia which had become so large and tender that he could not ride his bicycle over the rutted roads on his village circuit. Several Indian congregations were praying for the young American surgeon as he tackled that job in the bare operating room at the front corner of the old hospital. The operation was a success, and the young preacher was soon riding once more. Then came another preacher, an old man with cataracts so far developed that he could not see to read his Bible, a calamity for him and his whole illiterate congregation.

Cataracts! A delicate test indeed for a brand new surgeon! For, although Charles had assisted with eye operations and watched them, he had never before actually performed cataract surgery. A day or two before he secured some rabbit eyes and practiced on them, but that was hardly comparable to doing the operation on a fully conscious patient, under mere local anesthetic. The knife shook a bit when his fingers closed about it. The eye stared up at him with mute—was it accusation? Pleading? No. Trust. He knew it was not going to be easy. But his hand was steady when he made the first neat incision. He was surprised to find how tough the cornea was, even though the cataract knife was needle-sharp—and how delicate the iris! To his consternation, when he pulled on it the patient jumped.

"Come now, brother. Lie still, please. We're nearly finished."

The shadowless lights were good. The Indian students were already proving excellent scrub nurses. They had quickly learned the hand signals for the different instruments. Gritting his teeth but smiling calmly, Charles pursued the operation to its conclusion. The patient was bandaged, carefully nursed through the days of delicate care and immobility. Then came the test. Charles held his breath when he took off the bandages.

"God be praised, Doctor Sahib! I can see!"

Good so far! But—could he read? When the glasses came and he put them on, again the young surgeon held his breath.

"*Achchha!* Give me the Bible, Doctor Sahib."

The hands turned unerringly to a certain passage. The face became wreathed in smiles. "Here it is! I can read it, Doctor Sahib, clear as day. 'Whereas I was blind, now I see!' "

Such operations were soon routine work. As the reputation of the new surgeon spread, the twenty beds in the men's ward were soon filled. Villagers who walked many miles, carrying their precious shoes on the end of their bamboo poles or staves, came with sore eyes, hernias, venereal disease. Workers from the match factory at the edge of Bareilly came with hand injuries inflicted by the automatic machinery or were sent in with terrible burns. The lives of several of these burned factory workers were saved by the use of the pressure dressings devised by Dr. Sumner Koch, with whose use of massive dressings padded with mechanic's waste Charles was in emphatic agreement.

One of the factory patients was Raj Bahadur, a mechanic who had been hurled to the ground, suffering a nasty fracture of the upper femur. They rigged him up in ropes and pulleys. Three months later he was smiling radiantly as they helped him into the pony cart to take him back to the factory. But the next day he was brought back again. The cart had been involved in an accident. Raj Bahadur had been thrown to the ground and his bone refractured. Another three months in the men's ward! But when he left this time he took more with him than a reset femur. His bed was next to that of a Christian preacher, and the two spent many hours discussing the meaning of suffering and other problems. Raj Bahadur became a Christian and the lay leader of a new Christian community at the match factory.

Nursing service in the new men's department was a real problem. When the ward was first opened the woman nurses were afraid to nurse the male patients. Each night the male nurse was locked in with them, and Miss Mary Gordon, the nursing instructor, held the key. One night when she went on her rounds, she unlocked the door and found the male nurse fast asleep in a hospital bed!

The barriers between the men's and women's departments, however, were not long in breaking down. With a married couple in charge of the hospital, both departments became more or less a family matter. Patients and their relatives in the women's side would hear of the activities of the new man surgeon and ask why his services should be denied to women. So Dr. Charles found himself in the women's wards, being escorted on either side by a senior nurse, visiting his surgical patients. Though he would try to keep his eyes straight ahead, he could not help noticing the rows of beds with each patient carefully hidden under a sheet pulled up over her head. A few days later he could see eyes peering around some of the sheets, and it wasn't long before a hand was motioning to him and a timid voice was saying, "Please come and feel my pulse, Doctor Sahib. I'm sick too."

Some of his first women's operations were large ovarian cysts, and, though Dr. Charles tackled them confidently, his skill was sometimes severely challenged. One of the largest cysts turned out to be a sticky dermoid, adherent everywhere. Lifting and retracting the slippery 22-pound tumor proved too much for the student nurse assisting. She fainted dead away. After the growth was finally hoisted out, the surgeon also experienced a sickening sensation as he gazed down into the huge cavity and identified 7 inches of the inferior *vena cava*, the large vein, projecting into the field of his recent sharp dissection! Surely it must have come within an eighth of an inch from his scalpel!

Dr. Wilma also was having her problems, successes, frustrations. Unlike Charles, she was not India-born. She must learn not only the language but the elementals of a new culture, many of which were of vital significance to a doctor specializing in the health problems of women and children. She was deluged by a constant stream of poor childless women seeking her help. In India, she soon discovered, the childless woman was accursed. For many, bearing sons was the sole purpose in life. If a woman could not produce them, better that she had been created a cow, which was at least considered sacred! Ask a Hindu woman how many children she had, and she would usually mention just her sons. Only if pressed further would she admit that she had daughters also. Other women with failing health came with the opposite problem. By the age of thirty they might have given birth to ten or twelve children, most of whom had died in rapid succession. In the family planning clinic which she soon established, Dr. Wilma gave not only sympathy and understanding but, as her knowledge and experience developed, an increasing amount of practical help.

Many of her childbirth cases were complicated, like that of the village woman brought twenty-five miles in an ox cart. With difficulty she extracted some of the history from the ignorant village midwife. The woman had been in labor for at least five days. The infant's arm had prolapsed four days ago, and the midwife had tugged on it valiantly to no avail. The arm had been purple for three days and was necrotic when the mother was admitted.

Her condition had been "bad" for two days—and no wonder! At first Dr. Wilma consulted her textbooks faithfully. Many of their comments, such as "This condition should never be allowed to occur," or "Treatment is extremely difficult and the outlook is discouraging," were of small help indeed! Many of her cases had reached an extremity never even imagined by an American obstetrician. Within a few months she herself could have written a fairly complete treatise on the complications of childbirth.

Her surgical skill developed also. Many cases came to her with such a degree of pelvic contraction that instrumentation was impossible. Frequently, as in the case of the woman previously described, they had been in labor for as long as five days or more. With Charles's help she did a remarkable series of Caesarians in which she was able to save twenty-two out of twenty-four mothers. They developed their own highly successful technique, delivering the pregnant uterus out of the abdomen and packing it off before opening it, then carefully washing out traces of cow manure or other "medicines" introduced by overzealous midwives. Closure in most cases was effected by interrupted cotton sutures with the use of a little sulfonamide powder, and infection seldom followed. The next time these patients became pregnant, they came to the hospital more promptly, especially those who did not have a living son. Dr. Wilma's reputation for handling difficult cases successfully was soon bringing her patients from a wide area.

But it was the children's work which was always closest to her heart. Babies, she discovered, had a hard time in India. The lucky ones were breast fed; the rest, fed out of unwashed brass nursing bottles, usually died. Even the fortunate ones had a rugged time when they were weaned, for they were usually put immediately on a diet of rice and hot curry.

The Perrills received a grim education in child mortality on their first visit to the Barcilly crematorium. They learned about it following the death of one of their poor patients. A new Hindu crematorium, they were told, had been established near the city so that even the poor were treated with compassion. Precious firewood was supplied at cost, or even given free for the destitute. Dr. Charles asked his lawyer friend, Surya Prakash, who had been responsible for the building of it, to take them there for a visit. After court hours Prakash took them around the grounds and eagerly described his plan to make this *Shamshan-bhumi* (cursed ground of death) into a place of peace and courage in the quest for Truth. Close to the crematorium, built on a huge mound left from the rubble of ancient brick kilns, had been established a center for Truth-meditation, with a beautiful garden close by.

"Here in this garden and the Satya-ashram," explained Surya Prakash, "the grieving relative may find his heart responsive to serious thoughts about life, about eternity, and final Truth."

The project was a noble and highly efficient demonstration of how one of India's problems, the disposal of her dead, could be solved. It was not the fault of the good Surya Prakash that it gave painful evidence of another of her problems.

"What are those little mounds?" asked Wilma. "There are so many, hundreds of them!"

It seemed that in the crematorium, which was still very new, about ninety adult cremations were performed in the course of a month. However, children under five were not cremated but buried in shallow unmarked graves. The rate of burial was more than two hundred per month. The hundreds of little mounds were pitifully revealing.

If the mother died in childbirth, Wilma soon discovered, the case was almost hopeless. Once a poor sweeper brought to her what looked like a bundle of rags. Inside was a tiny wizened infant, limp and almost lifeless.

"Take it, please take it, Mem Sahiba," he pleaded. "I can't do a thing with it since its mother died weeks ago. At first it did nothing but cry, so I gave it a little opium. That stopped the crying and the eating too."

Dr. Wilma took the bundle gladly. She named the tiny girl Shanti, Peace, and soon cured her of her opium addiction. In a few weeks, fat and healthy, the baby was transferred to the Baby Fold next door, where she would spend a happy childhood, attending the girls' school nearby as soon as she was six.

The Baby Fold also was Dr. Wilma's special province, where she watched over the health of thirty to forty tiny Indian children. And with the children's ward constantly full of ailing infants and skinny children, there were few idle moments in any day. It was all she could do to find a few hours for language study.

The maternity wards and delivery rooms, however, were excellent schools for learning not only language but Indian customs. It was considered very important that a new baby, if a boy, be given the right start in life. Sometimes the grandmother would send in an alarm clock with instructions that the exact minute of birth be recorded, in order to calculate his horoscope. Also, his left ear must be pierced with a black thread and a potent medicine applied to the umbilical cord. Wilma dutifully obeyed, careful to apply the doubtful substance to the placenta end rather than to the baby's. Then would come the proud exhibition to all the relatives of the new arrival, complete in his infinitesimal bright-colored jacket and red tinseled hat. Sometimes a band of musicians would be brought into the ward or private room to celebrate the birth. As an act of thanksgiving one family sacrificed two goats and hung them from a tree.

Other Hindu customs caused conditions peculiar to an Indian hospital. Though Christian patients gladly ate the food prepared for them, Hindus would not touch it, and each patient brought along a relative to do the cooking in one of the little fireplaces provided behind the wards. The relative also brought half a dozen brass vessels, some trays, several bags of supplies, and a bundle of firewood. And this whole assortment might be found under the patient's bed . . . including the relative, as the Doctors Perrill sometimes found when making their rounds at night. And, though this latter addition was against the rules, it did simplify the communication system!

As they prepared to leave for the hill station in the spring of 1942, for several months of language study as well as a much-needed holiday, the Perrills could see many indications of progress. The hospital was now performing creditably the modern major surgical procedures. Equipped with oxygen-gas, anesthesia apparatus, blood-transfusion apparatus, all kinds of surgical instruments (even though second-hand), sterilizers (effective, though contrived out of a couple of old pressure cookers), the services of a skilled nursing staff, and a team of four doctors, operating was already becoming a matter of precision and speed. In the little more than a year since Dr. Charles's arrival, some seventy-five operations had been performed.

The long-awaited running-water system was close to completion. Almost a thousand feet of plumbing pipes had been laid. A large pressure tank, with pump and automatic motor was being installed. Like most improvements involving automation, this one would have its liabilities. The two faithful *bhistis* (water carriers), who had trotted about the compound for years on end with bulging, dripping goatskin bags astride their shoulders, would be thrown out of work. But when the time came they were taken care of. For one a job was found elsewhere. The other was kept on in a menial capacity until he died. Then his son took his place. Years later, when Janette Crawford returned to the compound after a long absence, the son came running to meet her, a wide smile on his face.

"Look at me, Miss Sahiba!" he crowed. "See my clothes!" To his great pride and joy he had been made an *aid* in the hospital, and he wore a uniform, a triumphant promotion, he felt, for a man of his caste.

The Perrills had many reasons for satisfaction in their first year's achievement. A male nursing staff had been provided and was functioning efficiently. The nursing department was competently running under the supervision of the nursing superintendent, Theresa Lorenz. The nurses' training school, under the efficient leadership of Mary Gordon, was continuing to supply training for Christian girls in this much-needed profession. The quality and scope of its nurses' training program had increased immeasurably with the larger opportunities to be found in a general hospital. Housing arrangements for the staff and student nurses were being improved.

The laboratory was undergoing changes and rapid expansion. Using new photoelectric colorimetric apparatus as a nucleus, the hospital was ready to offer a series of quantitative blood chemical analyses.

Important public health work was also being done in the city and nearby villages by Miss Fernstrom and Dr. Kipp, based from Bareilly.

But some of the most effective "health work" was done by Dr. Charles himself, not with intention or forethought, but merely by being himself. As adventurous a sportsman as in his Indian boyhood, he was soon prowling through the country north of Bareilly on hunting trips which brought him into contact with hundreds of villagers. Almost as Indian as American in his cultural background, and charged with uninhibited friendliness, he could not only talk to the villagers in their colloquial idiom, to say nothing of their language, but he understood their attitudes, their cautious acceptance of strangers because of age-old exploitation, their fear of the absentee landlord, their distrust of anything new until it had been tried, their innate fatalism, their inimitable patience in the face of adversity. It was not long before many of them were coming to the hospital, and the time would come when his name would be known all through the region.

"Where you come from?" Ten years later a doctor visiting villages far up in the foothills would be asked the question.

"From Clara Swain Hospital. You have heard of it?" The face of the inquirer would look blank. "Dr. Perrill's hospital."

"*Achchha!*" Invariably there would come the light of recognition. "I know." Then the villager would tell how his son, or his wife, or some member of his family had been made well by the Doctor Sahib at Bareilly.

Charles even had the knack of turning potential enemies into friends. One day soon after coming to Bareilly he went hunting, saw a fine *nil-gai*, and wounded it. Then he found to his dismay that it was a pet of the neighboring village. Expressing his deep regret, he treated the animal as well as he could and left the villagers 50 rupees for its care. A month later some of the villagers came to the hospital. The animal had recovered, they explained, so they would give him back the 50 rupees. No, Charles told them, he would put the money in a fund in the hospital clinic, and the villagers could draw on it for treatment for themselves whenever one of them needed it. The incident made every person in that village his friend forever.

But for Dr. Charles all these small successes of his first year were only preliminaries. The old hospital, with its rectangles of rooms and verandahs built helter-skelter, could never be made the basis of a modern hospital plant, ministering with proper efficiency through clinics, in-patient facilities, and a developing service to the surrounding area. Already he was working on plans for a new plant, to be built in one part of the huge hospital courtyard, plans providing for operating rooms, a delivery room, laboratories and work rooms of the most modern type. All he needed to get started on this new building program was a mere $10,000!

3

The work of all Westerners during those first years of the forties was vastly complicated by the war. After the fall of Singapore and Burma, all of India was plunged into a state of emergency. Cities like Calcutta and Madras, close to the eastern coast, were in deadly fear of being bombed, and there was evacuation of Europeans and of many government agencies. Urgent appeals came to the Perrills and other missionaries to leave India before the Japanese troops invaded. But Bareilly was a thousand miles from Assam, the province nearest the Burmese border, so these appeals were not taken too seriously. Yet had the missionaries realized how completely isolated India had become when the Allied navy in the Indian Ocean had been wiped out, some might have changed their minds.

The war increased the difficulties of the medical work immeasurably. Drugs, such as quinine and emetine, instruments, and many other supplies were impossible to procure. Dr. Charles's ingenuity in finding substitutes was never more severely tested. He was able to get some surgical instruments made in India to his specifications. With the aid of his skillful mechanics he fashioned a bone chisel with a double curve, for shaping femoral heads, out of a broken spring leaf taken from an old Ford car. Carbarsone for treating amebiasis became unobtainable, but he found that liquid extract of the bark of the Kurchi tree contained an alkaloid which was fairly effective. They used this until the Indian army bought up all the supplies of Kurchi bark. Running out of calcium lactate, they substituted calcium carbonate made from marble chips which they sent to be ground in the Bareilly flour mills; not a bad substitute, since tests showed that almost half an ounce of this fine limestone powder could dissolve in satisfactory amounts of normal gastric juice. For hypertensive cases he even resorted to the use of a local medicine called "Serpina," whose active ingredient (Rowulfia) was still to be isolated and advocated in the West.

Occasionally they found that the improvisations helped rather than hindered the process of healing. With beds at a premium and other patients constantly waiting, early ambulation and rapid convalescence became a necessity—years before they had proved their superior value in the United States. Lacking comfortable Gatch beds with adjustable knee rests, they were spared the postoperative embolic complications. Unable to procure catgut for sutures, they used No. 30 sewing cotton for all types of surgery, even on the bowels. After 3,000 of such cases they were to conclude that cotton was superior to catgut or silk and found many of their friends in the United States were using it.

The orthopedic cases tested to the limit all of Charles's talents for improvisation. For traction pins he used steel knitting needles, with a Sears Roebuck breast drill which he found was less likely than the chrome-plated variety to tear precious rubber gloves. Lacking stainless steel wires, he cheerfully substituted "stove pipe" wire in imitation of Dr. Magnuson's practice. For six years they were without an X-ray machine, but they did not feel helpless without it. Their locally manufactured Thomas splints with Pierson attachments became suddenly in demand for potential air-raid victims, and they made and shipped scores of them to the principal hospitals and medical colleges in the area, losing some of their enthusiasm for this type of service, however, when it took months, plus endless red tape, to recover the expense.

Though active fighting never came close, they were surrounded by war activity, and Bareilly with its large cantonment became a big military medical center. The two military hospitals, one British and one Indian, were expanded until they had a combined strength of 3,200 beds.

Contacts of the Clara Swain staff with doctors and nurses in military service widened the horizons of both groups. A modern cement air strip on the edge of Bareilly brought in patients from the Burma front, and Charles was privileged to see some of these cases within twenty-four hours after they had been wounded on the battle fronts 2,000 miles away. A medical open house was held at Clara Swain for the Birmingham doctors and nursing supervisors working in the area. The latter had the opportunity of seeing local tropical diseases at close hand, and the hospital staff of associating with eminent specialists. Some of the army orthopedic men assisted Dr. Charles with bone operations, and their brain surgeon operated on a couple of neurological cases. One of the anesthetists performed the genuine feat of giving a spinal anesthetic to the fattest man in Bareilly, a patient weighing about 400 pounds!

There was another valuable by-product of the war activities. When the Japanese were bombing Calcutta and western India was observing air-raid precautions, a basement room was built in the hospital as an air-raid shelter. So successful did it prove to be, so cool in hot weather, so comfortable in winter, that it was to inspire Charles to fresh thinking about building possibilities in India. In fact, it was to supply one of the essential features of his future, highly original, building operations.

The two American nurses, Theresa Lorenz and Mary Gordon, also were discovering that the war was not an unmixed evil. True, some apparent assets turned into liabilities, like the matter of sawdust. The hospital instruments were sterilized over charcoal fires. With the advent of war, charcoal grew scarce and expensive, so the sterilizers were converted into sawdust burners. Fine! The sawdust was obtained free from a sawmill. Then, as the new fuel caught on and became popular, the price went up—and up!

Yet certainly without the war's exigencies, involving the inevitable breaking down of barriers, the students would not have been able to adjust so easily and quickly to the requirements of general nursing. Seeing them go about as naturally in the male ward as in the female, they knew that progress had been made.

It was no easy task to develop young nurses not only of high professional caliber but with that additional plus of personal concern and service which differentiated this Christian hospital from most government institutions. Many of the Indian girls came from primitive homes, perhaps from one-room village huts or city tenements where the whole family huddled together in poverty. Yet somehow during their three years of training they were transformed into poised, efficient young women, appreciating orderliness and beauty, alive to the needs of others, and able to act on their own initiative. It was the patient skill and Christian spirit of these two women which accomplished the miracle.

Mary Gordon, the assistant principal of the nursing school, spent her afternoons lecturing to the students, while in the mornings she followed up the theoretical work by supervising them in the wards. The training she gave was stamped with American thoroughness. But it was not only expert bandaging and skilled nursing which she taught them. From her example they learned the true spirit of service. Forever smiling, hands briskly efficient but cap often rakishly askew, always willing to take upon herself the most menial job which needed doing, she was a living textbook of that lesson so many Indians needed badly to learn, the dignity of manual labor.

And considering the multiple duties which both women performed in addition to their medical ones, whether in wartime or otherwise, it was amazing that they could remain serene and kindly. Besides acting as superintendent of nurses and helping in the operation and delivery rooms, Theresa Lorenz was in charge

ARY

MISS CLARA A. SWAIN, M.D.,
FIRST WOMAN PHYSICIAN TO COME
TO THE ORIENT
1869.
SHE ERECTED THIS BUILDING IN 1873
FOUNDING THE FIRST HOSPITAL
FOR WOMEN & CHILDREN IN ASIA
REMODELLED 1951

Dr. Clara Swain

Nawab of Rampore's Gift: The Palace

Dr. Ernest Sundaram and family

Charles and Wilma Perrill

Waiting room of Women's Out-Patient Department
at Clara Swain Hospital, with Indian nurse in charge

Dr. Wilma visiting Maternity Ward

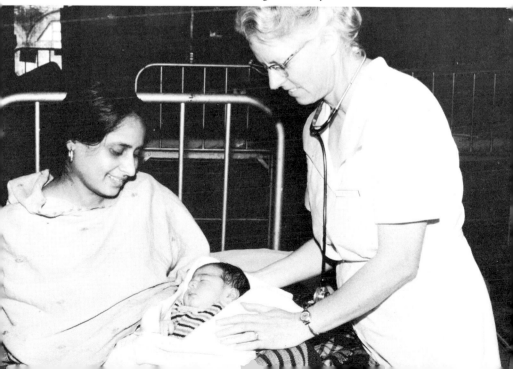

Nizam Masih in Bareilly

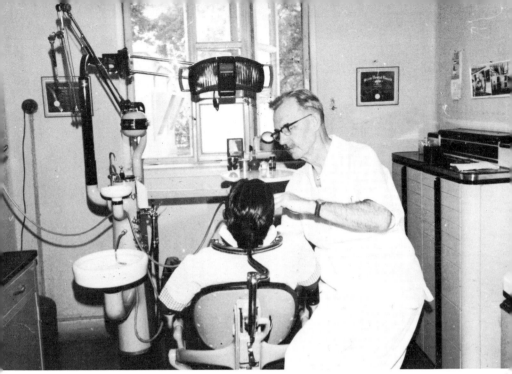

Patient being cared for by Dr. Riel
at the Clara Swain Dental Clinic

Frances Allen (right) and author enjoying afternoon tea

Although new machinery is now being used for laundry (above),
old methods still exist (below).

of the vast hospital grounds, coping with a legion of problems, from how to keep goats out of the compound or supply water to the vegetable patch in Block A, to whether an orchard would be practical in Block C and, if so, what fruit trees should be planted. Add to this the still more frustrating problem of getting all the *malis* (garden coolies) to do their job properly! As she cheerfully went her rounds, in wards or hostel or gardens, Sister Lorenz was invariably accompanied by Biddy, her tawny, loping Alsatian hound.

"Strange," commented a somewhat pompous retired English civil surgeon as he watched Dr. Charles going around accompanied by Sister Lorenz with Biddy on a leash, "to see a doctor going on rounds with a matron and her dog! I never could have done it." Then rather wistfully he added, "But I wish I could have."

Biddy had little chance to pursue her hunting talents except in the pursuit of rats, but she was an excellent watchdog. Though she tolerated her mistress's friends and acquaintances with an aloof friendliness, woe to the stranger who trespassed! Not an undesirable accompaniment to one's bicycle when one rode alone to the station to meet a patient in the middle of the night!

In spite of difficulties caused by the war, the hospital program slowly expanded. There were already some excellent members of staff, like Mrs. Minnie Paul, the trained compounder, whose versatility in service to the hospital would be matched only by that of her sister, Miss Premi Singh, a graduate of the school of nursing in 1932. Mrs. Paul took competent charge of the women's side of the dispensary, writing all the women's cards and the children's below age ten and dispensing all the medicines.

But there was need also for a compounder on the men's side of the dispensary, as well as desperate need of a male nurse who could give anesthesia. In 1942 Mr. S. P. Dan was secured to fill both offices. For a long time he was the only trained male nurse in the hospital. Then, after the course of male nursing training was started in 1944, he also became an instructor in physiology. Like Mrs. Paul's, his service to Clara Swain was to be long and faithful.

The end of the war brought no immediate end to the difficulties it had aggravated. In fact, for Dr. Charles it increased rather than curtailed his extra responsibilities. The American soldiers, leaving India in a hurry, left behind huge stocks of war surpluses in Calcutta and Assam. By an act of Congress charitable institutions in India—Christian, Muslim, Hindu—were entitled to buy some of these surpluses. A committee was organized, with Methodist Bishop J. Waskom Pickett of Delhi as chairman, representing all these organizations and charged with the task of distribution. Bishop Pickett chose Dr. Charles as his technical adviser to help in determining the supplies to be bought for 115 groups, which eventually paid a total of almost 4 million dollars for their purchases. For the most part Charles's advice was sound, but, perhaps fortunately for him, his furlough arrived before many dissatisfied customers appeared.

With seventeen other people he spent the last hectic two months of his first term in India in Calcutta unscrambling the huge piles of army surpluses, thrown helter-skelter into a warehouse by the hastily departing United States army. To get all these supplies sorted and shipped thousands of miles all over India was a herculean task; another was to make out the bills correctly. The job was still far from finished when the time came for him to leave.

His last months were complicated also by the building program going on at the hospital. At last some funds were being made available, and as fast as materials could be secured additions to both buildings and equipment were being made. The Woman's Division of Christian Service was undertaking the modernization of some of the wards, expanding the nurses' hostel, and building new staff quarters. In cooperation with the Division of World Missions they were planning to erect a new hospital wing to house X-ray, laboratory, and maternity departments. In addition the block would contain central supply rooms, stock rooms, and special teaching facilities.

Charles had his own ideas for building, and he had helped to formulate the plans for all these additions. It was torture to leave India while all these changes were taking place, even though he knew he would return long before they were completed. But he needed just as urgently to be in America, to do further study, to collect needed equipment, to go on speaking tours, to interest church groups in other special projects. And his term of six years was finished. It was time to go home.

4

His six years in India had roused in Charles an intense concern to learn more about those diseases which were India's worst curses: malaria, typhoid, respiratory diseases, and, especially, tuberculosis. A million Indians were reported to die of malaria each year, and sixty miles to the north of Bareilly, along the foothills of the Himalayas, was a marshy belt a thousand miles long, known as the *terai*, where malaria and typhoid fever were common. Respiratory infections had a high incidence. In five years he had performed over 300 tonsillectomies.

And tuberculosis, as he had written in a short transcript back in 1944 called "The White Plague of India," was of all diseases "India's scourge." A conservative estimate indicated that there were more than two million infectious cases at large. This meant that about 10 per cent of the whole population of Bareilly had the disease in some form. Almost half of the hospital's patients were suffering from tuberculosis of one kind or another, of bones, joints, lungs, intestines, skin, in fact, of practically every part of the body. These included the youngest, the oldest, the poorest, the most wealthy. He was being forced to believe that anyone with signs of fever or an obscure infection had the disease unless definitely proven otherwise.

It was to increase his own knowledge and usefulness in this area that in 1947 Dr. Charles completed a fellowship in thoracic surgery at the famous Sea View Hospital in New York. Some of his associates there were doing early experimentation with isonicotinic acid hydrazide, one of the newest drugs, and he immediately applied for an import permit to get supplies for his Indian patients. It was denied, however, until the government could satisfy itself that there was no danger of Indians being used as guinea pigs.

He also spent much time on his furlough inspecting and ordering new equipment: incubators, a vacuum pressure pump, a photoelectric hemoglobinometer, and other instruments. He investigated plumbing fixtures. He tracked down the X-ray machine which had been ordered long ago but delayed by the coal strike. He visited hospitals, electrical plants, factories.

But the major part of the Perrills' time on furlough, like that of most missionaries, was spent in traveling, telling the story of their work, arousing interest among church groups to support the new projects. Charles was an eloquent and persuasive speaker. He believed passionately in his subject, and his enthusiasm was contagious. In his letters back to the staff in India he jubilantly reported offerings of several hundred dollars, the promise of free beds and nurses' scholarships, and—at Evanston—a far more exciting development.

"What an eventful visit!" he wrote in December, 1947. "I started out by addressing the Covenant Church men's group, about 200 of them; then Wilma and I appeared in Indian dress for the Church School; a week later was the thank offering, when we both spoke. More than $800! There was such enthusiasm that Dr. Newham asked me to return for a meeting with the Official Board several days later. In the meantime he had gotten my blueprints and showed them to some of his officials. At this meeting they decided that they would like to build us a chapel, and made plans for securing $5,000 for this purpose by June. Hurray!"

Full though they were, the months of furlough seemed to crawl. He was like a race horse held in after the starting gun has sounded.

Meanwhile in India the building program was proceeding according to his specifications. To Theresa Lorenz, Janette Crawford, Mary Gordon, and others who had known the long lean years of scarcity and deprivation, leaking roofs, impure water, makeshift tools, the growing abundance seemed like a miracle.

"Our lovely new X-ray machine," wrote Mary Gordon in December, 1947, "is almost too good to be true. There are only five others like it in the country. Its total cost came to just under $12,000, and of this $9,000 came from gifts here in Bareilly through the efforts of an English official who was interested."

The building, part of the new block, was ready for it. And in 1945 Mr. I. C. Singh had gone to the big interdenominational Christian Medical College Hospital in Vellore to take training under Dr. Ida B. Scudder, head of the radiology department. He was soon taking pictures and training a nurse and another hospital worker as his assistants. A new missionary, Miss Mildred Althouse, took his place as laboratory technologist, and the following July, 1948, she started a school for laboratory technicians with a first class of three students. Offering a one-year course, only a high quality of candidates who had passed their matriculate examinations being admitted, the school was soon graduating technicians to serve in mission, government, and private hospitals all over India. Another big step of progress!

"Our other fulfilled dream," wrote Mary Gordon, "is the beautiful new addition to our nurses' home. Now each of our supervising staff nurses can have her own room with bath. (Not your Western idea of a bath, of course! Here we use the 'pour system' in a much simpler cement cubicle.) There is a lovely dining room, with big windows, quartet tables, and a serving room. Gone are the days when each nurse must supply her own dishes and wash them! In the basement are comfortable, quiet sleeping rooms for night nurses (no longer any need to sleep in the old chicken house to find quiet!), a store room, and library study room which now has over thirty new reference books. On the second floor is a large light room now used as a chapel. There is a little prayer room, too, with nothing in it but a rug. However, the rug has an interesting history. The children in our boarding school at Bijnor wanted to do something for the hospital, so they planted cotton in their garden, gathered it, and spun it on hand spinning wheels, then dyed the thread and wove the rug. Our girls sit on it for meditation and prayer."

There were other causes for rejoicing. Beautiful supplies from the Indian Red Cross and the American army surplus! For the last two years they had been coming from time to time in quantity: wheel chairs, books, phonograph records, trays, surgical supplies, knitted sweaters, robes, gowns, sheets, towels! The men in the male ward could now wear beautiful striped pajamas instead of dirty loincloths. Small wool blankets had been made into capes for nurses and used to keep babies warm. From the army surplus they had been able to purchase enamelware, bed springs, scales, instruments, office supplies. How wonderful after all the lean years to see shelves stacked with decent equipment! But they could certainly use them, with the year showing 140 more in-patients than the previous one and 500 more than five years ago!

"It begins to look as if we might have a *real* hospital when our 75th anniversary comes next year!" exulted Mary Gordon.

Janette Crawford, the business manager, also had reason to rejoice. For a quarter of a century she had been the human dynamo which kept the whole machinery of the hospital running smoothly. That she had done so without losing her dry good humor and infectious laugh spoke volumes for the quality of her administrative ability as well as her good disposition. For the job involved far more than keeping books. It meant coping with the maddening methods of local workmen, the wiliness and obduracy of shopkeepers, the constant dearth of available funds, to say nothing of the recent thousand-and-one restrictions of wartime conditions and the scarcity of goods. Guests were also her responsibility, for she was hostess at the women's bungalow, a caravanserai for a continual stream of people: refugees from China, Singapore, and Burma; fellow workers from other missions; travelers from abroad; government inspectors; medical observers from all over India. All were welcomed and made to feel at home by Miss Crawford, who moved humorously and imperturbably through red tape, constant annoyances, and crises both petty and great.

The hospital had been without a business office until 1930, and there had been almost no previous records kept. The patients' charts had been stored in a tin trunk. Later a large cupboard had been used. After ten or twelve years this had become inadequate, so cement shelves had been built into the wall at one side of the office. Now bazaar-made files which fitted into the cement shelves had been added. A woman had also been added to the staff to do some of the work of a medical record librarian, and an alphabetical file of in-patients was being started.

There was similar improvement in the handling of money. In 1930 most of the income from patients had come into the office in the doctor's pocket. Only an occasional bill had been made out and a receipt issued. Then gradually the weight of silver had become too heavy for a uniform pocket, so padlocked boxes had been placed in the dispensary. The medical and financial records had always been kept together, but now a method was being evolved to separate them. The work of the cashier was being carried on by a very able assistant, college trained.

One of the most valuable additions to the staff was Miss Beatrice Bonjour, an expert bookkeeper, who had worked fifteen years in missionary institutions. But her activities soon included much more than the competent management of all the business of the school of nursing, which was no small boon to its superintendent. She was also a gifted artist. Every evening at five she held "open house," usually on the lawn, where the nurses and others could learn creative handwork—painting, drawing, sewing—except for Saturday, which was reserved for basketball. With her artistic talents she had soon equipped an attractive drawing room for staff and students. Her originality was boundless. She could turn a faded old sari into a costume fit for a rani, or a handful of broken glass into a floral centerpiece.

But her creativeness was even more valuable in human areas. "Aunt Beatty," as she was soon called by almost everyone on the compound, was a catalyst, uniting discordant elements, melting barriers, infecting every phase of hospital activity with a bit of her own resourcefulness and good will. Her room was not only a favorite meeting place for staff, students, employees, and visitors, but a clearinghouse for either little worries or big problems, an anteroom through which the students passed from a contracted, often secluded existence into the wider, fresher atmosphere of a new world. Always available for confidences, the sharing of joys and triumphs as well as fears and problems and tears, Aunt Beatty cajoled, sympathized, advised, occasionally scolded, stimulated fresh thinking, all with the happy enthusiasm of the rare individual wholly concerned with the spiritual well-being of other persons.

There were other humbler but equally valued additions, like the *darzi* (tailor), who came faithfully each morning to the hospital and sat on the floor of the bungalow verandah and sewed, making new uniforms, repairing old ones as well as all the hospital linen, the droning presto of his sewing machine interrupted only by the patient click of his scissors. Day after day, hour after hour he would sit cross-legged on his bit of striped matting, head bent over his tiny machine and work laid out on the floor, too intent to look up at passers-by. Every working day in the week he would come for the next quarter of a century—except one, Friday. For he was a devout Muslim, and on Friday he took time out to go to his mosque and pray. He had touched his forehead to the floor so many times that it showed calluses beneath his round black cap.

Like Kallan and Nizam, like the two *bhistis* (water carriers), and Dulari the sweeper woman, and many others of the faithful, more menial staff who gave most of their lives in service to the

[125]

hospital, the loyal *darzi* with his sewing machine became himself one of the strongly binding threads in its stout and enduring fabric.

But there were serious losses as well as gains. In the early spring of 1948 staff and students joined in sad farewell to Sister Theresa Lorenz, who for more than twenty years had rendered untiring service, much of it as superintendent of nurses and principal of the nursing school; and recently, during the absence of the Perrills, as acting superintendent. The printed tribute, as necessary for a formal Indian farewell as garlands for a greeting, listed all her many achievements—the new school of nursing building, the gradual rise in the standard and status of nursing services, the provision for male nursing and midwifery training, and the recognition of the nursing school as a Class A school by the state medical council.

"We are indebted to you not only for all that you have meant to the hospital but also as our companion and friend. Our interests were yours. You shared with us our joys and sorrows, failures and successes. Our hostel is a living miniature of your ideals of democracy, of fellowship, and individual responsibility...."

It was a tribute which any doctor or nurse might well have coveted.

But changes in the hospital during these years of the Perrills' absence seemed minor indeed beside the momentous changes taking place in the world around it. Soon after independence came rumors of refugees moving in vast migration across the new border, Muslims toward the north, Hindus toward the south. The people in Bareilly did not realize the magnitude of the crisis until the terror struck Delhi. Then news of the mounting tragedies came in chilling crescendos. Both Hindus and Muslims were being murdered by the thousands. Within three months a million were massacred. Another million refugees were pouring into Delhi, being herded into temporary camps, fed meager rations by government and charity organizations in hastily improvised soup kitchens. Disease was rampant. An epidemic of cholera was wiping out thousands who had survived the massacres.

Bishop Pickett, head of the Methodist Church in Delhi and General Chairman of the Christian Committees in Relief Work in India and Pakistan during these tragic days, was an active and tireless worker. The National Christian Council sent out an appeal to all mission hospitals for volunteers to help, and eight staff members of Clara Swain went to Delhi the first of October at the height of the cholera epidemic and gave several weeks of service. The reports they brought back were unbelievable.

The extremity of terror passed, and though there were tension and insecurity in Bareilly, few among its large Muslim population were killed. The city officials, chiefly Hindu, were wise, moderate, and efficient in their control of the situation. But the Christmas pageant given by the staff, nurses and fifteen nursing students for patients and relatives on the twenty-third of December, 1947, beautifully depicting the message of "peace on earth," was more sobering than triumphant.

5

The furlough was over at last, and the Perrills were back in India. It was good to inspect all the changes, to greet old friends and meet new ones, to enjoy a reunion with Dr. Charles's parents, still in Lucknow where Dr. Fred Perrill had been for sixteen years editor of the *Indian Witness*, Methodism's all-India periodical; to share new ideas, new plans, new acquisitions, with his colleagues; but most of all to get to work again. With all the vigor of his intense and energetic nature Dr. Charles plunged into the new surgical and building program.

He had original and very definite ideas about building. Many of his theories were the result of his father's forty-three years of experience as a missionary. The two had already prepared a *Manual for Building in India* which was soon to be published. Some of his conclusions were an abrupt reversal of traditional ideas of missionary architecture. Height in a room, for instance, was no insurance of coolness. Perhaps in the old days of the majestically swaying, starched and ruffled punkah, 20-foot ceilings were necessary, but not in this age of electric fans and air conditioners, of reinforced concrete and fiberglass and sponge-foam insulation. A low ceiling with a circulating air space above was far superior. Nor were the ubiquitous verandahs more than a waste of space, likely to be misused later by being enclosed as rooms, and thus shutting off light and air from the inside of the house.

He had equally definite ideas about roofs and ceilings, about the angles of houses so they would get the maximum of sun in winter and the minimum in summer; about lighting and sanitary installations and room partitions and basements. Especially basements!

The first basement room at the hospital, built as an air-raid shelter, had proved so successful that Dr. Charles continued to use basement rooms in all his building plans. The new block containing X-ray, laboratory, maternity department, infant nurseries, central supply, stock rooms, and special teaching facilities had the first basement rooms ever built in Bareilly. Here were rooms for storing linen and machinery, refrigeration and air-conditioning equipment, an office for the Indian engineer, and an ice plant, with a potential of 500 pounds of pure ice a day. In addition, it had one of Dr. Charles's pet contrivances as a cooling system, a method developed by Professor Wilbur Thoburn, a nephew of Isabella and a long-time missionary professor of physics at Lahore. It made use of an underground tunnel through which air was slowly drawn for natural cooling on its way to the army-surplus air-conditioning machines. Professor Thoburn worked out the crowning feature, which linked the tunnel system to an old well in the hospital courtyard. The plastering up of the well's stone wall added an extra bonus to that of coolness, the elimination of the family of cobras which had emerged each year from cracks between the bricks. No longer did the nurses have to travel the brick walks gingerly at night, escorted by the hospital *chowkidar* (watchman) with his kerosene lantern and bamboo pole!

This tunnel 16 feet below the ground was a practical masterpiece. The earth temperature at this depth remains constantly at the mean temperature of the local climate (79° in Bareilly compared with 55° in Chicago). When the outside west wind was blowing, the temperature in Bareilly might reach 120, even in the shade. Then the tunnel felt cool indeed. In winter, when there was an occasional frost, it remained warm. That first tunnel with 1,000 square feet of surface area provided a lot of cooling or warming during extremes of temperature. On a hot day it doubled the capacity of the 5-ton air-conditioning machine placed under the new operating-room wing of the hospital.

But Charles's father was never to see the publication of their book or the completion of the buildings for which some of his novel theories had been the inspiration. He had worked through the height of the hot season of 1948, burdened with the extra responsibilities of an acting bishop and district superintendent. He was on his way to the mountains for a much-needed rest when on the train between Cawnpore and Bareilly he was overcome by a heat stroke. He died in Bareilly on June 12. For Charles the shock was like a thrust from one of his own scalpels, sharp, sudden, painful, cleanly revealing as it probed into life's deep and elemental verities.

But if Fred Perrill never saw the completion of the hospital buildings he had helped plan, by his death he became even more a part of them. For his wife Mary insisted on using a legacy from her brother, the late H. Chris Voigt, to construct a surgical wing in her husband's memory. The Fred M. Perrill Memorial Surgical Unit was begun immediately, an integral part of the whole new building program.

Yet even with all these signs of progress Dr. Charles was far from satisfied. With his tremendous concern for the tuberculosis problem and his recent experience at Sea View, where he had studied the new developments in thoracic surgery under such distinguished surgeons as Dr. Charles P. Bailey, he was impatient to get a chest department in operation at Clara Swain. On his return from furlough he was designated also as the superintendent of the Almora Sanatorium in the mountains, and he attempted to develop a program of close cooperation between sanatorium and hospital. He began chest surgery, using a new thoracoscope which had been his father's last birthday gift to him, and a few chest beds were arranged on an isolation basis for these patients, most of whom were afterward transferred to the sanatorium as their condition improved sufficiently to stand the trip of 145 miles into the mountains. But it was a makeshift arrangement which kept Charles champing at the bit. What he needed was a real chest ward, a separate unit, and he could hardly wait to get it.

But a greater need at the moment was for a new dispensary. The old building built by Clara Swain in 1873 was completely outmoded. Available funds having been exhausted, he looked about for other sources.

"Nizam," he said to the hospital's motor driver, handy man, interpreter, preacher, medical assistant, repository of information, "could you get me a list of the leading citizens of Bareilly?"

Nizam cocked his head. "Certainly, Doctor Sahib. From what standpoint?"

"Financial, Nizam. Money."

"*Achchha*, Doctor Sahib. Can do."

Nizam soon returned with the promised list of citizens, graded with remarkable accuracy according to wealth.

"Wonderful, Nizam, perfect! But—how did you do it?"

"Ah, Doctor Sahib, it was easy. I saw my friend, a clerk in the local bank, and he went over all the bank accounts, and it was no trouble at all."

The name of Murli Manohar, owner of a large sugar factory in Bareilly, like Abou Ben Adhem's, led all the rest. The hospital board of managers voted to put on a campaign to try to raise the funds locally. The names were divided among members of the board. Dr. Charles was chosen to approach Murli Manohar.

Charles was a very simple man, never putting on airs and usually wearing the most ordinary clothes. Finding him typing one day in his small office in the basement, a visitor of importance mistook him for a *babu*, clerk. But, understanding Indian psychology, he now dressed carefully in formal clothes and took the hospital's best car, with Nizam, tall and dignified and impeccably uniformed, in the driver's seat. Both knew that a man like Murli Manohar would understand and appreciate proper respect.

"This is how Dr. Swain must have felt when she went to the palace of the Nawab," thought Charles as he was ushered into the distinguished man's presence. Though he had always been on good terms with Sri Manohar, he was unprepared for the extremely cordial welcome he received.

"Ah, my good friend Dr. Perrill! Which will you have, tea or coffee? We'll have a cup together; then, since I know you are interested in building, I would like to show you some improvements I am making in the factory. And then you must tell me what you are doing at your fine hospital."

Dr. Charles drank tea, conversed pleasantly, toured the factory, admired, all with outward aplomb but the inward impatience Clara Swain had once felt touring an endless succession of gardens and palaces. But the moment came at last.

"Ah, and now—what about your fine hospital?"

Charles told him of the urgent need for a modern out-patient building. He showed him the sketches of the unit, which would have offices for nine doctors. He explained all the advantages of such a building to the city of Bareilly.

"How much would it cost?" demanded Sri Manohar bluntly.

"Say—fifty thousand rupees," replied Charles. He almost opened his mouth to ask for a donation of 5,000 rupees to get the campaign off to a good start, but his courage failed him.

There was a brief pause, then Murli Manohar said, "All right. I'll give you the whole building. I have been wanting to erect a memorial to my father, Sahu Ram Narain. This is a good opportunity."

Charles expressed his thanks, performed the amenities of farewell, and departed in a daze. He felt as if the wind had been knocked out of his sails. Wonderful, incredible triumph, to be sure! And yet—the very first person on the list had ruined the whole campaign plan!

"Doctor Sahib disappointed?" inquired Nizam anxiously, finding his expression enigmatic.

"Disappointed? Well—hardly! No, I should say not! He—he's going to give us the whole building!"

Nizam looked a bit smug, as if he had maneuvered the whole operation. "*Achchha!* Was hoping he would."

The board shared none of Charles's frustration. They were jubilant.

"And it comes just in time to announce at the Jubilee and dedication!"

Plans had been made to combine the approximate 75th anniversary of the hospital with the dedication of the new buildings. Originally scheduled for March, 1949, the event was postponed because of the death of the Governor of the province. The dates were now fixed for October 20 and 21.

It was the most dramatic celebration to date in the hospital's history. Preparations began months ahead. Bishop Pickett and his wife came from Delhi. The First Secretary of the United States Embassy and his wife, Mr. and Mrs. John Steeves, were also present, arriving and leaving in a government plane.

"They think no more of ordering a plane," observed one of the staff drily, "than we do of sending for a ricksha."

But the outstanding guest was the Honorable Rajkumari Amrit Kaur, Minister of Health of the Republic of India. A Christian, intensely brilliant, a dynamo of energy and of selfless dedication to her job of creating health for almost four hundred million newly freed people, she dominated the occasion from the moment of her arrival from Delhi in a private car, complete with retinue of secretary, gunman, and servant. But in spite of these necessary appurtenances, she was humility and simplicity personified.

"I prefer to stay in a home rather than in a government house," she had specified firmly. Local police guarded the bungalow where she was entertained during her stay. Though she addressed the public three times at the hospital and several times at other occasions in the city, she managed to find time for becoming one of the bungalow family, whether at the dining table where staff and guests ate or in a group about the piano singing hymns and carols. Once she even sat down at the piano and played song after song while they sang. She could not have done any of these things at Government House.

Diminutive, eloquent, vivacious, clad in the Gandhian homespun which she wore at all times, a "princess" in fact as well as in name, for her father had relinquished his right of succession to the throne of a native state rather than renounce his Christianity, this remarkable woman became the living embodiment of the hospital's seventy-five years of healing service to her people. She examined the new block with keen interest, admiring its natural air-conditioning system, the layout of the new theaters and their equipment, some of it ingeniously homemade; visited the classes in nursing and laboratory training; was especially enthusiastic about the proposed course in hospital administration designed to relieve medical superintendents of routine duties and to enable them to devote more of their time to professional service.

The nurses gave a tea the first afternoon in the courtyard of their hostel. It was hard restricting the number of guests to fifty to comply with government restrictions on food. Later Sri Murli Manohar gave a dinner to about twenty-five guests in his palace of a home not far from the hospital, the silver dishes used for serving a marked contrast to those from which Rajkumari ate in the hospital bungalow. And at the anniversary meeting that evening his gift of 50,000 rupees for the new dispensary building was announced.

Paying a tribute to Clara Swain, who had traveled so far to plant a seed in Bareilly, Rajkumari in her opening address expressed the hope that this seed would continue to expand until its healing ministry touched surrounding villages.

"The salvation of the world," she affirmed, "lies not in power politics and the atom bomb, but rather in service on a cooperative basis through the World Health Organization and kindred bodies of the United Nations."

The following morning she took time out from city functions to help Bishop Pickett dedicate the three memorial tablets in the new hospital chapel now under construction. The first recorded the gift from Dr. Wilma's church in Evanston. The second commemorated the Easton Chapel of the Wellesley School for Girls in Naini Tal, after which the chapel was designed and from which the furniture and some of the fittings were secured when the school was closed. The third was in memory of Bishop Robinson, father of Mrs. Pickett, whose interest and assistance the hospital so highly valued.

But the crowning event of the two days was the dedication that afternoon of the new Jubilee building containing the delivery rooms, infant nurseries, and the Fred M. Perrill Memorial Block. Again Rajkumari addressed the large group assembled. She spoke of the appalling needs of village India and of the government's commitment to raise the health standards of her people.

"But what are two years in the life of a nation? What are even ten years in the life of a nation of three hundred and sixty million people? India is a vast field calling for service from every one of us. . . .

"Doubts sometimes have arisen as to whether there is any need for foreign missionaries in our country now that it has attained its freedom. The activities of persons like Dr. Perrill must remove these doubts. . . . It has filled me with pleasure to see that the staff of this institution has as its members men and women derived from all communities. It should be so because this great art of healing, this science par excellence, knows no barriers of race or caste or color or class."

But the Jubilee was merely an incident, the dedication a slight pause in continuous activity. Even before the celebrations were finished, the next seventy-five years of service had begun. With 140 beds now in the hospital, a daily average of 132 filled and many days patients overflowing into verandahs and corridors, with at least 150 people coming to the dispensary each day for treatment, there was little time for reminiscence. The number of patients had doubled in a single year. But there was more staff to take care of them. Besides the two missionary doctors there were Dr. Roshan Masters, a Parsi, Dr. Vera Choithramani, a Hindu, and Dr. Sama Mahamoodian, a Muslim. These non-Christians entered with surprising ease into all the hospital activities, including those religious. One day they had a good laugh on themselves. The three non-Christians came together at mealtime, the others being late.

"Let's not wait any longer," said one. "Let's have grace and begin."

Then suddenly they looked at each other and laughed. Three non-Christians thinking they must say Christian grace before eating!

The securing of medical supplies because of restrictions on imports was difficult. The fame of the new X-ray department spread, and the hospital was swamped with fracture cases and others needing casts. After the army surplus supplies of plaster of Paris and crinoline were exhausted, there was a hectic struggle to secure good-quality plaster and any kind of usable cloth. Finally they were able to place a standing order with the Christian Medical Supply Agency in Bombay for plaster of Paris. But they could do nothing about ether. At one time they got down to 2 pounds, then were able in the nick of time to get a small quantity from Lucknow.

But some new drugs were making their appearance. To Dr. Charles's delight, the availability of streptomycin was proving a Godsend in the treatment of tuberculosis. Patients responded to it in amazing fashion. The problem now was to find a place to keep such infectious cases in the hospital, for his few chest beds were soon filled. Nor would the patients remain at Almora over long periods. They insisted on coming down to the plains during the winter months and demanded treatment in Bareilly. He finally permitted a small number of them to pitch tents in the compound, to live in while they were receiving injections. Soon there was quite a tent colony. Then he devised a small prefabricated house which could be taken up to the sanatorium in summer and brought back in winter. Made of wood and asbestos board at a cost of less than four hundred rupees, one of these provided a room for the patient, accommodations for the attendant, cooking and other facilities. Knocked down, they could easily be transported between hospital and sanatorium while the patients made the trip by car. But all these were poor substitutes for what was really needed, an adequate chest department.

Slowly the hospital was fulfilling Rajkumari's hopes of moving out into wider service. The laboratory technician students made four trips to mission schools of the area and did routine examinations on the children. To their dismay they discovered that the average hemoglobin count was only about 25 per cent and that at least a third of the children were infected with some sort of pathogenic parasite.

The hospital staff were also able to begin the weekly clinics in villages, which had had to be stopped during the war. Securing an International truck chassis, they watched with fascination its conversion into an ambulance on the hospital compound. It was hardly a de luxe job. It had two reclining cane-bottom seats for patients which could be removed to convert it into a station wagon. On the outside the names of the hospital and of the Almora Sanatorium were painted in three languages. Each Wednesday when the out-patient department was closed, the ambulance with two doctors and a nurse went out to two village clinics, the farthest one thirty-four miles away. There was no woman doctor in either of these villages.

The new dispensary was nearly finished when Dr. Charles discovered that the 50,000 rupees were barely enough to cover the cost of the actual building operations. There would be nothing left for fixtures and furnishings. A quandary! Sri Murli Manohar had asked for permission to defray the full expense of the building. But he had already given the full amount specified. It was unfair to ask him for more. Yet he must be given the opportunity to offer. Again Dr. Charles dressed with respectful formality and departed in the best car with chauffeur, the latter compensating in dignity for the serious deficiencies of the former.

He explained the situation to the sugar magnate, then tactfully suggested that since he had already been more than generous, doubtless the money for fixtures and furnishings could be obtained from other interested citizens of Bareilly.

Sri Manohar was distressed by the very idea. "You never knew my father," he said earnestly. "Sahu Ram Narain was a very kind and generous man. Please do not take away from me the honor of erecting a worthy memorial to my respected father."

They did not take away from him the honor. Not only was the new building properly equipped and furnished, but it was even possible to construct an extensive basement connected to an underground tunnel with an air-conditioning machine. The whole project cost Sri Manohar 90,000 rupees (more than $25,000).

Certain members of the hospital's board of managers became worried about these developments. Accept such large gifts from a non-Christian? And how would they provide the upkeep after the first costs had been met? There were rumors also that Sri Manohar was not satisfied with this gift alone and talked of building a new section for children. What might happen next? Would the hospital begin to lose its Christian emphasis?

The answer to this came during the last stages of the building project. In the front of the new dispensary was a large circular window, in its center a frosted glass cross clearly visible down the main road. At one time an agent of Sri Manohar came to inspect the building operations. He saw the cross and frowned.

"And what is that?"

"A cross," replied Dr. Charles.

"Is it necessary?" inquired the Hindu inspector.

"No. It's not absolutely necessary."

"Then why is it there?"

"Because, my friend, this is a Christian hospital. And the cross, a symbol of suffering and service, is a Christian symbol. It's our trademark."

"But—in the end all religions are really the same. They all lead to God."

"Then why," asked Dr. Charles, "did Murli Manohar come to this Christian hospital in preference to the others which are non-Christian?"

The cross remained on the door.

Only later did they discover why Murli Manohar had responded so generously to the need of Clara Swain Hospital. The year before, an Indian woman, badly crippled by a fall, had come seeking help. She had been to all the specialists, including those in the government medical college.

"I've been everywhere," she said, "but I've come to you because I know that I can trust you Christians to tell me the real truth. Will an operation help me, and would you be able to perform it?"

To Charles she was just another patient, like all his others. He knew of no special family connections, and it would not have mattered if he had. He performed the operation, a laminectomy, one morning in May, a blazing hot day. He found the spinal cord damaged beyond repair. It was a long operation, and it made him late for his out-patient office hours, so he hurried to get his lunch at the nearby bungalow. The brother of the woman operated on had come to the hospital that day to visit his sister. There was no waiting room, so he stayed outside, seeking relief from the heat in the shade of a large mango tree near the path leading to the doctor's bungalow. He saw Dr. Charles hurry by and a little later hurry back to the dispensary clinic, and he was greatly surprised.

"Doesn't this foreigner know how to take care of his delicate health?" he wondered. "He must have a divine love for his patients. Yes, that's it. Why, he might even be an incarnation of God himself!"

The man was Sri Murli Manohar. Sitting there under the tree, he experienced a feeling of shame that he, a leading citizen of Bareilly, was not doing something worthy for his own community. During the weeks that followed he did not come to the hospital, but the efficient nursing care and the personal interest of the doctors in his sister were well known to him. His resolution to do something worthwhile did not meet with the approval of some of his business associates, but their objections only intensified his purpose.

For Dr. Charles the demonstration of divine incarnation had been all in the day's work. ("What a description," he disclaimed wryly, when he heard the story, "of a hot and tired doctor hurrying late to his clinic!")

"What about your Christian witness?" was the question often asked by devoted churchmen back home, anxious to be sure their hard-earned dollars were really going to "convert the heathen." Did he preach a lot? No, Charles had to admit, his heavy load of medical work left little time or energy for preaching, even if he had that special skill, although all the missionaries took their turns in nurses' chapel and in the annual Hospital Sunday church service.

"But," he expressed it once in writing, "our Christian witness sticks out all over. For instance, when Ram Gopal, a villager, falls ill with an attack of appendicitis, what happens? A local quack doctor is summoned. Some herbal medicines are given or plasters of mustard and leaves may be applied to the abdomen, and prayers and incantations are said, amulets placed around his neck. He becomes worse, and the case is declared hopeless. It is his fate, his kismet, or karma. The relatives then think of one last chance. They've heard of that Christian hospital in Bareilly. So they bring him, jouncing and bumping over twenty miles of rutted village roads. Hours later he arrives at the hospital, more dead than alive. Yes, he will undergo an operation. Why not? There is no alternative.

"To his surprise he wakes up afterwards, finds himself in a surgical ward. His relatives are getting excited now; they want him to recover. After all, they have paid the $25 operating fee, and it would be a shame to have the money wasted. There are other patients in the ward. They have wonderful tales to tell. One man tells about his operation, a gastroenterostomy. 'I had constant stomach pain,' he says. 'I couldn't eat a thing. I was becoming a bag of skin and bones. So I agreed to an operation. They took me into the operating room and covered me with a big white sheet; they put some poisonous medicine over my nose, and I died right then and there. The doctor took a big butcher knife and cut me open from top to bottom. And do you know what they found inside? There was my stomach, upside down. And do you know what they did? They took that knife and cut the stomach right out and turned it over and stitched it back, right side up. And they sewed me up like this, and then I woke up and now I am a new man. I can eat anything, but the doctor says, "Not yet." '

"Everybody asks questions. Why is this a Christian hospital? Why are the Christians more interested in poor folks than anyone else seems to be? Are you paid huge salaries or given a big bonus when somebody becomes a Christian? Is it something to do with your religion?

"We tell them that we Christians are the followers of Jesus Christ, a carpenter who lived in a neighboring country. Jesus went about among the common people preaching, teaching, and healing the sick. So some Christians are preachers or teachers, and some of us try to show our love by helping the sick. Then what did Jesus teach about God? He taught that God is our loving Father and, if God is our Father, then we are all brothers. That is the reason why the folks in America are interested in helping the folks in India. Well, then, they say to me, the folks in India should be interested in what happens to the folks in the United States.

"They tell us they will watch to see whether we live up to the ideals of our leader, Jesus. This means that about 6 million Indian Christians are being watched by 350 million fellow countrymen. We cannot be satisfied that the Clara Swain Hospital has grown since 1940 from 50 to 250 beds. We must do much more."

One patient, a woman very ill and needing medical care, expressed it with great pertinence and simplicity. She entered a city and walked a long distance to the mission hospital, passing another on the way.

"Why did you not stop there?" she was asked. "It was much nearer, and the medicines are the same."

"Oh," she replied, "the medicines may be the same, but—the hands are different."

6

The dispensary was finished, dedicated, and put to immediate use. But still Murli Manohar was not satisfied. He could not rest until a new children's ward, big enough for sixty beds, was also opened, again built in memory of his father.

The increased work load which the new facilities brought to Dr. Wilma Perrill spurred rather than diminished her untiring energy. The more women and children to whom she could apply her skills of healing, the more strength, it seemed, was given her to serve them. The slender sprightly figure in its white uniform, fine light brown hair a bit wind-tossed, lips smiling, blue eyes glinting behind rimless glasses, could be seen day or night hurrying between bungalow and hospital, bending over sick beds, examining long queues of patients in the dispensary, stopping to pick up or fondle tiny babies, patting older ones on the head, or, enveloped in mask, gown, and gloves, delivering infants and with ever-increasing skill performing delicate operations.

The presence of young Teddy Perrill, the baby they had adopted while on furlough, raised her prestige among Indian women in immeasurable degree. She was now the mother of a son, blessed by the gods, the highest estate to which any woman could aspire, an evidence of divine favor even more indicative of healing prowess than a medical degree. But even with these additional insignia she was expected to deliver the goods, as she once discovered when she had the ill luck to deliver eighteen girl babies in a row! The maternity ward almost had to shut down. No woman informed of the tragedy would come to her. But the situation was finally saved when she did a Caesarian section and delivered twin boys!

Her deliveries did not always follow conventional patterns. Once during chapel she was called out of the service just in time to deliver a baby on the steps outside. Another she delivered in a taxi which had managed to get the mother inside the hospital compound. More than once she performed the necessary service at the hospital gate.

And in at least one "delivery" the natural process of birth was not involved. It was on Christmas Eve. Dr. Wilma heard a high plaintive cry and thought at first it was a distant jackal. Finally, hearing it again and again, she went to the front porch. There in a wicker chair lay a tiny baby, about five days old. It wore a woolly sweater and was wrapped in a cotton covering.

"Well," she announced, bringing it into the house, "it looks as if somebody had just delivered a baby, and it wasn't Dr. Wilma."

The arrival created great excitement among both family and servants. Teddy, aged about two and a half, was especially impressed.

"*Ohe*, what a beautiful, beautiful baby!" breathed the ayah, reaching out her arms for it.

They named the baby Noel. She was taken care of in the hospital until July, when she graduated to the Baby Fold. When she was eight months old the ayah and her husband, the *chowkidar*, took her for their own. Though in India there could be no legal adoption for Christians, by their making a will in the child's favor the arrangement was recognized by law.

Another equally unusual "delivery" came via the mailman. Dr. Wilma took the letter to Janette Crawford and stood by her desk while she read it. It was from one of the missionaries in village work. A mother, wife of one of the village pastors, had died after giving birth to twin daughters. The babies were frail and needed special care. Could the hospital take them? The two women looked at each other and smiled. Both knew what the answer must be. But they had to be practical, especially Miss Crawford, the business manager. How much should they charge for their care? In spite of the hospital's constant operating deficit it was not difficult to persuade each other.

"Of course, for little babies the biggest item is the milk bill."

"And, after all, small, weak, newborn babies can't take *much* milk!"

They agreed they could give free care for at least two months.

It was easy enough to diagnose the situation. Most pastors in villages were on starvation wages. There would have been no money to pay for extra food for the expectant mother. She had given birth to two other living children and to twin boys who had died. No wonder her weak, anemic body could not stand the strain. When her husband had been a student at the theological school, she had been taught the elements of nutrition and child care. But how put them into practice with no means to secure the basic necessities of health?

It was a common problem. As one missionary said when preparing to teach a class on child care, "How can I tell these women their children need milk when I know they cannot buy milk?"

The twins arrived, via a missionary carrying two baskets, a baby in each. "This one is Beauty, and that one is Sweetie," she said. "The nurses at the government hospital named them." Looking into the wizened little faces, Wilma wondered at the nurses' optimism. Sweetie, the weaker one, remained for a long time in doubtful condition. There was no thrill in the world, Dr. Wilma often thought, like seeing such little bodies fill out, such little wizened faces brighten and take on the look of healthy, happy childhood.

The family planning clinic was also proving one of her most rewarding activities. It ministered to both groups of women, those unable to have children and those who already had too many. Many childless women were helped, and many were surprised when laboratory tests demonstrated that the deficiency was with the husband rather than the wife. Certainly a variant from traditional Hindu concepts! But science was fast coming into its own in India, and the laboratory reports were usually accepted even when they disagreed with theological dogma.

Those with the opposite problem, often weak and anemic but still too fertile, were also being helped by the new, simpler, and more inexpensive methods developed through recent research. But the need here was stupendous and with each year of population growth (at the rate of 11 million a year) becoming more acute. The government was cooperative. Margaret Sanger's visit to India some decades ago had resulted in a number of clinics in the larger cities. But how combat the ignorance and apathy of 600,000 villages, even with the simplest and cheapest of methods? And unfortunately the latter had not yet been found.

It was hard for a Westerner to learn that changes must come slowly in a land like India. People had to be shown the value of innovations, taught patiently how to use them. But Charles was as much an Indian as a Westerner, and he not only understood the psychology of the country, but he had imbibed a goodly amount of its patience. He was as skillful in dealing with his patients' fears as with their bodily ills. He understood well the terror of a poor villager about to mount an operating table for the first time and knew how to allay the fears of each one.

"Is this a—a dangerous operation, Doctor Sahib?"

"If it were really dangerous," he might say jokingly, "I wouldn't want to do it, because I wouldn't want to waste time on a patient who was going to die."

Or—"Well, yes," he might admit frankly, "but you know, it's dangerous riding in a ricksha, too."

Or to the anxious relatives he might say, "Lots of patients have operations at the Clara Swain Hospital, and just about all of them get through safely. I'll tell you what we'll do. We'll call in one relative to show him the trouble when we find it. Which one of you will it be? The nurse will come and help you put on a cap and gown and help you adjust your mask."

It was an assuring experience just to see him operate, for he was a skillful surgeon, swift, confident, precise in every motion.

"It's beautiful to watch him," said the Parsi doctor, Roshan Masters.

And he had a marvelously sure hand. There was the boy who came to the hospital after swallowing a safety pin. An X-ray was taken, and the object was revealed—open. Using an extra-thin forceps, Dr. Charles proceeded to close the pin and bring it up.

It was no wonder his manner and reputation inspired confidence in patients, even when it was a bit unfounded. One patient came whose relative had previously been treated by Dr. Perrill. "We have great confidence in you," said the patient trustingly, "because you treated a relative of ours."

"Oh?" replied the doctor. "And how is he?"

"He's dead."

Like Dr. Wilma, he had his share of unusual cases. Several of his patients had been attacked by tigers. One, a woodcutter, had walked into a thicket, surprising a tigress with two cubs. Dr. Charles was on his way to a meeting of the Annual Conference in Bareilly when he was called to mend the terribly ripped face. Many of the visitors flocked to see the victim instead of going to Conference. Such accidents were not too uncommon. That these patients could live to reach the hospital was proof that the tigers were not man-eaters. Their intent was only to drive away an unwelcome intruder. But the damage inflicted by one swipe of the tremendous paw—crushed bones and shredded skin—had to be seen to be believed.

And of course he could report his cases of "longest" and "biggest." In north India urinary-tract stones were numerous and so large that after a long succession of cases far outweighing anything he had seen in the West, they seemed no longer worth reporting. One bladder stone he removed weighed 25 ounces. Many were five times the weight of a normal kidney, 140 grams.

But perhaps the operation which brought him the most widespread fame was a case of transvestitism, occurring several months after the international furore aroused by the incident of "Christine Jorgensen." A schoolteacher, about eighteen years of age, was admitted to the women's wards because "something was wrong." Dr. Charles was called to consult with the puzzled staff doctor, who said she wasn't even sure of the sex of the patient. Neither was he, and neither was the patient. Even though "she" had known that something was wrong, she had gone to a girls' school and had finished two years at a women's college. She had even been examined at a neighboring hospital and told that nothing could be done.

Suspecting that the patient might be a true hermaphrodite, Dr. Charles suggested an operation, to which she readily agreed. Since she had reached the full marriageable age, her parents had been urging her to let a marriage be arranged, a prospect which filled her with fear. On laparotomy the doctors found the "girl" to be not a hermaphrodite but a male without doubt, and she was transferred to the men's side of the hospital, creating a tremendous stir among her relatives, to say nothing of the nurses.

Soon, as with the similar incident in the West, newspaper reporters were at the doors. Dr. Charles had a hasty conference with his lawyer friend, Surya Prakash, who advised that, since there was no escaping publicity, if the hospital were to avoid the sensationalism which could well attend a case of transvestitism, it would be best to permit a well-known newspaper syndicate to publish a series of dignified articles adhering to the scientific truth. This was done, and the patient "himself" wrote in a most interesting style about the heartbreaks of a sensitive and intelligent person whose sex was in doubt and who had the misfortune to be reared as a girl instead of the boy he really was.

"It was dark where I was born," ran the simple but intensely dramatic story. "The sun had gone down, but it was before the moon and the stars had showed up. A perfect hour for the start of my nondescript existence! My anxious relatives asked the midwife the age-old question: 'Is it a boy or a girl?' 'Girl,' she announced after taking another hard look at me.

"Seventeen years went by.

"It was a July day, dismal and dripping. I was in a hospital and excited over what was coming. I had undergone an operation so that the doctors could determine my sex. After anxious hours Dr. Perrill pronounced me a boy and told me to cast off my sari, cut my long hair, and cut off my bangles. I took to *kurta* and pajama (men's clothes). From Chameli Devi I was transformed into Chandra Prakash."

Dr. Charles's syndicated articles explored the scientific background of such a case, explaining the general problem of mistaken sexual identity occurring, by no means rarely, in cases of retarded male development. He estimated that there must be about 350,000 of such unfortunate individuals in India alone and recommended that every effort be made to locate such cases and offer them expert scientific help. A series of six of these articles was syndicated throughout India.

In spite of these precautions results were sensational. Some newspapers amplified the story to proclaim that "Dr. Perrill at Operation Changes Girl into Boy," and he received letters from all over India asking how much it would cost to have daughters turned into sons. However, the publicity did bring two interesting patients into the hospital. One was a six-months-old baby "girl," a retarded male, whose mother had read the articles and noticed a slight peculiarity in her infant. The second case journeyed 600 miles to reach Bareilly, another teacher, about thirty-four, rejected by her husband because of abnormalities. A series of plastic operations was performed on both of the older patients, and hormones were given to help both develop into as normal males as possible. It was attempted also to give wise and sympathetic counsel in the far more complicated problem of mental adjustment. Certainly it was in such areas that the deep human concern of a Christian hospital could make its witness profoundly significant.

Yet it was not always the professedly Christian doctors and nurses who best exemplified the spirit of the hospital. For example, no Christian could have been more kindly, generous, concerned about each individual patient than the Hindu Dr. Das. A graduate of the Lahore Medical College, he started his work in 1951, asking for the privilege of serving the hospital part time. He was unimposing, quiet, unassuming. At first he did a few little menial jobs about the hospital, always thoroughly and with no apparent feeling that they were unworthy of his talents and training. And he always gave the right answers to questions. Dr. Charles noticed that he was interested in surgery, and he took him on as his assistant. Dr. Das showed a remarkable aptitude and mastered all the skills with amazing rapidity. He was soon in full charge of the men's surgical section of the hospital, and in 1955 he was to become head of the department of surgery.

His surgical triumphs through the years were many. There was the case of the sugar magnate's wife, operated on two years before in Calcutta, suffering from severe gangrene and almost pulseless when she was brought to Clara Swain. Dr. Das operated successfully and sent her away in good health. Then there was the farm woman who had been hit on the head by a servant and was not brought to the hospital until the following day. The wound was so deep that the brain was showing. Dr. Das cleaned the wound and repaired the defect. Not trusting his own skill, he asked Dr. Jacob Chandy, the famous neurosurgeon, to come from Vellore.

"It's as good as I could have done," commended the eminent doctor.

But it was in the area of human relations that Dr. Das displayed his finest skills. When not in the operating room, it seemed that he was always with his patients. Even after he was afflicted with a severe heart condition he continued to serve with selfless devotion. "Take it from my salary," he would often urge when a patient was unable to pay.

He put many of the Christian doctors and nurses to shame.

7

It was in 1950 that a dentist in Portland, Oregon, made an unusual decision which was to have far-reaching consequences for Clara Swain Hospital and the area to which it ministered.

"I believe that only spiritual life can give human existence its full meaning," Dr. Robert Petersen once expressed his philosophy. "Unless one has made an adjustment to God, to Providence, to the Creator—whatever designation one chooses to use—one cannot lead a mature, happy life. We have to make up our minds about the significance of our tiny part in this vast complex of life. Until we do this, we cannot lead pointful, fruitful, intelligent lives, personally or professionally."

And this was impossible, he came to believe, spending his entire life building up his excellent practice in Portland, Oregon, where there were plenty of dentists to attend to all the needs of his prosperous clientele—yes, even of the many less-prosperous patients whom he treated gratis.

So after much thought and discussion over a period of years Dr. Bob, with the full agreement of his wife Mary, came to a decision. If possible, he would donate a tithe of his lifetime career, perhaps three years, to dental work in a mission hospital in some place where a dentist was most needed. He began corresponding with the Methodist Board of Missions about possible openings. Seeing the name of Dr. Charles Perrill in one of his church magazines, he also wrote to him, explaining his desire. Charles, always receptive to new ideas, was enthusiastic and urged him to come to Bareilly.

But it was decided by the Board that Seoul, Korea, was the place where the services of a dentist were most needed. Plans were completed, and one Saturday the Petersens received their application papers for travel and visas to the Far East. The excitement of the family soared high. The next morning, Sunday, Dr. Bob opened his newspaper and read that North Korea had invaded South Korea. The whole plan burst like a bubble. The correspondence with Charles Perrill was reopened. Finally Dr. James K. Mathews, secretary of the Board of Missions for India, heartily in favor of the project from the very first, appointed Dr. Petersen to Bareilly, the first dentist to be sent out to India under the Board of Foreign Missions.

"What shall I bring with me to India?" wrote Dr. Bob to Charles.

"Everything," was the reply.

So Dr. Petersen closed his office, packed up all his equipment, took his wife Mary and their three-year-old son Peter, and started. Destination: exactly half a world away.

Charles had made careful preparations for his coming, setting aside a room which he considered adequate in the new outpatient building. Dr. Bob inspected the small space, then turned to Charles in obvious bewilderment.

"And where am I going to work?" he inquired innocently.

If Charles felt consternation, he did not show it. "Come with me," he said without batting an eye. Leading the new dentist down the stairs to the unfinished basement, he waved his hand in a grandiose gesture. "We'll remodel this," he said blandly. "Naturally, we wanted to leave the planning to you. It shall be done any way you wish."

After a few weeks the vast quantities of supplies began arriving from Bombay—X-ray machine, dental chair, cabinets, sterilizer, a complete laboratory including thermatrol, water bath, inlay furnace—in short, Dr. Bob's entire office. When it all arrived, there were ten barrels and crates of dental equipment, supplies, and materials. Of course, there was no room for it in the small space immediately available, but he set up his chair and started work while waiting for the basement rooms to be remodeled.

The strange country, language, customs, lack of space were no deterrent to this energetic and ingenious enthusiast. During World War II he had gone across Europe as a dental officer attached to an armored division, and he found it a simple matter to organize and set up a dental unit in strange territory. Mary also was soon absorbed into the busy routine. A graduate in pharmacy from the Oregon State University, she rendered some professional service, but her greatest contribution was in presiding over a beautiful and well-ordered home always open to guests.

Until Dr. Petersen's arrival the so-called dental department had been operating one or two mornings a week with one local practitioner in charge, using instruments easily classifiable as "antiques," but rendering a valuable and faithful service with very little equipment and supplies. This dentist, Dr. G. Madan, soon became Dr. Bob's friend and proved a wonderful colleague, making possible several dental meetings of local practitioners at the clinic. With his help Dr. Bob was able in time to organize the Bareilly branch of the Indian Dental Association, of which he was at four different times to act as president. But all this was still in the future.

Dr. Bob started work in the small room. Ignorance of language proved no drawback. Two short sentences in Hindi sufficed: *"Munh kholo* (Open your mouth),*"* and *"Dard kahan hai* (Where does it hurt)?" There were amusing reactions from patients to the new equipment. Some thought it a "strange chair" and observed its up-and-down motion with the fear and fascination of children. Some tried to sit on the footrest. Others used the seat, but, Indian fashion, pulled their feet up under them and sat cross-legged. One mother nursed her child while her teeth were being extracted.

The new doctor set up a busy schedule, adhering to an eight-hour day, an unusual precedent for the mission field, and quickly set about training his colleagues: his assistant, Sister K. Dadel, a graduate nurse; Mr. Ghosh, the X-ray technician who had worked in the laboratory; Mr. Prabhu Dayal, another laboratory man; and Miss Paul, the business manager. None of them had ever worked with a dentist before. On Wednesday afternoons all hands pitched in to clean up the clinic, and on Saturday afternoons all took a vacation, another radical idea.

There were setbacks. A Christian boy whom Dr. Bob had hired to help with the equipment stole a large quantity of instruments and dental supplies, disposing of them in the bazaar. Dr. Charles secured the chief of the C.I.D., and they went down in the bazaar and uncovered a half-dozen shopkeepers who were acting as fences, selling the goods to local dentists. When the C.I.D. man discovered some of the articles, the shopkeepers gave them back without a word of protest. All part of his Indian education, Dr. Bob maintained cheerfully.

The bazaars educated him also in some of the cruder Indian dental practices. On his first holiday in Almora he saw itinerant dentists setting up their little folding chairs in the bazaar, perhaps in a fly-infested market. In front of the chair several hundred teeth would be laid out on a blood-stained cloth, many with missing roots. The sign over the "shop" might read: WATCHMAKER AND DENTIST. A few practitioners were also snake charmers, their experience derived from extracting cobras' teeth. This was done by holding a rag in front of the cobra, then, when the snake struck, deftly pushing the rag into its mouth. Jerking it out violently, the skilled operator would bring the snake's fangs with it.

Occasionally Dr. Petersen saw the consequences of such treatment. One poor Muslim villager came to the clinic, his jaw swollen to twice its normal size, so sick that his two sons had to hold him upright. He had had his teeth pulled by the unclean instruments of a village snake charmer. The doctor removed a sequestrium of large proportions, and the man recovered.

Of course, India had her qualified dentists as well, perhaps a thousand of them, with many more of Class B status. When the dental act was passed, anyone who had been doing any kind of dentistry had been able to register as a "B Class" dentist, a condition which was later regulated by more stringent laws. Taken all together, there was probably one dentist for about 133,000 of India's population.

The doctor's services were of value in other departments than dentistry. With him he had many modern "carpules" of long-acting local anesthetic for his dental syringes, and he offered to use them if necessary for other patients. One day Dr. Charles ran to the dental clinic and summoned Dr. Bob to come quickly with his syringe and local anesthetic. A patient had come with scorpion bite. Hurrying to his side, they found him moaning with agony.

"Where is it?" demanded Dr. Bob. "Show me."

The patient had sat on the scorpion!

"That's the lowest-down injection I ever gave!" the dentist commented.

Word of the new doctor and his wonderful equipment spread rapidly not only in the city but among all the missionaries of the area, and they came swarming. During his three-year term 320 different missionary names were entered in the dental register, with an average of four appointments each. The remodeled suite in the basement of the dispensary was completed in record time—for India, and after the other makeshift quarters it seemed the height of modernity. It contained two operating rooms, a large laboratory, a waiting room, and a business office. With its air-conditioned comfort, it soon became a meeting place for all kinds of people, including the two Doctors Perrill. But before it had been occupied four months something happened.

One day an Indian banker came to see Dr. Charles. "I would like to inspect the hospital," he said, "and with your permission I will bring a lawyer." Charles agreed with some trepidation. Trouble? Official red tape? The following morning the man arrived, accompanied not only by a lawyer but by two other determined looking gentlemen. Still in the dark, Charles showed them about the hospital, the wards, the infant nursery, the operating rooms, the labs, the upstairs classrooms for student nurses and technicians. They saw the old white building built by Clara Swain in 1873, the new dispensary with its dental clinic.

"Is there anything else we can do for you?" he asked.

"No," one of them replied. "There's nothing you can do for us; we want to do something for the hospital. We are the trustees of the Bareilly Corporation Bank, and we have a trust fund for building a worthy memorial to the bank's founder. We would like to build something at Clara Swain Hospital."

Dr. Charles tried to appear nonchalant, as if such things happened every day. "Very good, gentlemen. How would you like to build a new surgical ward?"

No. That apparently did not interest them. He tried again. "Then how about a children's ward?" Still they did not seem enthusiastic. "Well, what would you like to do?"

The spokesman for the group cleared his throat. "We are impressed by what Dr. Petersen is doing in the basement dental clinic. The little daughter of our banker has been his patient, and now we have seen it for ourselves. We want to give the hospital a new dental clinic building."

Charles called Dr. Bob, who came bounding up the stairs in his white jacket. "How would you like to build yourself a new dental building?" He tossed the bomb without warning.

"Oh—*no!*" The young dentist groaned. "I've got enough trouble keeping up with my work in the basement, without looking for more!"

[150]

"Better be careful," grinned Charles, "or you'll be hurting the feelings of your friends here. They want to build you one."

Dr. Bob's eyes popped open, then narrowed in swift appraisal of the situation. Well, he agreed, maybe a new building would be all right. In fact, it might be pretty much all right. But he was not going to move from his basement unless it was into a real *pukka* clinic.

The banker nodded slowly. He regarded the dentist with even more respect. "What kind of building do you think should be erected, then?" he asked. "We would want it to be a fitting memorial to the worthy founder of our bank."

That was the beginning. Charles and Dr. Bob drew up careful plans, adapted to conditions in Bareilly, and the dentist sent the plans to two different dental houses in the United States for expert guidance. Every detail was meticulously checked. The plans provided for hot and cold running water, sewage, drainage, steel windows, gas, light, compressed air, and even air conditioning, all detailed down to the last plug and socket. Their Indian building contractor had never seen such plans. Neither had Charles and Dr. Bob. But it was built exactly as specified, and they kept a complete record of expenditures. It cost 13,761 rupees. The fund allotted by the builders covered everything but the cost of an air-conditioning machine, but Dr. Bob obtained that by taking one from what he considered a less important section of the hospital. The building included four operating rooms, an examination room, an X-ray room, two rooms for dental hygienists, a recovery room, a lab, a waiting room, and a business office. It was the finest dental clinic in all of Asia. Its dedication was a triumphant occasion, both for Dr. Bob and for the hospital. Once again Rajkumari honored the event with her presence.

Dr. Petersen introduced many innovations in Bareilly. He seemed unaware that there were things which just couldn't be done in India! He brought the first rubber garden hose to the compound, and fascinated Indian boys spent hours spraying the plants in the planter boxes, built for the more important purpose of keeping the back wheels of the bicycle rickshas from scarring the smooth cement walls of the clinic. On at least one occasion the hose was used to break up a noisy gambling game of the ricksha men too close to the clinic windows, a sport that was a sort of cross between checkers and throwing dice.

There was even a medical-dental photography room in the

dental clinic, which used some of Charles's equipment. The photographer, Mr. Ghosh, was a young man Dr. Bob "borrowed" from the X-ray department, who proved both clever and ingenious at the craft. There were two toilets in the clinic, one European, one Indian, the squatting plate of the latter shaped like a large keyhole in the floor. Each had its own septic tank and flush arrangement, a contrivance which so impressed the banker that he ordered one made in his own house by the building contractor. The two doctors were invited to inspect it when the gleaming terrazzo had been given its final polish.

With the new building in operation, Dr. Bob's work load increased. Nor did he confine his service merely to the hospital. He procured some army field dental chests with tray and foot engines and started visiting Methodist schools in the area, sometimes examining up to three hundred students a day. The children from the villages, he discovered, had almost no cavities. Those from the cities, who were able to get candy, often did. He was even able to make a small start on a public health program of prophylactic or preventive dentistry.

Many Indians were as baffled by his purpose in coming to their country as his associates had been back home. Why was he here? Surely he was sent by the United States government and was receiving a huge salary?

No, Dr. Bob would explain over and over, he was sent by the Methodist Church of America, at a salary much lower than his income in the United States, to serve the people of India as an expression of Christianity in everyday practice. Many of his Indian listeners then looked at him askance. They simply did not believe it. But he was not annoyed by this reaction. It merely intensified his desire to do everything he could to prove to them, and to himself, that Christianity could "work." But—why make such a sacrifice? would be the next skeptical question.

"I realize," he once said with a good-natured grin, "it would be much more dramatic if Mary and I were able to say that we received a vision that indicated we must serve in the mission field. Actually, our decision was the result of much thinking over a long period of time. It was, therefore, not a sacrifice. If anything, it was a selfish decision, because we felt our happiness lay in the pleasure this kind of service gives us."

Other pleasures were less altruistic. The Perrills and Petersens often went picnicking together on Saturday afternoons. There was a large irrigation canal with a private maintenance road not far from Bareilly which ran for miles through beautiful fields near an old river flanked by large sand dunes. The wife of the canal officer had been delivered of a son in Clara Swain Hospital, and the proud father had presented Dr. Wilma with a pass to the canal road. It was an ideal spot, not only for picnicking but for hunting, and Dr. Charles and Bob became experts at bagging the pea fowl, a good substitute for turkey at Thanksgiving and Christmas, and stalking the *nil-gai*, a large antelope to be found in the area. To hunt the latter it was necessary to approach within 50 yards of the game with one's shotgun and then make every shot count. The hospital ambulance was also a necessity. The back seat could be removed and the tail gate lowered like a station wagon; then the antelope, weighing perhaps 500 pounds, could be hoisted inside. On returning to Bareilly, Dr. Bob would take charge of supplying meat to the local Christian community of about five hundred. He had once worked in a butcher shop and knew how to wield a meat saw and cleaver. Those with refrigerators filled them with roasts and steaks, doubly welcome in a land prohibiting the slaughter of the cow.

Later, when Dr. James Pomeroy, the new chest surgeon, arrived in 1952 with his wife and three lively boys, there was still more jolly activity. Christmas was especially exciting, each family celebrating with its tiny arborvitae tree loaded with tinsel and gifts, one for each of the household servants and their numerous family members. Then the nurses put on a pageant depicting the Christmas story, and there was a large community Christmas tree, with a jovial Indian Santa arriving in an ox cart and distributing presents to all the hospital workers and their families.

But the Pomeroys were not the only interesting arrivals in 1952. June saw the advent of little Polly Elizabeth Petersen. Her parents were up in the mountains, in the missionary colony at Landour, when it happened, and the experience presented some novel features.

When Peter had warned of his arrival, Dr. Bob had merely backed the car out of the garage, tucked Mary in, and driven leisurely to the hospital. Not so the approach of this blessed event! Polly started her activities at two in the morning. First Dr. Bob woke up the *khansama*, cook, who raced to the local bazaar. Here he wakened five coolies, one to carry Mary's hospital necessities, four to carry her in a "dandy," a chairlike arrangement on poles. They bundled her up, put her in the dandy, and trudged off to the hospital, Mary thankful that it was dark, with few witnesses to the odd procession. After about twenty-five minutes of trudging up one steep slope and down another they reached their destination. Here all proceeded as in any modern American hospital, for the doctors and nurses were mostly American missionaries, with a competent Indian staff to assist them.

Flowers! thought the proud father as soon as Polly had put in her healthily robust appearance. Must have flowers for Mary! But how? No telephone call to a convenient florist this time. He had to hire a coolie to walk four miles to gather some. It cost him the whole sum of 3 rupees, less than seventy cents.

Every day he made the trek down to the hospital to visit Mary, walking from their cottage at about 6,700 feet, over the 7,000-foot crest, and down to the hospital on the 6,000-foot level. Quite a hike! But when he got tired he would think of the coolies he had seen climbing the whole 7,000 feet, each with as many as seventeen 10-pound cans of *dalda* (shortening) or three maunds of charcoal (about 240 pounds) on his back!

8

The arrival of Dr. Pomeroy in March of 1952 was another of Dr. Charles's dreams realized. His plans for a chest department had progressed slowly. Though he had continued to treat as many tuberculosis patients as possible in his "spare" time and a small group shuttled back and forth between Almora in the summer and the tent colony in winter, the arrangement was uneconomical and unsatisfactory. Now, with its first qualified thoracic surgeon, the chest unit could really be started.

Assigned as Dr. Pomeroy's assistant was young Dr. Ernest Sundaram, a recent graduate of Calcutta University Medical College, who had been doing a rotating internship under Dr. Perrill. From the time he assisted at Dr. Pomeroy's first chest operation he exhibited a remarkable interest and aptitude in chest surgery. The surgeon encouraged him to specialize, and in a few months Dr. Ernest left for study at the Vellore Christian Medical College to work under the eminent thoracic surgeon, Dr. Reeve H. Betts.

A program to provide a separate department of about thirty beds for Dr. Pomeroy's patients was immediately sanctioned, with a plan to increase it to forty beds by 1953. Since there was no nearby sanatorium, an outdoor chest clinic was established, and the basement of the out-patient building became the chest-clinic dispensary. Dr. Pomeroy, very meticulous, deeply spiritual, intensely humble in spite of his great skill, was a valued addition to the staff.

The thirty beds were filled so rapidly and the rush became so great that some of the poor patients were left lying out under the trees, many of them under the huge mango tree which was a central feature of the compound. Something had to be done. Nizam Masih's list was again consulted, and Dr. Charles and his associates challenged their friends in Bareilly, merchants, small shopkeepers, businessmen, workers, and many contributed generously. Work on the new unit started at once, and with some additional help from the Methodist Committee for Overseas Relief, the new chest wing was well under way when the Perrills were preparing for their second furlough in 1954.

Other departments were showing progress. Three technical schools were now in operation, one for lab technicians, one for X-ray technicians, and a full course in nursing, which now included a fourth year devoted to the study of midwifery and the care of new-born infants. Several years, under the leadership of Mary Gordon, now superintendent of nurses, the school had enjoyed the distinction of "100 per cent pass." In ten years enrollment in the school of nursing had risen from a low of thirteen to a high of over fifty. Similar changes had taken place in staff. Back in 1942 the teaching staff had included one Indian staff nurse, the business manager who taught an English class, and three American nurses. In 1956 it included five Indian sisters and one American.

Standards in the school had risen constantly through the years. 1950 had marked a step forward with the first "matric pass" nurses graduated. In the first years when they were trying to raise the standard for admission it had been difficult to get candidates who had passed their matriculation examinations, but that hurdle had been surmounted. Nursing was no longer a course for a girl not bright enough to take teacher training or go on to college. It had assumed its rightful place as an opportunity for educated girls with the keen desire to be nurses.

"Why do we want this?" wrote the superintendent. "Let me illustrate. Ten years ago B/P was a procedure carried out only by a doctor or perhaps a senior sister. Now young nurses are required to take B/P readings many times a day. Four years ago we had seven transfusions in a whole year. Recently we had seven in one day. Hundreds of injections are given in a week. Student nurses are learning how to use the very intricate apparatus required in care of patients following chest surgery. Professional nurses must be an important part of the health team that must work together for a patient's recovery."

Patient, competent, always in motion, always smiling, Mary Gordon was as much the spirit of Clara Swain Hospital as Nizam was its mascot. Her motions were so swift that occasionally she stumbled and fell, but even in her falling she maintained her innate dignity. Concerned with every individual, very devout, she always prayed when her girls came to her with their problems. She distributed Christmas cards to every patient, always attended their Sunday church services, read the Bible to those who could not read. She was meticulous with records and correspondence, so that there was a clear and easily located picture of every student's work for the past twenty years. And she loved her students. Many, like Kheti, could testify to that.

Kheti's mother had died when she was a baby, and her father had brought her to the hospital to be cared for, where she became the special interest and concern of Janette Crawford and Theresa Lorenz, as well as of Mary Gordon. From time to time the father would come to see how his child was getting along. Then for several years he failed to come. Meanwhile Kheti attended the school, became interested in Christianity, and asked to be baptized. Suddenly the father appeared. He explained that he had married again and that at first he had not told his wife about the child. The girl came to her missionary friends.

"They'll come and take me away and marry me off, and I'll have to leave school, I know they will. And I don't want to—not yet. There are so many things I want to do, to help people!"

Yes, the missionaries were agreed. That was probably just what would happen, and the child was scarcely in her teens.

Unless they did something to prevent it! Taking full responsibility, they sent the girl to another school and assumed the cost of her education. Later, to Mary Gordon's delight, Kheti decided to become a nurse. It was a proud day for both of them when she received her nurse's cap at Clara Swain.

For the capping ceremony was a much-coveted achievement. During the first three months of their course the students wore white saris. At the end of this trial period, if they had completed their work, they were given uniforms. But the donning of the cap was the first real milestone. The service took place in the hospital chapel, usually decorated with white flowers and white candles. At the beginning of the service on one end of a long table were the caps, on the other tiny replicas of the Nightingale lamps with small white candles in them. The sister tutors "capped" the students, but it was Mary Gordon who had the privilege of placing in their hands the tiny lamps and lighting them.

As time passed there were other, more mundane improvements in the hospital. One was in the laundry. The usual, time-honored *dhobi* system of India employed a number of strong-armed Indian *dhobis* (washermen) who took the clothes to the banks of a local pond or river and beat them over a rock or heavy board. The hospital laundry was not much better. It consisted of a pair of shallow cement water tanks in which the washermen stood and beat the sheets and other articles over wooden slabs. The whacking resulted in partially clean, but shredded linens. Following this they were steamed over a large copper kettle set in a primitive wood-burning stove, and the bleaching process was completed by spreading them on the "grass," mostly sand and weeds, to dry in the strong sunlight. If all went well, the wash would come back sweet-smelling and white. But much could go wrong. Cows and goats were no respecters of sheets. Often a surgeon would discover in the operating room that the linen was full of tiny sand particles and that weed seeds were dropping out of the laparotomy sponges. And in the monsoons everything was damp and often mouldy.

The installation of a modern laundry system seemed impossible. Machines were bulky and heavy to ship. They demanded live steam, soft water, and large quantities of electricity. However, the Woman's Division of Christian Service spurred them to action by a gift of $5,000. The result was improvement, but hardly modernization. They walled off an area to exclude wandering cows and goats. They graded the site and put in brick platforms and drains around new cement water tanks. And they completed five simple but modern apartments for the hospital *dhobis* and their families. Each had a large porch for ironing and sorting, a cubicle for steaming, and a drying shed with long lines of shiny new wire. More water was needed, so they drilled a 4-inch pipe and installed a 5-horsepower pump connected with a 3,000-gallon water tower 40 feet high. Hot water came from a 50-gallon oil drum enclosed in masonry and fired by wood chips obtained from a local factory. All this used up the $5,000. The washing machines were yet to come.

The water supply for the compound was now fairly adequate. In 1940 there had been no running water. By 1954 they had added five deep well borings and devised a "grid" of looping water pipes so interconnected that every point had an ample water supply. Bareilly was one of the last big cities of India to get a water system, largely because of the local union of *bhistis* (water carriers), who were fearful of losing their jobs carrying water in their goatskin bags.

The problem of correct time was only partially solved. It was important for a hospital team to keep on schedule, immune to the pranks of students who liked to tamper with the clocks when late to meals or duty stations. There were twenty-five clocks in the wards and operating rooms, each securely reposing in a locked box behind a small glass window. They were Nizam's province, and he operated with the faithful efficiency of an ancient lamplighter. Each morning he went to a friend's house to set his Swiss watch on correct radio time. Then he went his rounds, unlocking each box, winding and setting each clock, and recording any gain or loss in his "clock book." He made plusses where a Westerner would have recorded minuses, saying that he must "add the lost minute," and he put down a queer check mark whenever he adjusted the timer of an ailing clock. A twenty-sixth clock had recently been purchased to start a system of clock rotation. This provided each clock with two weeks' leave of absence each year at a clock shop.

Charles had dreams of buying 26 eight-day clocks for the hospital. What box-unlocking time that would save for poor Nizam, winding four instead of twenty-five each day! And what a boon a master clock would be which could run all the others! But already patients were complaining because the hospital was getting too mechanical and impersonal.

In fact, it was becoming so complex that it was hard for doctors to understand or cope with many maintenance problems. To meet this need, Clara Swain had just hired a fine young Indian engineer, Jai Narain, graduate of one of India's engineering colleges, and he was being encouraged to go to the States to further his knowledge, especially about such complicated mechanisms as air conditioning. Not that much could go wrong with the underground tunnels! However, plenty could happen to the machine which provided auxiliary cooling, and it was a blessing to have Jai Narain to keep it in order during the hot months.

But it was as much the humbler workman as the trained professional who kept the hospital wheels running smoothly. For instance, there was "my-man-Thursday." The hospital was blessed—or cursed—with wheels of all sizes, from the small castors on dressing stands to the large wheels of bicycles. The small castors would clog and bind as they picked up scraps of thread or catgut in the operating rooms or gathered lint in the wards. The bumpy courtyards and halls played havoc with swivel wheels, and the sideways pushing and pulling were especially hard on the bearings and tires of the bicycle wheels used for a smoother ride over long stretches between wards.

When the engineering department admitted defeat, Dr. Charles asked a bicycle shop for help. The owner and a young helper brought a bag of tools and came every Thursday, their "free day," when the bazaar was closed. Near the central supply room was the workshop for ailing hospital wheels. They found castors which had been jammed for months and even painted over; "frozen" wheels, worn flat on one side; wheels with bearings gone, or bushings worn twice the size of the axle. For many weeks they worked in a mechanic's nightmare, for castors and good ball bearings were scarce in India, and the hospital wheels came in odd sizes. But the mechanic and his helper worked on patiently, adjusting faulty swivels, using grease and oil where needed, and cleaning away the lint and grime each week. The wheel chairs and stretchers stopped squeaking and scraping, and the nerves and tempers of busy hospital workers were spared for more important stresses.

The reputation of "my-man-Thursday" soon spread around the hospital, and on Thursday mornings the nurses would roll the bothersome wheels to the service workshop. He soon took on other special projects, such as cleaning and oiling door hinges on the wards, or helping to adjust the gears of an ancient operating table. In other parts of India wheels might squeak and stick, but in Clara Swain Hospital there were smooth rolling and perfect synchronism of gears, at least on every Thursday afternoon.

Nizam Masih was another of the nonprofessionals whose value to the hospital vastly increased through the years. In many ways he and Charles were kindred spirits: both were cannily practical, both extroverts, both audacious in attempting new ventures—and they had the two loudest voices in the hospital. When either of them was talking, he could always be located, regardless of the intervening distance! In time Dr. Charles conferred on the amazingly versatile Nizam the title of "public relations officer" of the hospital. Thus he became semiofficially what he had long been in actual practice: a go-between linking the practical interests of staff and patients.

Indian patients, even those from the villages, were becoming remarkably canny. Though most of them had no recourse to popular magazines and couldn't have read them if they had, the village radio kept them informed of new and successful procedures in medicine elsewhere in the world, and they came to Clara Swain expecting the staff to know all the latest developments. Nothing should prevent them from doing the latest types of cardiac or brain surgery! They came meaning business and prepared to pay—at least what they could. The villagers might have sold their precious grain or borrowed money, and they wanted to know exactly what the treatment would cost. And here problems began.

Dr. Charles—or another staff doctor—would examine the patient carefully, recording the details on the old typewriter in the consultation office, and the admission card would give an estimate of the time the patient must stay in the hospital. Each expensive item would be noted down, such as operation fee, X-ray examinations, or antibiotic drugs. If the estimate was wrong—well, it had better not be! The hospital would lose face as well as money.

But many patients could not pay for their treatment. And here was where the "public relations officer" entered the picture. The examination and estimate would be made just as carefully. The patient would then go to see Nizam. He would listen to the problems of each one—social, financial, medical—and arrange what was needed, regardless of the patient's ability to pay. But each one was expected to pay something, or, if possible, supply his own food. The hospital was not handing out charity to paupers. It was helping self-respecting citizens who were slightly embarrassed financially. The treatment might cost 200 rupees and the patient could scrape together only 5—about a dollar—but he was doing what he could, and the hospital was doing what it could, and so they could part as friends and equals. It was Nizam's job, with all his accumulated wisdom, to decide what the patient was actually able to pay.

And how would the difference be made up? For in a land like India, with the average per capita income about $60, there must always be a difference. This must be a matter of Christian conscience, the practical Christian conscience of all those believing in the brotherhood of man.

Not infrequently the hospital was in the stream of new medical discoveries which were only beginning to flow out to the rest of the world. For instance, shortly before the Perrills left for furlough, the hospital was visited by Dr. Paul Brand of the Vellore Medical College, fast becoming one of India's most eminent surgeons and in time to receive worldwide recognition. Within the last half-dozen years he had been experimenting with new techniques of surgery and rehabilitation which were already revolutionizing the treatment of leprosy.

He and Dr. Charles proved to be kindred spirits. Both were skilled surgeons. Both were explorers, innovators, taking pride in making the best of whatever tools or materials they might have at hand, often creating "something" out of "nothing." Both, in spite of their achievements, were simple and humble men.

This characteristic of humility was dubiously exemplified when Charles took his guest on a hunting trip. After a long trek into the jungle they saw tiger footprints. As they kept on, the prints kept getting fresher and fresher. Finally they disappeared into a thick grassy patch.

"You go in," urged Dr. Charles magnanimously, "and chase him out. You're the guest. I'd like you to have the honor."

"No, no, you go," urged the guest with an equal display of self-denial. "I wouldn't think of depriving you of the privilege."

Neither of them went, and the tiger remained in his retreat.

They stayed overnight in the foothills in a little hunting lodge, sleeping on *charpoys*, string cots, provided for such transient occupants. In the middle of the night Dr. Brand was awakened by suspicious sounds and the occasional flare of Dr. Charles's squeeze torch.

"Zwing! Zwing! Zoom! Ungh! Ungh!"

Familiar enough sounds to anyone forced to cope with the frequent small denizens of Indian hotel beds and train bunks! Lying in unmolested comfort, Dr. Brand smiled sympathetically as he heard his roommate kill scores and scores of the unwelcome visitors all through the night. Again Charles had proven himself the perfect host!

While in Bareilly Dr. Brand demonstrated the techniques of his new operation of muscle-tendon transplantation on the "claw hands" of leprosy patients, fascinated young Teddy with tales of his lively and unpredictable four children (there were two more to come), and inspired both staff and students with the Christian witness of his friendly and dynamic personality. Being both surgeon and builder, he was especially interested in some of Dr. Charles's ingenious devices in the new buildings and operating theaters. Now working with enthusiasm on the rural hospital idea, Dr. Brand believed that modern surgery could be simplified drastically and hoped to demonstrate under primitive conditions new methods for his young surgeons. He studied the shadowless lamp made of circular sheets of aluminum beaten into parabolas, and later made a similar one for Vellore's new Rural Hospital.

Simplicity had long been the keynote at Clara Swain. Charges to patients were cut to a bare minimum. The largest European-style rooms for private patients cost about $3 a day; ward bed care came to 30 cents; major operations were not more than $25. Not infrequently missionaries would come to the hospital for surgery *before* returning to the United States. But for an Indian patient this scale of costs was not as low as it sounded. A month's salary for a government clerk was only $25, and the daily wage of a laborer was no more than 50 cents. Much service was given at far below cost. The medicine might cost a dollar, and the patient could pay but 5 cents. But even that small payment made him self-respecting.

"Free medicine degenerates into 'red water,'" was Dr. Charles's caustic appraisal.

9

When the Perrills left for furlough in the spring of 1954 after a spate of farewell parties, they hoped to slip away quietly, so they picked a train which left at 10:30 at night. But when they arrived at the station, there were their friends, several hundreds of them, to see them off.

"There were tears in their eyes," recorded Charles, "and in ours too, only we could hide ours better among the dozens of garlands which almost hid our faces. They wished us Godspeed and hurry back. No matter how political winds may blow, or things turn sweet or sour, these Indian friends understand what we Christians in institutions of healing are doing in loving service."

The three years of the Petersens' short term had passed, and the two families traveled together, taking an Italian ship as far as Naples, where they parted, the Petersens to spend some time skiing in Switzerland, the Perrills to go on to London and New York. During the last intense hot season Dr. Bob had contracted infectious hepatitis, from which he recovered promptly but which left him with a residual ache. In spite of the fact that all his tests proved normality, the ache persisted. Later at a conference in Indiana the two men met and compared notes. With his usual drive and enthusiasm Dr. Bob had floated a loan, assembled another full supply of dental equipment, and started a new flourishing practice in Oregon.

"How's the ache?" asked Charles.

"Still there," returned Dr. Bob.

"I know how to diagnose that," said the other shrewdly. "It's an ache to get back to India."

The Perrills were not long enough away to develop the same malady. A year later they sailed by the new ship *Christoforo Colombo*, arriving in Bareilly in time to take up their work during the hot season—not the time of year when "sane" people planned to arrive in India, but it was important to be on hand when vacations came due for the overworked staff and the oppressive heat pushed hospital morale down to low ebb.

Again Dr. Charles took back considerable equipment: Strycker vibrating bone saws, window air conditioners, plans for an intercommunication telephone set, an improved camera, and, he hoped, additional know-how and enthusiasm. Since their arrival in Bareilly fifteen years before, the status of missionaries had been undergoing drastic change. The Indian church was developing its own efficient and highly trained leadership. Missionaries must come now as colleagues and helpers, no longer as administrators because of their superior training and leadership qualifications. The Methodist Church in India now had its own four Indian bishops, as independent in administration as those in the United States. It was right that it should be so. This was the goal toward which mission work had been moving for a hundred years, since William Butler had started schools, begun training Indian pastors, set in motion the printing presses designed to produce an educated and self-governing laity. And the Perrills knew that this third term of service must be one of extremely important transition, continuing the process of training Indian doctors, nurses, and technicians for assuming new offices of responsibility and leadership.

Immediately there were encouraging developments in this direction. In 1955 medicine was separated from surgery, and Dr. Das became head of the department of surgery. Sister Shanti Singh, assistant nursing superintendent, rejoined the staff after six years of study and experience in England and America to take charge of midwifery, and Sister Pauline Alexander, another assistant, having spent nine months in Vellore and two years as a Crusade Scholar in America, returned as director of nursing education.

Dr. Pomeroy interviewed a young Indian, Dr. Tara Chandra, a Rajput of the noble warrior class, who had secured his M.D. in general medicine from the Lucknow Medical College, and was much impressed with his high qualifications, his motives in choosing medicine as a career, and his desire to work in a mission hospital. Taking him into his department, he immediately began training him in chest surgery. Dr. Tara Chandra studied under Dr. Pomeroy until the latter left in the spring of 1956, then he continued his study under Dr. Ernest Sundaram, who returned just before the departure of Dr. Pomeroy to become head of the chest department.

Though Dr. Charles still acted as both hospital and medical superintendent, the increased efficiency of staff made it possible for him to undertake another major responsibility. For some years he had acted on a committee assigned the task of upgrading the Christian Medical College in Ludhiana, for years an interdenominational women's school, into a general medical college.

He well knew the difficulties the college was facing. India was in dead earnest about her educational program. When the British left in 1947 there were fewer than twenty medical schools; a decade later more than fifty were in operation, and a further 50 per cent increase was planned. Christian medical schools like Vellore and Ludhiana were facing a tremendous task of upgrading to meet the new demands of a progressive government. And Christian hospitals and medical schools had values to give which no government institution could possibly offer. At Ludhiana the deadline was approaching for approval or rejection by the Punjab state government.

"Indian regulations now require," Dr. Carl Taylor, an old schoolmate, pointed out on one of Charles's visits to Ludhiana, "that professors in the basic science departments must have two degrees, an M.D. and an M.Sc. Our problem at the moment is to find a doctor who also has a physiology degree. They're rare birds."

"Funny! I happen to have both," admitted Charles in an unguarded moment.

A few days later he received an urgent letter asking him to join the Ludhiana staff for four months as the assistant professor of physiology!

"You can spend weekends in Bareilly," wrote Dr. Eileen Snow, the principal. "Surely Wilma can keep things going at Clara Swain."

Knowing the seriousness of the emergency, he could not refuse. But the assignment lasted two years instead of four months! It was a strenuous interval. Commuting each week the 300 miles on the Punjab mail train was no picnic. Hard enough also to try teaching physiology after a gap of sixteen years! Often he was only one lesson ahead of the students. And he was soon involved in building as well as teaching, bossing a crew of seventy-five workmen, improvising laboratory equipment. In return for this service, some of his associates helped round up stray dogs and frogs for experimental physiology and pharmacology. With no proper animal house, the dogs were a problem. On a long winter night they kept howling next to the quarters of the overworked staff until a laboratory worker was induced to sleep with the dogs, under threat that Charles would do so if he refused!

Meanwhile Dr. Wilma, besides supervising the women's and children's work at Clara Swain, in itself a full-time job, was trying to run two households, one in the hills at Mussoorie during Teddy's school year, and the main home in Bareilly. She was also the draftsman and architect for their new bungalow being built at last almost to her taste, according to her husband's plan and supervision. She had the teaching responsibility for the midwifery course for the fourth-year student nurses plus the satisfaction of seeing these girls make high marks on the government examinations. She continued to serve as medical advisor to the Baby Fold next door and to respond to calls of church and civic groups in both Bareilly and Mussoorie. In addition, like most missionaries, she carried on a large and lively overseas correspondence.

Of course the new house incorporated some of Charles's experiments in building. Trust him to make use of such a prime opportunity! This time he explored the possibilities of solar energy. The new bungalow contained a device for securing warm water heated by the sun. Then as a further experiment, he took one of the shadowless operating room light reflectors, enlarged it, and tried it out as a solar cooker, for food. Wilma, however, found the method left much to be desired.

But for Charles the most satisfying achievement of this third term was the new chest department. In 1956 the chest clinic building was completed, a separate unit on the side of the hospital next to the chest unit beds, a modern building with facilities for diagnosis and simple treatment and follow-up for all chest patients.

That the Christian witness of the hospital continued to be noticed and appreciated was evidenced by a letter received by Mary Gordon just before Christmas, 1956.

To the Nursing Superintendent,
Clara Swain Hospital, Bareilly

Respected Madam:

On the eve of this divine rejoicing, we, the patients of Male-chest-unit, want to assemble and dedicate our sincerest gratitude to the spiritual background which, present in every sphere of activity of this hospital, inspires a new libido in us.

We earnestly request your gracious personality present among us and distribute presentations. We hope your kindness will oblige us. The function will be held at 5 P.M. Thanking you,

Yours sincerely,
Patients of Male-Chest-Unit

Dr. Charles was disappointed that plans for a complete thoracic unit had to be abandoned for lack of money. However, the surgical facilities were remodeled and increased to meet further needs for chest and cardiac surgery, and in 1959 a new upstairs chest ward with twenty-six beds was dedicated, conveniently located above the larger section and intended for women patients.

Just ten years before, the surgical unit in memory of Charles's father had been dedicated. It was a joy to all that his mother, Mrs. Fred M. Perrill, now retired in America after forty-five years of service in India, was present for the dedication of this new addition. Twice she had provided money during the interval for enlarging the original unit, until now it contained four large operating rooms. A worthy memorial it had proved, indeed, for during the ten years it had seen a total of 16,979 operations performed, over 5,000 of them major. The dedication service was impressive, with Bishop S. K. Mondol of the Delhi area giving the address.

The upper story of the surgical wing contained the much-improved laboratory, with its school for technicians, for in 1957 the hospital had started training compounders for the state government. Here also was the new blood bank, the only one in Bareilly.

Securing blood donors for transfusions, especially after the initiation of chest surgery, was for many years a problem. There was a feeling in India that it was usually fatal to give a blood transfusion. At first the only blood donors were the relatives of patients, and they had a way of vanishing except at visiting hours. Even when cornered, they would insist that they were only "distant" relatives, and when it came time to give blood they would be among the missing.

However, the prospect of a good fee proved a more powerful argument against superstition than education. A good source was finally discovered among the riksha drivers, the lads who operated the gaily painted taxi-tricycles which brought patients to and from the hospital. They were a good-natured, rough-and-tumble lot, always willing to tackle something new if it meant an extra rupee. The staff soon had a squad of these pedicab drivers scouring the city for prospective blood donors, paid at the good price of $3 for each transfusion. Certainly a pint of blood was cheap enough to pay for a good pair of spectacles (made locally in India at one-tenth the cost in the United States), or something equally useful!

At first they kept the bottles as best they could, in an old refrigerator equipped with isinglass compartments to keep the temperature constant. No bottle could be kept more than ten days. When a bottle reached the eighth day it was declared surplus and made available as charity for poor patients suffering from hookworm or other debilitating conditions.

Soon the blood bank became so popular with the donors that precautions were taken of printing blood-donor cards to prevent their trying to give blood too often. Stamped and sealed, bearing the photograph and thumbprint of the donor, they were prized by the pedicab drivers, who were often donors. They were valuable identification documents in case of a squabble with the police!

Established in August, 1958, in its first four months the blood bank furnished 442 pints of blood at an average rate of 4 pints a day. Soon it was sending supplies to other hospitals as well.

Even a terrific flood during the monsoons of July and August failed to diminish the blood supply. Roads were wrecked, railway bridges washed away, whole villages demolished. Village patients and their relatives were stranded, either in the hospital or away from it. Some managed to wade through the waters to get treatment or return home after recovering, many to find their village had vanished. But the blood bank flourished and the number of donors soon reached a new high. None was turned away, and all were paid cash on the spot.

"Where are you finding all the new donors?" the pedicab drivers were asked.

Easy! They had been going up and down the railroad station platforms, offering the travelers in the stranded trains the chance to come and recoup their finances by giving a pint of blood, with no extra charge for the pedicab ride, but a commission, of course!

For some members of staff there were improvements appreciated even more than the chest unit and blood bank.

"At last we have been able to buy a real laundry!" reported Mary Gordon in 1956. "We got it from army surplus, and it runs on electricity. It took many months to get it set up and connected. I am anxious to have it started before the rains begin, as that is the time we always have the biggest headache over linen."

But she rejoiced even more over a class of thirty-three nursing students. Not so long ago they had raised their standards to accept only high school graduates, and the first year they had been able to get only one student! Now there were many applications each year, all from high school graduates. Several men students were also in the group, graduate nurses who had had their training in other schools without benefit of experience in the care of men and their diseases. The coeducational setup was productive of more than nurses' training, for that year two of the students were married in the hospital chapel, having chosen each other and made all their own arrangements, an innovation indeed for India.

Before leaving for furlough in 1959 Mary Gordon saw other satisfying developments. The first unit of Aish Mahal, residence for staff nurses, was completed in 1958, leaving more room in the old hostel for students. One of her nurses, Molly David, took first place in the state final nursing examinations. In the same year a public health program was initiated with the coming of Miss Frances Allen, a public health nurse, from America. And not long before leaving, Mary Gordon had the pleasure of seeing graduation exercises for twelve nurses, four midwives, four lab technicians, three radiographers, one compounder, and two nurse anesthetists.

10

The arrival in 1956 of Dr. and Mrs. Eugene Riel, a retired dentist and his wife, from Dayton, Ohio, gave a new burst of life not only to the dental program but to occupational therapy, which was Alice Riel's specialty. "Doc," as his wife called him, with his fine singing voice, his kindly, quiet, serious manner, his intense love of children, was a perfect complement to his more outgoing, fun-loving wife, with her delight in people, her skill at the organ, her love of entertaining. Fond of young people, they were soon involved in a father-mother relationship with many of the students.

Immediately Dr. Riel became interested in the school health program which had been successfully instituted by Dr. Petersen, and he determined to develop it further. In 1957 he mailed a dental questionnaire to all the Methodist schools in north India, ranging all the way from Isabella Thoburn College to village schools in the industrial area around Asansol in West Bengal, and schools high up on the slopes of the Himalayas. The replies were revealing. Only about 10 per cent had any arrangements for dental service. He arranged a trial tour to get an idea of the time and cost involved and found to his delight and amazement that the children living in the hostels could be given complete dental care for less than 1¼ rupees per patient, about 26 cents. So he planned four major tours, with separate visits to the hill stations. In the first year forty-two schools were visited, and over 5,500 children were examined and given treatment where necessary. Over 6,700 dental operations were performed at a total cost of only $950.

It could not have been done without his efficient assistants, Dr. Edwin Anamiah, a graduate of Calcutta Dental College, and Miss Amerjet Singh, trained by Dr. Petersen as a dental hygienist, who gave examinations, oral prophylaxis, and instruction in oral hygiene.

The influence of such a program could not be overestimated. These 5,000 and more children would take the story of dental hygiene back to their homes in villages scattered all over north India. They would be leaven permeating a large section of society and arousing greater demand for proper dental service. India's six dental schools were doing almost nothing in dental public health education. This was not a bad beginning, certainly, aside from its immediate value, a program which created 5,000 young ambassadors for better dental hygiene!

But if Dr. Eugene Riel made important contributions to the program already started by Dr. Petersen, his wife Alice built a new department from rock bottom. She began work in occupational therapy in an old laboratory room, using the materials and equipment which she had brought from the States. Here in a space only 15 by 20 feet, where it was difficult to turn around, she carried on a busy daily schedule. Ambulatory patients came; others were brought in wheel chairs to do caning, painting, weaving, *sirki* mat making, lamp shade construction, wood-burning, metal work, leather crafts. It was thrilling to watch dull eyes brighten, idle hands become creative, deadened spirits quicken into renewed interest in life.

But the Riels made an even more permanent contribution. Prompted by the obvious need, they offered to defray the complete cost of a new building to facilitate the program! Plans were immediately made to build a 40 by 45-foot addition to the central service building to make more room available. Early in 1958 the occupational therapy department was occupying a new modern center with 800 square feet of floor space, including a screened verandah, and, believe it or not, a show window to display the articles which patients had made and wanted to sell! The room was cooled by two air conditioners which the Riels had brought from home, a boon to grateful patients when the thermometer soared to 120. The monthly patient load, including both ambulatory and bed patients, would average about ninety.

Even more pertinent to the future of the new department was the departure in 1959 of Shanti James, a graduate nurse who had been Mrs. Riel's assistant, for the United States. Accepted by Ohio State University, she was to study for three years, again at the Riels' expense, to earn a degree in occupational therapy.

The values of this new department were to be measured not wholly in terms of physical improvement, though in many cases it accelerated the recovery of patients, exercising unused muscles, releasing tensions, improving appetites and digestion, revamping mental attitudes. Frequently it gave new life to a patient, providing the incentive and "know-how" for making a living after hospitalization in spite of physical disabilities resulting from illness or surgery. And for Alice Riel this imparting of hope and faith was an even greater thrill than initiating skills and developing latent abilities, rewarding as this could be.

The Riels had come for just a short term of service, their commitment to the Board extending only from July, 1956, to July, 1958. It was with regret that they saw the two years coming to an end. But there was one factor which made leaving a little easier, at least for "Doc." He was turning over the dental department into good hands. Dr. Petersen was returning!

For the "ache," mental and spiritual if not physical, had persisted. In 1958 for a second time Dr. Bob made arrangements for the transfer of his practice and the rental of his house, packed up most of his equipment, and made ready to return to India. It was a decision which brought joy to the whole family, even baby Jane, the newest member. And this time they were going as full-time recruits, committed to a five-year term. On June 8 they were commissioned as missionaries in Portland, Oregon, by Bishop A. Raymond Grant, and Dr. Bob was soon back in Bareilly unpacking new equipment, exulting in all the improvements and developments, especially the expanded mission school program, joyfully welcoming old friends and making new ones, plunging into work with all possible speed.

It was just as he had remembered it, the hectic exciting days, the thrill of serving where one was most needed, the colorful panorama of patients' dress: women in saris, from rich silk to dingy white cotton; women with jewelry, from the massive gold of the well-to-do to the heavy silver ankle bracelets, toe rings, and nose loops of the villagers; children in gaudy colors with big black eyes and shining dark hair, or in scant rags with hair in dull, matted strings; men, some in Western clothes, some in loose shirts and pajamas, others in long fitted coats over leg-hugging *churidarhs*, still others in knotted skirtlike *dhotis* and *lungis*.

The satisfactions! He tried to detail them once in a letter to friends back home. But—"How describe the dramatic relief when an infected tooth has been extracted? the startling change of appearance when dentures replace diseased and broken teeth? when a cleft palate and lip are repaired by surgical procedure? when oral tumors and cysts are excised? when the misshapen mouths of otherwise handsome children are given the aesthetic results of orthodontic treatment and appliances?

"Or how can facts tell of the discouragements?" he continued. "The hopelessness of an inoperable oral cancer? the ignorance of those who refuse to have abscessed teeth extracted for fear of losing their eyesight? the disfiguring habit of *pan* and betel-nut chewing, so prevalent among the populace? the lack of knowledge of even the most fundamental principles of oral hygiene? the grim poverty which makes the goal of living the obtaining of food and shelter?"

But the satisfactions far outweighed the discouragements. For instance, there was the middle-aged Sikh woman who came with a growth in her mouth. When removed, it was diagnosed as a nonmalignant tumor. Wonderful to be able to report to the anxious woman and her bearded, turbaned husband (who had sought help for her in many places) that she could safely return home and resume her household duties without worry!

Then there was the Sikh farmer who, while cutting grass in his fields, was clawed in the face by a tiger. He was brought to the hospital from Pilibhit, a distance of some sixty miles, weak from shock and loss of blood. The open wounds were dressed by the hospital surgeon, Dr. Das. Several days later, when the swelling had reduced, Dr. Bob and Dr. Perrill managed to reset his splintered broken jaw. He was kept in the hospital for further treatment and convalescence. But the patient did not mend. He lost flesh daily. Dr. Bob was baffled until he discovered the reason. The family was able to bring him food from his distant village only once in three or four days, and the man was almost starving! Dr. Bob soon arranged to have him receive a good diet through Church World Service supplies, and with the help of good foods, vitamins, and antibiotics he made an amazingly rapid recovery.

"And today," reported Dr. Bob, writing home in 1960, "he is back on his land, growing a new beard (common to all Sikh men) to cover his scars, and keeping a wary watch for tigers!"

"We value the opportunity we have of residing here during these momentous times," he concluded. "Policies and personnel of governments change with events, but the church still affirms Christ's timeless message of love. Pray that India may respond to this love!"

11

Twenty-one years! The span of a generation, the best years of their lives had been given to this small mission hospital in a remote city of India. Leaving for furlough in the spring of 1961, the Perrills might well ask, "Have they been worth it? What return for such a costly investment?"

Charles well knew what most of his peers in America would say. He had been a fool. He had wasted what might have been a successful career. For his skill as a surgeon was far more than mere competence. In his own country it would have brought him fame and affluence, a comfortable sinecure, a big house and car, all the appurtenances which were considered the by-products if not the genuine ingredients of success.

And what did he have now that he was approaching fifty? A salary which they would consider pitiably small, barely enough to cover necessities. A job dependent on a newly emerging, sometimes unpredictable church officialdom in a land which did not always look with favor on the activities of foreign missionaries. The criticism of some missionary colleagues who did not approve of his unconventional, often highly individualistic ideas, and of some Indian colleagues who frowned on his acceptance of too large donations from non-Christians. And what else? Twenty-one of the most challenging, most exciting, most rewarding years any man could ask!

Take last year's cholera epidemic, for instance, which had swept north India. Nearly 12,000 cases had been reported, with 3,444 deaths. Seventy-four victims had been brought to Clara Swain Hospital, and they had been able to save all but two of them, even several who had come twenty miles in ox carts! What could be more satisfying than saving so many lives, and, equally thrilling, to help cut short the epidemic with the modern miracle of inoculations?

Satisfying also to witness the growth of this new free nation from birth to maturity, to have had a part in it! The expansion of the medical program alone was impressive, though sobering when one considered the huge distance yet to go. In 1950 India had had a few over 5,000 hospitals and dispensaries, with one hospital bed per 3,000 inhabitants, as compared with the rate of one per 100 in the West. There was now perhaps one bed to every 2,500. But more emphasis had been put on village work, where it was badly needed, with about 3,000 village units established, each with a doctor, a midwife, a nurse, and a health assistant trying to provide medical service to a hundred villages. A mere beginning, with villages numbering 600,000, nevertheless a valiant beginning! The number of doctors had increased from 59,000 to about 80,000, still only one for every 5,000 people. The number of nurses, still one for about 14,000, had doubled. Thanks to WHO (the World Health Organization of the United Nations), working in cooperation with the Indian gov-

ernment, the swamps of the *terai* had been cleaned out, apprecia
bly reducing the terribly high incidence of malaria.

They had seen Bareilly grow also. Was its population still
200,000 or had it grown another hundred thousand? It was expanding so fast that records could not be kept up to date. And it
was facing an even more tremendous surge of growth. The new
synthetic-rubber factory would employ 4,000 workers and gen-
erate about 20,000 added city dwellers in the next year or two.
Even if the government plan to increase the size of the local district hospital from 150 to 500 beds, and the number of doctors
from five to twenty-two, was successfully accomplished, this
would be far from adequate. The needs of providing health service for the rapidly increasing population, of meeting health insurance provisions, of expanding family planning education were
colossal.

And what of Clara Swain Hospital itself? He had found it
with about 60 beds, many of them empty. Now there were offi-
cially 264, full usually to running over. In 1940 he had been the
only male doctor on a pitifully small staff. Now there were ten
doctors, six men and four women. There were seventy-three
students of nursing and midwifery. The first tiny operating
room had increased to four, all well equipped. Electricity, water,
air conditioning, new dispensary, chest wards, dental depart
ment, housing facilities, maternal and children's blocks—the list
of improvements was almost endless. Still he was far from satisfied. To meet the needs of this new India, with its tremendous
population growth and urbanization pressures, there must be
ever more exacting requirements for personnel, increasingly expensive equipment. X-ray therapy should be provided at a cost
of many tens of thousands of dollars. Judged by present cost in-
creases, within ten years the outlay to keep up even the same
volume and quality of medical work should be twice the present
expenditure of $200,000 a year. Yet nowhere in the world could
money be invested with greater returns either of material or
spiritual dividends. Would Christian people in America have the
vision and the will to meet the challenge?

Perhaps Charles's greatest satisfaction was in seeing so many
positions of responsibility occupied by highly trained and efficient nationals. There were Dr. Das in surgery, Mr. Singh in X-
ray, Dr. Thomas in dentistry, Mr. Dan in pharmacy, William

Ram in laboratory. And, though another missionary, Mr. Wesley Ginn, was taking his place as hospital administrator, it was an Indian, Dr. Ernest Sundaram, who was to become medical superintendent as well as chief thoracic surgeon. Perhaps Charles and Wilma could render the hospital their greatest service of all by leaving it in the hands of these sons and daughters of the new India which during their twenty-one years of ministry had been tumultuously but gloriously coming of age.

PART THREE
Nationals

1

Ernest Sundaram became familiar with doctors and hospitals at an early age. Stricken with typhoid when a child, in days when there was no prevention and 8 per cent of the children affected died, he was a long time in the children's ward in Secunderabad, from which he emerged a mere skeleton but with a ravenous appetite. In the summer he often visited his aunt, Elizabeth Shantappa, and her husband, both doctors. They had early become associated with a small hospital in Bidar, not far from his own city of Hyderabad, doing their first operations on a kitchen table. Fascinated by their work, Ernest had watched the hospital grow to over a hundred beds. Then when he was fourteen he broke his arm, a supracondylar fracture.

"I'm afraid it will be stiff," the local specialist pronounced dubiously.

Ernest was panic-stricken. "But I can't have a stiff arm," he protested. "I'm going to be a doctor!"

The specialist shook his head.

Gabriel Sundaram, Ernest's father, had many friends and relatives who were doctors, and he was well informed. "We'll go to Miraj," he said. "There's a famous surgeon there, Dr. Vail, just returned from Germany."

They took the train to Miraj, a town 250 miles west of Hyderabad, where there was a Presbyterian medical school and hospital. Dr. Vail operated on the arm. While there, Ernest watched the great surgeon operate and was fascinated. He also became acquainted with Dr. Bruce Carruthers, the principal, and his wife and played with their children. Listening, observing, Ernest wanted more than ever to be a doctor. After months of physiotherapy he waited in an agony of suspense for the verdict.

"It's all right, boy. The arm is as good as new."

"You mean—I don't have to be careful of it? I can even play basketball again, and hockey?"

"Sure thing. It's just as solid as the other."

Ernest's family had been Christian for several generations. Tracing their conversion back to William Carey, they had been Baptist for many years, then British Wesleyan. But Ernest's father, Gabriel, when studying in the Nizam's college in Hyderabad, came under the influence of a Methodist missionary, Charles Edward Parker, and joined the Methodist Church. He took the Conference course of study and became a minister as well as a teacher in the Methodist Boys' School of Hyderabad, little realizing that after a term as head master, then twenty-five years as principal of the school and a brief period serving as secretary of the Council of Christian Education, he would be chosen one of the first four Indian bishops of the Methodist Church.

Ernest was three when his mother died in childbirth, and he and his sister Sarala, a year and a half younger, were cared for by their two aunts, Elizabeth and Rosie, until the two girls left for medical training at Ludhiana. Then Gabriel Sundaram married Rajabai Peters, a science teacher, and the two children were soon absorbed into the wholesome affection of a normal home, where they were presently joined by two sisters and a brother. With a father and mother who were both teachers, Ernest received every educational opportunity, and, with three aunts and an uncle devoted to medicine, every encouragement in following his chosen career.

He pursued all his high school courses with medicine in mind. He graduated with high marks. Then came disappointment. The Nizam's state government of Hyderabad refused to admit Telegu-speaking students to the local medical college.

"You can speak Urdu," said one of his father's government friends. "Tell them you are able to take the studies in Urdu. With my influence I can get you in."

No, replied Ernest. He would try other colleges. He wrote to Dr. Bruce Carruthers. "Remember the boy who used to play at your house and watched you work? I want to be a doctor. Can you give me a seat?"

"Yes," the principal wired back.

Miraj prepared students for the examination taken under state auspices for the L.C.P.S. (Licentiate of the College of Physicians and Surgeons) certificate. He emerged from the examinations in top position. The highest scorer in state examinations was supposed to obtain a scholarship to a medical college, where he

[180]

could qualify for the M.B.B.S. (Bachelor of Medicine, Bachelor of Surgery) degree, but in this case the scholarship was awarded to a lower-ranking student. Obviously the officials balked at giving the honor to a Christian. A second scholarship was also awarded to a Hindu who ranked lower than a Muslim, who was also passed over. Bishop Pickett heard of the injustice and was incensed. He took the matter to Rajkumari Amrit Kaur, the Minister of Health of the central government. After confirming the facts, she was equally indignant. Taking funds at her disposal, she awarded scholarships to both Ernest and the Muslim boy, and secured entrance for them to a class being organized in Calcutta to prepare holders of L.C.P.S. certificates to study for the M.B.B.S. degree. Two years later Ernest graduated with distinction.

It was during his student days that India became independent and partition came, creating a holocaust of terror and bloody massacre as thousands of refugees poured across the borders between India and Pakistan. It was difficult at the time to find Hindu doctors willing to enter the danger areas because of the hazards resulting from their religious status. Bishop Pickett with other Christians was actively involved in the program of refugee relief, tireless both in rendering service in the Delhi camps and in recruiting workers.

Ernest willingly dropped his studies and went with others to Pakistan, becoming one of those responsible for the care of 50,000 Hindu refugees and for bringing them over the border into India. There he labored with others to establish them in camps, helping to dig trench latrines, immunizing them from the terrible epidemics that swept the massed areas, struggling against fearful odds to keep them as healthy as possible. It was a sobering, racking experience, shocking him abruptly into maturity, testing and almost draining his physical and spiritual resources, yet providing knowledge and skills which no amount of academic training could possibly have provided.

After securing his degree he went to Clara Swain Hospital to do a rotating internship under Dr. Perrill. It was here, operating with Dr. Pomeroy, that he decided to specialize in chest surgery and went to Vellore for further training.

The Vellore Christian Medical College and Hospital was an exciting place in the early 1950s. It had just celebrated its Jubilee, marking fifty years since the founding of the medical work in 1900 by Dr. Ida Scudder. The Madras government had approved it as a fully qualified institution under the state university. Dr. Paul Brand, still only an obscure orthopedic surgeon, had barely started his remarkable experimental surgery for leprosy and had just built the first leprosy rehabilitation center in the world, a little cluster of mud and thatch huts up on the college campus. Sitting in Dr. Brand's postgraduate lectures every Tuesday evening, captivated by his clear thinking, his dynamic enthusiasm, Ernest became his devoted admirer.

There were other great doctors at Vellore. Coming in 1946, Dr. Reeve H. Betts had been the first and only thoracic surgeon in the country. Ernest could hardly wait to begin work in this area.

"After you finish general surgery," Dr. Betts told him, "come into my department."

Ernest needed no second invitation. He finished one year of general surgery under Dr. John Carman and Dr. Bhatt, then began to specialize under Dr. Betts. He was amazed at the latter's remarkable energy and dexterity. Dr. Betts could take six or seven hours of operations in one stride. His working hours were usually from 7 A.M. to 6 P.M. Instead of taking time out at noon, he would bring along a box lunch and dictate letters while he ate. Though an eminent authority in his field, he would always listen to other points of view, even his students'. An intensely humble man, if pictures were being taken, he would always insist on his assistants' being in them, not himself. It was Ernest and Dr. Gopinath, not Dr. Betts, who appeared in photographs publicizing the new department.

Dr. Brand was equally humble, always sharing credit with his associates. A patient once came to the thoracic department with a familial metaphysia dysplasia, a rare case of multiple fractures caused by inherent weakness of the bones. Ernest consulted Dr. Brand, the orthopedist.

"Let's send it to England to Fairbanks," Brand suggested. Ernest compiled the case sheets, the X-ray pictures, the history, and they were sent to England. The great bone authority said he would publish the X-rays in the *Journal of Bone and Joint Surgery*. Later Dr. Brand and Ernest published a joint article in the *Journal of Surgeons' Association of India* on the same subject.

There came another unusual patient, a girl with a tumor under her thumbnail. Ernest took it to Dr. Brand, who pronounced it a very rare case indeed. He operated and Ernest assisted.

"Write it up," he told Ernest, "and we will publish it."

Ernest did so. Dr. Brand corrected and compiled it, couched it in more specific language, and it was published in *The Indian Journal of Surgery*, later reprinted in a pamphlet entitled, *Glomangioma of the Left Thumb*, jointly authored by Paul Brand, F.R.C.S., Professor of Orthopedic Surgery, and Ernest B. Sundaram, M.B.B.S., Department of Hand Research.

Ernest was in Vellore when on a January day in 1954 a terrible tragedy occurred. A station wagon filled with young resident doctors was bound on a picnic when it left the road, catapulted down a bank, and strewed its occupants over a wide area of muddied field. They were brought back to the hospital in the bus which had caused the accident, carried in ghastly procession into the dispensary and laid on improvised tables, examined by a hastily summoned corps of doctors, and, if necessary, rushed to operating rooms. He would never forget the shock of the experience. He had worked with most of the dozen or more residents, knew them all by name. To one, a girl named Satyabama, he administered anesthesia while her severe injuries were repaired. Another, Sojibai, was barely recognizable. It looked as if every bone in her face had been broken. Fascinated, he saw the tremendous job of reconstructive surgery performed by his superior, Dr. Bhatt, and by Dr. Moody, the missionary dental surgeon.

But it was Dr. Mary Verghese, most severely injured of all, about whom the whole hospital was most deeply concerned. She too had had severe facial damage, but, unlike Sojibai and the other victims, no surgery could repair her injuries.

". . . back broken . . . spinal cord severed . . . never walk again. . . ."

Ernest was as shocked by the reports as the rest of the staff. He remembered Dr. Mary as an attractive girl, tall, strong, quiet, very poised. She had just finished training as a gynecologist, and now her career was ended. In subsequent weeks and months he heard of her amazing patience and uncomplaining courage, knew when she graduated from bed to wheel chair, caught glimpses of her scarred smiling face in porch or corridor, then marveled to see her working with the leprosy patients in the clinic. Then before the end of the year the whole hospital was electrified by the news that, still seated in her wheel chair, she was performing operations on leprosy patients, the delicate transplantations of muscle tendons devised by Dr. Brand for the correction of the claw hand!

His admiration was tinged with awe. "Suppose something happened to end my career as a surgeon," he thought. "Would I have courage like that to pick up the pieces?"

In 1956 Ernest asked for an extension of his leave, but Dr. Pomeroy was going on furlough, and he was needed back at Clara Swain. Returning to Bareilly, he worked with Dr. Pomeroy a month. Pomeroy was a lung surgeon, not a cardiac. Ernest saw tremendous possibilities.

"We should start simple cardiac surgery," he said eagerly, "perhaps also some surgery on cancer of the esophagus."

"Go ahead," urged Pomeroy, and put him in charge of the department.

In 1951 Ernest had been named for a Methodist Crusade Scholarship for graduate study in the West. He was getting older. Soon it would be too late to go. He waited until 1958; still Dr. Pomeroy did not return. He felt he could wait no longer. Arrangements were made by church officials for him to go to Canada to study for his F.R.C.S. (Fellow of the Royal College of Surgeons) degree. To his regret, no surgeon could be found to take his place at Bareilly, and the department had to be included in general surgery.

It was about this time that romance entered his life.

He received an urgent letter from Miss Edna Hutchins, principal of Lal Bagh School in Lucknow, started long ago by Isabella Thoburn. Three of her girls had come down with tuberculosis. Would he come and screen the other thousand students? Dr. Pomeroy had secured a portable screening machine and given about 3,000 examinations in the schools. Ernest welcomed the opportunity to visit his home, for his father, elected bishop in 1956, was stationed in Lucknow. Since all his three sisters had followed their mother's example in choosing Isabella Thoburn College as their alma mater, Lucknow had easily become home for the family.

Ernest found the three cases very positive and sent them, with others, to the city hospital. He operated on the three successfully, and later one became a teacher, one a nurse. The third, Premlatha, stood first in scholarship in the whole state of Uttar

Pradesh. She studied while sick and went on to graduate from Isabella Thoburn College.

"We must prepare the nursery children," Ernest told Miss Hutchins. "If they come into the dark room without warning and see me there wearing goggles, they will be frightened."

Miss Hutchins suggested that he visit the children in the nursery, and he did so, wearing his goggles and making friends with them. The children stared at him in wide-eyed fascination, while Ernest with equal fascination but slightly more discretion stole glances at their teacher.

"What do you think?" asked Miss Hutchins after they left the room. "Can you screen them?"

"Yes," he replied. "If their teacher explains it to them and comes with them. A very pretty teacher, by the way," he added casually. He could tell that the principal did not appreciate this comment.

Later in the day the children were brought, and the operation went through smoothly. They thought it a great lark. He screened them all, including their teacher, Sheila Wilson, who proved even more attractive on further inspection. Tall, fair of skin in comparison with most women of the south, clear-eyed and smiling, she possessed poise and serenity as well as beauty. He returned to the bungalow to have tea with the staff.

"There's an excellent movie at the cinema," remarked one of the teachers. "Would any of the rest of you want to come?"

"I'd be glad to take you," offered Ernest helpfully, "all of you."

But his invitation was refused. Sheila, it seemed, came from a very conservative family, and her parents had given her no permission to go anywhere with a man.

At home he told his youngest sister, Prem, "I saw a very attractive teacher today in Lal Bagh."

His sister's eyes brightened. An unmarried son over thirty years of age was a concern to any Indian family. Who was she? He mentioned the girl's name. Prem immediately mentioned the observation to a friend, Miss Lal, who mentioned it to Miss Hutchins, Sheila's local guardian. Then for some months nothing happened. Ernest wrote Sheila a letter. She did not reply. He wrote again, inviting her to dinner at his parents' home in Lucknow. She wrote back that she could not come without her parents' permission.

By now Miss Hutchins was convinced that he had serious intentions. She wrote to Sheila's foster mother in Dwarahat. Arrangements were already being made for Sheila to go to America to do graduate work the following year. A niece of Isabella Thoburn had provided the passage money, and the PEO sorority of American women was providing the scholarship. It was a coincidence that young Dr. Sundaram also was going to the West to study. If her parents approved and Sheila was agreeable, she could finish her Master's at Evanston National College of Education; then the two could be married.

But her mother was cool to the proposition. She disliked having Sheila marry a man from the south. There was too much variation in looks, culture, native environment. Her foster father, Dr. C. T. Wilson, an army physician, was also indifferent to the idea. To be sure, the medical career was in the family tradition. His father, Harku Thoburn Wilson, had been the first doctor to go into Tibet. But had not Sheila always expressed the desire to marry an army doctor like himself?

With his departure constantly drawing nearer, Ernest fumed with impatience. Would they never make up their minds? And suppose they did consent, what of the girl herself? So far she had received all his approaches with complete indifference, although he had managed a few meetings with the women of his family as intermediaries. He was too shy to confide his marital hopes to his father, who had always been strict in such matters with his children, boys as well as girls. Ernest was sure he would not approve of his becoming too involved on the eve of his departure to America. But his mother was a willing ally and often acted as an ambassador to his father. She even let him take the car without his father's knowledge and arranged occasions when it was logical for Prem and Sheila to accompany him. But as time passed and he had few opportunities even to get acquainted, the prospect was maddening, for he had known since that first meeting in the classroom that she was the one woman he wanted for his wife.

At last the answer came—too late. Her parents had decided to look with favor on the arrangement, but first they wanted to see the candidate. The date they gave was after his ship was scheduled to leave. "No time," he had to reply regretfully. Then fate intervened. He went to the Canadian Embassy to get his visa.

The official looked at his letter from the American Board of Missions.

"This is no guarantee! You need a Canadian affidavit."

The delay caused him to miss his boat, but at least it gave him a chance to visit Sheila's parents. He traveled alone by train and bus. The girl's brother met him. Her father greeted him with obvious skepticism. They had expected him to come with a retinue, Indian style, and here was just one youthful-looking, insignificant-appearing young man, thirty-one years old but looking less than twenty, weighing not much over a hundred pounds! The doctor asked three questions: When was he going to Canada? What was his specialty? How old was he? Ernest answered them, ate a good dinner, slept that night in Sheila's room, and returned to Lucknow, sure that the decision would be negative.

More time passed. His visa arrived. And finally, a week before sailing date, a letter came to Miss Hutchins. If she really thought this marriage would work out and would like them to get married in America, the parents would permit Ernest to date Sheila, but preferably in other company. On their first real date he took her to the cinema and had to pay for four other teachers, a decided liability in more ways than one. But his mother came to the rescue with extra funds as well as the loan of the car. Sheila came to the bishop's house with Premleela, and Ernest's father, influenced perhaps less by his wife than by the lovely Sheila herself, gave his approval. Rajan, one of Ernest's friends, gave the couple a dinner party. Still Sheila gave no indication of a decision. He left for America tortured with uncertainty but hopeful.

A year passed, during which he did further graduate study at McGill University in Montreal. At last Sheila started replying to his letters, and hope burgeoned. Then when she sent him a sweater which she had knit herself, it burst into full bloom. For an Indian girl such an act was equal almost to commitment. She came to Evanston in the fall of 1959, and their plans became more definite.

"As soon as my exams are over," he wrote her, "I'll call you. Then if I get through successfully, I'll come to Evanston and we'll make our plans."

He was one of the only two Indian students to pass his F.R.C.S. exams, one of the highest achievements in British medicine. As soon as he heard the news he called her long distance and told her he was coming. He took the last plane out from Montreal before a raging snowstorm. There were only two passengers who braved the flight. But in Toronto, where he had to change, planes were still running. His arrival in Evanston was like a homecoming. His sister Premleela was there, studying to be a medical dietitian. It was Miss Hutchins' home, and she was there on furlough. He met the pastor of the Evanston church which had built the chapel in Bareilly, the home church of Wilma Perrill. And, of course, there was his beautiful Sheila, studying for her Master's degree in education and child development at Evanston's National College of Education.

She had made up her mind, and the answer was positive. Wanting to buy her a ring but not knowing her tastes, Ernest took her and Miss Hutchins with him to the jewelry store. "Please tell me which one you like," he told her with expansive confidence. "Pick any one."

"This one," she decided without hesitation.

His heart came up in his throat. The price of the ring she chose was $300. He didn't have that much money. Miss Hutchins guessed his predicament and unobtrusively loaned him the extra money. Of course Sheila had no idea of the price. It was the last time he ever bought her such an expensive present. Both thrifty and simple in her tastes, she herself saw to that.

They set June 24, 1960, as their wedding date, when Ernest's parents would be in the States for the Methodist General Conference. Ernest went to Duke University that winter to take his fellowship in thoracic surgery. When the time came, he had no money to go to his wedding. But fortunately he had friends. His landlady took him to a bank and went surety for him to borrow $300. He bought a 1950 Chevrolet and started to drive the thousand miles to Chicago. It was a frightening experience. Techniques learned in India, where one drove on the left instead of the right, had to be unlearned. The hazards of bullock carts, bicycles, cows, goats, rickshas, were nothing compared with those of American traffic. In Virginia he was stopped by a highway patrol on the turnpike because he was going too slowly. But he reached Dayton, Ohio, safely and found his parents there, together with their friends the Riels. All went on to Evanston, including the Riels' grandchildren, who were anxious to see an Indian wedding.

They were not the only ones. Covenant Church at ten o'clock on that June morning resembled an international festival. Ernest's father, with Bishop Mondol and Dr. Hunt, minister of the church, performed the ceremony. Doris, one of Sheila's friends, a Jewish girl, sang a solo. Her local guardian, a Mr. Shaw, gave her away. There were many Indian friends, some attending the theological school there in Evanston, others in the country for General Conference. Mary Gordon, home on furlough, surprised them by traveling all the way from the state of Washington.

"Are—are you really Miss Gordon?" asked Ernest, who had never before seen her out of uniform.

After the reception and the lunch in Miss Hutchins' home Ernest bundled his bride into the car. He could sense if not detect her slight shock at its contrast with Mr. Shaw's sleek, streamlined model. But his discomfiture was only beginning. On Lake Shore Drive, with its eight lanes, the engine balked. At every red light he had to ask a car behind to give him a push. In Gary he had to stop to have the battery recharged. The weight of their luggage threw the lights out of line. But they finished the trip finally, stopping three nights on the way.

Her second shock was his apartment, all he could afford on $140 a month. But Sheila was as serenely poised in temperament as in physical grace. She secured a position teaching in the Duke Memorial Nursery School, and together they paid off his debts and were living in a better student apartment before the year was over. She was as skilled at cooking as at teaching, and loved it. It was Ernest who had to make the most painful adjustments, forcing himself to cooperate, American-fashion, in such chores as dishwashing and floor cleaning, tasks completely foreign to the experience of most Indian males. But such minor sacrifices, much as he hated them, were a small price to pay for having Sheila.

One Saturday when Sheila had gone on a short trip with their landlady, Ernest received a telephone call. It was from a Reverend Mr. Harbin in Greensboro. His church was interested in supporting a medical missionary, and Ernest's name had been suggested by the Board of Missions.

"That's odd," commented Ernest. "It happens that my wife is visiting the women's college in your town right now."

Sheila was contacted and asked to appear before the congregation the following morning. She was horrified, for she was not used to public speaking; a bit angry also, for it looked to her like a prearranged trap. But she went and captivated the audience, if not with eloquence, at least with her charm and loveliness. Later Ernest was asked to come and preach, the first sermon of his life, though he had spoken many times on missions. The church decided to assume the couple's full support, an arrangement which was to continue indefinitely.

In fact, it did more than assume his financial support. When there was a big conference of thoracic surgeons in Philadelphia, with Dr. Betts attending from Winston-Salem, North Carolina, the church in Greensboro gave Ernest the money to go, plus furnishing him with a typewriter and tape recorder. The people had really adopted the couple as their own.

The fellowship at Duke completed, the young Sundarams left for India with the Riels. Arriving in Europe by ship, the Riels bought a Microbus, and the two couples took a long motor trip through Europe, driving from Amsterdam to Naples. Sheila did not enjoy the ocean trip that followed. Added to her being a poor sailor was the fact that in three months she was to bear her first child. They landed in Bombay June 8, in a burst of furnace heat, and celebrated their arrival in India with bouts of painful dysentery. In Lucknow they were greeted with another of the country's extremities, terrific floods, but finally they reached Bareilly.

Ernest was informed that he now had two jobs in the hospital, administrative assistant to the able superintendent, Mr. Ginn, and head of the chest department. For the past two and a half years there had been no specialist in chest surgery, and the load of the department was tremendous. He was operating almost every day. There was no opportunity for a vacation, scarcely time to go to Lucknow to visit his wife and new daughter.

And presently even these responsibilities were multiplied. Mr. Ginn was sent to Vellore. The hospital board of governors decided that the jobs of hospital and medical superintendents should be combined, and finally Ernest was appointed to this position. Yet to many, the wisdom of such appointments, while recognitions of ability and achievement, was to remain doubtful. To make an administrator, even a medical superintendent, out of a man who has spent seven years in the finest graduate training available in order to become an expert thoracic surgeon, is, to say the least, questionable procedure. And this in a land where one person dies from tuberculosis every minute!

2

A new era was beginning for Clara Swain Hospital. Under Ernest Sundaram's superintendency the years of the sixties were to see not only an increasing Indianization of staff but intensified specialization in an attempt to develop the institution into a first-class hospital. New departments were introduced. Attempts were made to secure qualified specialists in each area, nationals if possible, but missionaries when it was proved that they were better qualified. And always the hospital would place a major emphasis on increasing involvement in the life of the community and in health programs of the Indian government.

In addition to his two administrative jobs, Dr. Ernest maintained a full surgical schedule. Dr. Pomeroy had not returned to India, and Dr. Tara Chandra, the brilliant young Indian who had taken his training under Dr. Pomeroy and Dr. Ernest, was no longer at Clara Swain. In 1959 the government of Uttar Pradesh had advertised a post for a thoracic surgeon in the Bhowali Sanatorium, largest and most notable institution of its kind in the state. Situated high in the Himalayas, with 400 beds, it had been patronized by many famous people, including Prime Minister Nehru and his family. Dr. Tara Chandra had been the unanimous choice of its governing board. It had been a difficult decision for the young surgeon and his wife to make, but the opportunity for larger service had been irresistible.

The decision had evoked some criticism. After giving him all that training, certain persons had grumbled, and sending his wife to Vellore to learn anesthesiology, what value had it been for the hospital? Nothing but a waste! Ernest did not agree with them. The question was fundamental to his whole philosophy of the missionary enterprise. For what was the function of a Christian institution in a developing secular society? To perpetuate its own life? To win adherents and prestige through a jealous guardianship of its superior skills and personnel? Or to act as leaven, losing its identity if need be in trying to raise the whole body of society to new levels of human well being? The answer had been given long ago. An institution, as well as a person, could find its life only in losing it.

Immediately Dr. Ernest began training a new intern, Dr. Bimal Chandra Roy, a graduate of Ludhiana in 1961, to become his assistant in chest surgery. Slight, wiry, energetic, Dr. Roy was extremely conscientious and eager to learn. His wife, also a doctor, became a welcome addition to the department of gynecology and obstetrics.

In spite of the country-wide BCG program and clinics conducted under the government health service, tuberculosis continued to be India's number-one health problem. At least half of the patients coming to Clara Swain were afflicted by the disease in some form. Many were treated in the clinic, returning each month for screening and every second month for X-rays. The seventy-seven beds in the chest wards, forty-seven for men, thirty for women, were almost always full. In-patients averaged four months in the hospital, but it was often impossible to persuade them to stay more than a month. They would become impatient and insist on going home. Because of this and the fact that many patients delayed treatment until the disease was in its last stages, cures could be effected in only 20 to 30 per cent of the cases. Education in prevention was as necessary to the program as treatment and surgery, and far more difficult. In the case of lung cancer, for instance, indifference and obduracy were as potent factors as in many other parts of the world.

"I have yet to find a case of cancer of the lungs," asserted Dr. Roy after five years of work in the chest department, "where the patient does not smoke. But can I convince smokers that they are endangering their lives? No. They refuse to believe it."

As years passed the program of tuberculosis control and domiciliary treatment at Clara Swain Hospital gained increasing approval and support from both church and government agencies. In 1967 the British Council of Churches donated 42,000 rupees to the program without any application having been made. (Hearing of the work at Clara Swain, one of their representatives came and discussed the possibilities with Dr. Ernest and was so enthusiastic that even before a request could be made he handed over the check!) Plans were soon made to use the money in construction of a new building which would house the

500-MA X-ray machine which the hospital hopefully expected the Board of Missions to donate for its Centenary in 1970.

Government also was expressing approval in material form, contributing all kinds of antituberculosis drugs so that poor patients coming to the hospital for treatment on an out-patient basis could be taken care of free of charge. Later, when the government District Hospital Center was able to attain the necessary status, X-ray films would also be made available.

Closely related to progress in the chest department were the constant improvements made in the X-ray program under the supervision of Mr. I. C. Singh, who, after earning his diploma at Vellore, had completed an M.B.R. course in radiography by correspondence and examinations. This training, plus much innate mechanical ability, made him of great practical service both in his own department and to the general needs of the hospital. He installed a hospital telephone exchange, constructed a call-bell system, whereby any patient could call a nurse from his bed through an interconnection of lights both over his door and at the nurses' station. By explaining his original plan to a blacksmith, he manufactured for only 25 rupees a tomographic attachment for body section cutting which would have cost 5,000 rupees in a manual or 25,000 in an electrical model secured through regular channels.

Progress in the X-ray department during Mr. Singh's twenty years of service was impressive. When he came there had been only four books in the library. Now there were over a hundred, many bought at his own expense. But still the X-ray equipment consisted of only one 200-MA, two 30-MA, and one 25-MA units. A new X-ray block was badly needed, as well as a larger machine.

In the meantime Dr. Ernest conceived another idea. The dental tours to the schools of north India were proving a triumphant success. Why not a similar X-ray service? He remembered his own dramatic visit to screen the students at Lal Bagh School, resulting in health benefits whose satisfactions had been eclipsed only by his attendant discovery of a wife. With a traveling X-ray van hundreds of incipient cases of tuberculosis might be detected early and treated in time. He wrote to the Board asking for such a mobile unit.

The request came at an opportune time. Just as Dr. Brewster, the medical secretary, was reading the letter in New York, a man from the United States Public Health Department came into his office.

"How would you like to buy a mobile X-ray van?" he asked. "We have one which was going to Honduras. Now circumstances have changed, so we no longer need it."

Dr. Brewster's eyes kindled. "Why don't you donate it?" he asked promptly.

"Sorry, but we can't do that. However, we can give it to you for a very small price."

The Board was able to secure it for perhaps half its original cost. It was what the army called a "disaster unit" and was fully fitted with modern X-ray equipment. It was equally serviceable set up under a tree on the hospital compound or in the yard of one of the mission schools a hundred miles away, where it might screen 350 students in a single day. There was no similar piece of equipment in the whole state of Uttar Pradesh. It was an invaluable contribution to the program of public health carried on in the various schools and could also be used in village work.

The work of this X-ray van brought a satisfaction to Ernest which only a chest surgeon, deeply concerned with India's number-one disease scourge and dedicated to its eradication, could possibly understand.

3

"What about missionaries? Are they still needed in this rapidly expanding society of the new India: doctors, nurses, medical technicians from other countries?" More pertinent yet—"Are they still *wanted?*"

Dr. Ernest was constantly facing such questions in these years of the sixties. They were being asked by concerned church leaders, by proud patriots jealous of their country's professional attainments, by members of his own staff, by the missionaries themselves.

Needed? The answer seemed simple. In a country which still had only one doctor to every 5,000 people, one nurse to every 11,000, and medical technologists in even less percentage—yes, he had to reply. Of course they were needed, desperately. But—he was forced to qualify this answer—not *every* missionary. Only that one who had both a high sense of dedication and academic and clinical excellence.

"Gone are the days," wrote Dr. Ernest in a recent report for a dialogue held in New Delhi between the Methodist Church in Southern Asia and the World Division of the Board of Missions, "when a missionary need not be well trained, for in our own government hospitals the time is coming when postgraduates will be employed for junior positions. Even in our mission hospitals postgraduates from government and mission institutions are seeking employment.

"The medical missionary must be able to adjust to the local situation. This is difficult since he often comes from an institution or a country where the standards are exceedingly high. He must be prepared not only to make tremendous adjustments but to foster confidence among his colleagues and be able to lead them into an improvement of facilities and techniques. Without ever emphasizing his own importance he must be able to delegate authority. If he feels superior and wants to change the mode of operation of the institution within a few weeks or months, he may find much resistance from his co-workers. The ability to introduce new systems to the best advantage of a local situation needs much thought, patience, wisdom, and tact."

Fortunately the missionaries on his staff were men and women of this caliber. Two, Dr. Petersen and Dr. Riel, were in the dental department, and their combined skills, material assistance, and adaptability to the ways and needs of their adopted country not only raised the department to high efficiency but contributed much to the health program of the entire state.

Returning to India with Ernest in 1961, Dr. Eugene Riel gave the school dental work a tremendous impetus. In his previous term he had been highly intrigued by the pioneering extension work started by Dr. Robert Petersen. He visioned developing a far better program for taking care of the children in the mission schools and colleges, perhaps later to be extended to include village work. Before leaving his home in Dayton he directed the building of a mobile dental van by the Trotwood Trailer Company, equipped by himself and a friend with two dental chairs and other accessories. Mr. Eugene Kettering heard about the project and donated an International truck to tow the trailer from school to school.

Besides the van the Riels brought 4½ tons of dental and occupational therapy equipment on this return trip. By now practically all the dental equipment of Dr. Riel's thirty-two years' practice in Dayton had been transported at various times to India. In addition the Dayton Dental Society and the Ohio State Dental Association, recognizing the fact that he was serving as a missionary, had given their full support, remitting professional dues for the years that he was on active mission service and through different members making much dental equipment available. Through the generosity of the Weber Dental Manufacturing Company of Canton, Ohio, he brought with him in 1961 the first air dental drill to arrive in India. Other manufacturers of dental materials were very cooperative, especially the Crescent Dental Manufacturing Company.

The van arrived in Bombay in late August, 1961, and through the auspices of the Indian government under the Indo-American agreement and Church World Service, it was shipped by rail free of charge to Bareilly, where it was unloaded amid great excitement on September 22. Both vehicles, car and trailer, showed dents, holes, and scratches, as well as broken tail lights and screen, but no damage which interfered with their operation. The van was put to work immediately visiting mission schools. On October 16, 1961, there occurred a historic event which gave the program a tremendous impetus. Dr. Riel described it graphically in a letter he wrote home:

"We are just finishing a ten-mile drive from Butler Mission School in Old Delhi. By we, I mean myself, Dr. Balaram, area secretary of the Methodist Church; Dr. Philips, my Indian associate dentist; Elvin Singh, our driver-secretary, and last but not least, our mobile dental unit. And since this is such an important trip, I am taking the driving responsibility through the crowded streets of Delhi.

"We make a turn and enter a long street, with parkways on either side, and approach an imposing arch and gateway. Getting out of the car, Dr. Balaram has a short conversation with the attendants at the guard-house by the gateway, after which he re-enters the car with a guard and we proceed through the gate and draw up in front of a large, imposing residence. We park the car and in twelve minutes have the unit stabilized, equipment reassembled, and the gasoline-powered electric generator out of the car and ready to operate. Now we leave the driver in charge, enter the house, and find ourselves in a very large, beautifully decorated and carpeted reception hall.

"At 9:15 a man comes walking down the stairway alone, dressed in typical Indian summer clothing, and approaches our group. I find myself shaking the hand of the Prime Minister of India, Mr. Nehru, or, as he is lovingly called by the Indian people, 'Pandit-ji.' This interview is possible only because Mr. Nehru himself directed the issuance of our visas for India and is therefore interested in us and our dental program.

"After a few words of greeting we all walk out to the driveway, where Mr. Nehru tours the unit and asks a number of questions concerning its procurement and use. He is very cordial, and we feel highly honored that he would take fifteen minutes of his valuable time to talk with us about our program. Of course the dental unit is unique here. In fact, there are no trailers of any kind here in India."

Pandit Nehru was indeed interested. One of the questions he asked was, "Couldn't you undertake this type of work for the whole of India?"

Dr. Riel regretfully shook his head. "I'm sorry. It would take from ten to twenty units of this kind to take care of the whole population in even our own state of Uttar Pradesh. But it is certainly something for all of us to envision as a goal."

Happily, he was able to fulfill another request of the Prime Minister, and eighteen members of his personal staff had their teeth examined and cleaned and some of their cavities filled that morning!

Though a whole week's tour, examining and treating hundreds of children, cost only $50, funds were not available that first year. But Dr. Riel was not one to be inhibited by lack of funds. Support was soon given for the dental extension program by Trinity Methodist Church at Chillicothe, Ohio, which donated about $2,000 a year to the project. Dr. Philips and Dr. Thomas, the senior dentist, took their turns visiting schools all over north India, sometimes as far as 500 miles away. The hot season was no deterrent. Even though the trailer was parked in the shade wherever possible and there was an awning over the front, Dr. Thomas often found it so hot inside that he could not work during the middle of the day, only in early morning and late afternoon or evening.

"Five dollars from every tenth person or group receiving this letter," wrote Dr. Riel to friends in May of 1962, "would mean that we could buy a good small air conditioner for our trailer. And of course five dollars from every one on our list would mean that we could extend our work to many more schools. I am sure Dr. Thomas and hundreds of school children would breathe a fervent 'thank you.' "

The plea was effective, and an air conditioner for the van finally came through.

In its first year the dental unit traveled 1,800 miles in a circle to the west, south, and east of Bareilly. More than 3,000 patients passed through its doors. Already Dr. Riel was planning, on faith, to send out a second team in the following year, using his old portable equipment and traveling by train and bus. But when Dr. Sushila Nayar, the Minister of Health for India, wrote her commendation of the pioneer work and begged that it be extended into villages, he was forced regretfully to refuse due to lack of sufficient equipment, personnel, and money—regretfully, for the need for dentistry was appalling. In Bareilly, with its 300,000 inhabitants, there was still only one licensed dentist in the bazaar, and in the villages of India, all 600,000 of them, the needs were almost untouched.

Dr. Riel's own work days began early, heralded perhaps by the repeated calls of the "brain-fever" bird, bane of the hot season, rising in monotonous crescendos to such a feverish pitch that one felt inclined to wring its neck; or by the thunderous drumming of a monsoon rain on the asbestos-cement roof; or by the cracking of the same roof under the mounting heat of a June sun just coming over the horizon. Or perhaps he would be roused by one of the frequent predawn telegrams.

"Abscessed tomato," one such wire announced. "Request appointment on the 18th."

A natural but ludicrous error on the part of the telegram clerk, mistaking the word "tooth" for "tomato"! No laughable matter, however, for the sender, a young missionary wife who lived in a city over 300 miles from Bareilly!

Dr. Riel would eat breakfast, walk with his wife past one of the nurses' hostels, the old red bungalow called "Lal Kothi" where the lady missionaries lived, and the hospital chapel. In the space beyond would be crowds waiting for the out-patient dispensary to open. Some of them would have been there all night, sleeping under the trees. Usually there would be a bullock cart or two with the patient inside lying on a pile of hay or bedding. Here they would part, Alice Riel going through the main gate of the hospital to the occupational therapy department and Doc going to the dental clinic building beyond the dispensary.

The clinic would be already bustling, the sweeper dusting and scrubbing the floors, Mr. Ghose getting out his books and records for the office, the junior dentists chattering away in Hindustani. Probably Dr. Petersen would be already at work, possibly in the laboratory, for during his present term he had been specializing more and more on bridge work. Mrs. Selim, the faithful office nurse and dental hygienist, was always on hand, together with one or two girls in training. And no matter how the size of staff might fluctuate, with some away for graduate training, others out with the van on field work, there were usually enough patients to keep all six operating rooms busy.

But it was the activities of the mobile dental clinic which brought Dr. Riel his greatest satisfaction during these last five years he spent in India. Thanks to Dr. Anklesaria, a woman dentist who came to Clara Swain in 1962, the van was kept almost constantly in motion, traveling as far east as Arrah, as far north as Jullundur and up into the Himalayas, visiting schools in towns all over the areas between, until in all some thirty mission schools were being served by the program. It was a triumphant pioneer achievement.

Dr. Villoo Anklesaria was a young Parsee girl, a member of the Zoroastrian faith, brought up in a well-to-do joint family in Poona. After taking her basic training in an English-medium school and her B.Sc. degree in a coeducational college in Poona, she studied dentistry in the Nair Hospital Dental College in Bombay. Because she had a deep concern for those less fortunate than herself, she welcomed the opportunity to work in a mission hospital.

Her new job, traveling hundreds of miles each year and treating thousands of children, was intriguing but not easy. She approached it with much trepidation—not half so much, however, as the children, many of whom had never before seen a dentist and had been fed all manner of frightening rumors. Moreover, her Hindi being scanty, since she came from a Marathi area, she was unable to convince them that she was not going to hurt them. The language deficiency, however, proved a blessing of sorts, for they could not help laughing at her queer speech, which meant that they stopped crying. Being children, they were not slow about correcting her and proved excellent language tutors, so she was soon speaking Hindi fairly fluently.

There were still many scared patients, especially among the newcomers. At one school where the pupils, mostly day students, came to school and saw the van, they all ran home. When the van was left parked in the same schoolyard for a couple of months, several pupils failed to show up during the period. In one case the school faculty gave out cyclostyled copies of forms so that the day students could obtain their parents' signatures permitting them to receive dental care. Somehow the hostel children also got hold of some of the forms, and all the new children appeared with "No" written in the blank space.

"That's funny," thought Dr. Villoo. "Why should parents write 'no' for one of their children and 'yes' for another?"

The answer was simple. The older children had frightened the new ones by dire tales of wholesale tooth extractions. Hence the newcomers had written "no" themselves.

Occasionally the reaction to advance rumors was just the reverse. In one school of boys aged four to ten on her first year's round she had to extract a number of teeth.

"What fine boys you are!" she praised them. "I knew such brave boys as you wouldn't mind a little thing like that."

The next year all the boys wanted to have their teeth extracted.

She often marveled at their cleverness. In one school when she re-examined the teeth filled on her last trip, she found that every filling had a scooped-up appearance. She was nonplused. Could the alloy have been defective? She stumbled on the answer by accident when one of the youngest asked to have her teeth filled when they were as sound as ivory tusks. It seems that she had told the children she was filling their teeth with silver, and one bright nine-year-old, knowing that silver was expensive, had hit on the idea of taking out the fillings and giving them to the sweets-*walla* as media of exchange. So as soon as the fillings had been put in, all the children had tried to pry them out with pins! Time-consuming, of course, to have to repeat all the fillings, but Dr. Villoo could not help admiring the bright one's ingenuity!

And usually the little patients were far more helpful than annoying. When she had no hygienist in the team, the older children would wash and sterilize her instruments, mix the cement and amalgam, and run errands. They often turned the center of the van into a stage for a talent show, dancing and singing in keen competition and making time pass quickly for both doctor and patients. They taught her to be patient and fun-loving and kind, and at one time when she was passing through a period of great discouragement, they helped her look toward the future with new hope.

"My little angels," she called them, looking back on her period of service with nostalgia. "Oh, they were much more to me than patients!"

Always the goal was to give dental education as well as treatment. The hygienist who usually accompanied the team demonstrated correct methods of cleaning teeth and promoting oral health, so that the children (hopefully) would go back home and spread the information among families and friends.

Wherever it went, except possibly among prospective patients, the van was the center of attention. Passing through a town, the driver would find it almost impossible to maneuver car and trailer, because everyone on foot or wheels stopped to watch and invariably clogged the passage whenever he wanted to turn.

Once when they were going from Hissar to Ambala, they were told to take a short route. "Is the road good?" the driver asked some passers-by. "Oh, yes," was the emphatic reply. "Good," perhaps, compared with the farm roads they were used to, but hardly for a car and trailer! It grew narrower and narrower, more and more rutted and muddy. After a few miles it was impossible to turn back. Then for the first time in three years, a tire blew out. They were in the middle of nowhere. There was not even a brick in sight to support the jack. Then Dr. Villoo had an inspiration. She offered her tin trunk. They pushed it under the van. The lid broke, but it supported the van while the driver took the car and tire to the next village. When he returned, they couldn't get the tire fitted. Fortunately, along came a jeep driven by five robust-looking Sikhs. They quickly gave assistance, lifting the van easily while the tire was adjusted. After three hours in the burning sun the team was again on its way. But troubles were not over. Next the ball-and-socket hitch gave way. They tied it with wires and crawled along gingerly, stopping every few feet to inspect. At about 7:30 they stopped at a petrol station to camp for the night. At perhaps 4:30 in the morning they were wakened by a terrible racket.

"Open up!" shouted a voice in urgent Hindi.

Outside were about twenty people all crowded into a ricksha, on their way to a wedding. They were insistent on hiring the van, and had to be shown the inside of it before they would believe it was not a public conveyance. Later in the morning the van crawled over the last few miles of the "short cut" and finally arrived at Ambala. Eighty miles in twenty-four hours! It was the most tiring and eventful journey of Dr. Villoo's years of service.

After its nearly five years of travel under Indian conditions, most people considered it a miracle that the dental van was still in one piece. And indeed it did bear small resemblance to the sleek car-trailer which had pulled out of Dayton back in 1961! But the Riels had brought it to India to be used, and over 14,000 children and young people had been given complete dental treatment within its small confines. An achievement indeed, the first of its kind anywhere in the Orient!

Dr. Anklesaria worked with the project for four years, and she loved every one of them. She started out on every tour with excited anticipation, yet looked forward with equal enjoyment to her return. The woman residents of Lal Kothi, where she stayed in Bareilly, were all friends, especially "Aunt Beatty" Bonjour, whose room was always a thoroughfare and sitting room not only for the house residents but for nurses and students, a light usually burning there late into the night. And the dental department was like a close family group, with Dr. Riel himself, always sympathetic, gentle, kind, taking the place of her own father. She was glad that when she had to leave, in April of 1966, the Riels were still there, though they were leaving for America the very next day. Without Dr. Eugene, the dental staff, in spite of its intimate friendliness, would have seemed like a family suddenly bereft of its head.

4

And—"Are financial and other forms of support from abroad still needed and welcomed?" was another question which Dr. Ernest Sundaram was often asked, not by persons on the receiving end of such aid, but by boards, churches, and charitable groups in America and other donating countries, anxious to co-operate in rendering the wisest and most acceptable help to the newly independent churches in a developing nation.

Ernest's answer to this was always an emphatic "Yes." They were not only still needed and welcomed but essential if the mission hospital was to render quality service to those who needed it most. Even in an affluent country, he had discovered, a community hospital must depend heavily on gifts and endowments. How much more in a country like India! And to justify its existence a *Christian* hospital must render service to the poor, who needed it most. Even though Clara Swain was becoming more and more self-supporting with the help of the community in defraying its running expenses, for buildings, special projects, and new equipment, it must be dependent on foreign subsidy for many decades to come.

One of the most vital areas of such help was in providing scholarships so that young doctors, nurses, and medical technicians could take advanced training both in Indian institutions and abroad, and during his superintendency Dr. Ernest was able to promote many such projects. For him, as well as for Dr. Riel and Dr. Petersen, one of the high points of his first years was the departure of Dr. K. T. Thomas, the senior Indian dentist, for two years of graduate study in the United States.

On July 3, 1963, the Riels took all the members of the dental clinic, ten of them, in the Volkswagen bus for a picnic at a *dak* bungalow several miles from Bareilly, a festive occasion complete with ice cream and cake. It was a farewell party for Dr. Thomas. His departure was of interest and concern to the whole hospital, for he was not only beloved, but he had been working on its professional staff longer than all but two of the other members.

It was a special satisfaction for Dr. Bob Petersen, for Dr. Thomas was to study at the University of Oregon, his own alma mater, and he had personally made arrangements for his gifted colleague's postgraduate work. Since he himself was leaving on furlough in November, the two would soon be meeting in America.

The Petersens' second term at Clara Swain was proving just as busy as the first, and far more satisfying. For India had become home, and now that they were commissioned missionaries, they felt that they really belonged. Even the language had ceased to be strange, although Dr. Bob's fluency never got too far beyond the *"Munh kholo"* and *"Dard kahan hai?"* stage. Even though he and Mary concentrated on language study the summer they returned and engaged a tutor for continuing instruction after they got to Bareilly, the small Janie was soon chattering away in Hindustani with far greater proficiency than her father.

"How come?" people would ask Dr. Bob.

"Guess I should hire myself a nice young ayah," he would respond cheerfully. But Mary vetoed this suggestion with prompt vigor. She would do all the hiring of ayahs for the household.

The fact was, he was always too busy to take study seriously. From May to September he conducted a clinic at the Landour Community Hospital up in the hills, ministering chiefly to missionary families who, like his own, populated the hill station in the summer months because of Woodstock School, where their children were sent for an American education. These months were a boon to him and Mary, since they made possible a home environment for Peter, Polly, and Jane, separation from whom the rest of the year was one of the high prices paid by them and other missionaries for serving where the need was greatest.

"How can you bear it to send your children away to school?" Mary was often asked by shocked friends at home. "And when they're so small, too!"

"Well," she would reply thoughtfully, "I believe we missionary parents make a greater effort to make the times we do have together very meaningful and enriching, so we develop a special relationship with our children which most parents who never undergo these separations cannot understand. And," she would add with some pride, "I'd like to point out that the majority of missionary children become creative, outstanding citizens of the world."

However, this rationalization made it no easier to leave Peter and Polly and Jane in the hostel when she went down to the plains in the fall, nor did it make the big bungalow in Bareilly seem less empty.

Empty? Hardly the word to apply to a house which averaged twenty-five guests a month from September to May! For part of her work consisted in running a guest house for many of the patients who came for dental work at Bareilly. "Ma Petersen's

Boarding House," she called it laughingly. But it was an invaluable service, for it afforded Dr. Bob a unique opportunity to see exactly how his out-of-town patients were progressing and to know and appreciate them as persons rather than just patients.

Not only did Dr. Bob's work at the hill hospital give him more opportunity to be with the family, but it offered a chance for unique service. Though much of his work was with missionaries, it was a backward area with great needs, and he squeezed in as many emergency cases as possible. One such dental emergency treatment was for the wife of a local *dudh walla* (milk man). She had suffered toothache for several days. Dr. Bob guessed her age as between forty and fifty. Then he learned that she was a mere twenty-eight and the mother of six children. Her mouth was in terrible condition, but he did what he could, while the patient held an enormous nose ornament out of the way so he could work in the oral cavity.

Some of his most rewarding work was with Tibetan refugees from a nearby colony. It was hard to realize the difficulties and hardships of these people without a land to call their own and their problems living in a country whose tongue and culture were so foreign. Yet in spite of it all the smiles on their faces were wide and friendly. (Their smiles indicated, by the way, their past wealth and position according to the number of gold teeth in the front of each mouth!) They were as appreciative as they were cheerful. Once the Dalai Lama visited the hospital and expressed his gratitude for the treatment his people had received.

In his years of service in India Dr. Bob discovered that there were many children with teeth defects leading to malocclusion. He invited Dr. Gupta, a highly trained orthodontist, to visit Clara Swain Hospital and do some orthodontic work, not only to help the children with crooked teeth, but to give advice on the many who had to be operated on for cleft lip and palate. Since the Indian doctor had fine training but access to few materials, he was only too glad to come from Lucknow and give his services to Clara Swain on a once-a-month basis, forerunner of the time when the hospital could have a much-needed orthodontist of its own. Since materials for orthodontia were not available in India except by expensive importation, such service could be given only to those whose parents were well-to-do. However, the many with cleft lip and palate and other defects in mouth and teeth could definitely be helped. Although cleft-lip operations were outside the dental field, Dr. Bob began doing them with the help of Dr. Das and a highly trained Vellore-Ludhiana postgraduate, Dr. Bimal Masih, M.S. Results were gratifying.

When furlough time came, the Petersens felt they could spare only three months, and part of that must be spent in taking some refresher courses in dental schools. America now seemed the "strange" world, especially to the children.

"Do they have potatoes already sliced, ready to fry, for potato chips?" asked Polly. After five years of seeing the delicacies prepared "from scratch," she had to stretch her imagination to picture them even in the ready-to-fry state.

But three months of crisply packaged potato chips and other luxuries, including a lavish and hectic Western Christmas, did not spoil the family for India. They were glad to be back the following year for the slower-paced, Eastern-style Christmas, with its birds singing and flowers blooming, its *Bara din mubarik ho!*" ("Blessed be the big day!") instead of "Merry Christmas!", its colorful dramas with Indian dress and music giving such oriental authenticity to the story of Christ's birth. Dr. Bob unpacked his new American purchases and gifts of contour chairs, high-speed drills, and other equipment, and with all his engaging friendliness and intense enthusiasm was soon plunged into the work again.

The department continued to progress. Dr. Thomas returned from Oregon to become an associate director of the clinic, with a special interest and training in periodontia, his speech glib with terms relating to ultrasonic sound, supersonic vibrations and revolutions. The new equipment, shipped to India through Church World Service, contained a cavitron, one of the few in India. This instrument, a supersonic device with 28,000 vibrations per second, for the removal of tartar from teeth, was another contribution from Dr. Petersen and his friends. It promised to relieve one of India's worst tooth defects, since 99 per cent of Indian patients were sufferers from periodontia, the result of neglect, of chewing *pan*, of cleaning with the neem twig, of using such remedies as clove oil, charcoal, and mustard oil.

Other fine equipment, usually unavailable in India but possible to import through Church World Service, made Clara Swain's the most up-to-date clinic in all of India. A new Supplex chair had been obtained at greatly reduced cost. A mobile unit made by Swivel-Stool and purchased by a church in Paoli, Pennsylvania, with drills and octopus which could be removed and pushed against the wall, was not only efficient but reduced fear in patients. A high-speed turbine drill with 200,000 revolutions a minute made it possible to cut through teeth like butter.

"You're going too fast," some people objected. "Such specialization! The poor Indian farmer can't afford all these privileges and doesn't need them!"

But Dr. Thomas, Dr. Petersen, and Dr. Torbert, the new energetic young dentist who arrived early in 1966, do not agree. The opportunity through Church World Service to import such fine equipment, unavailable to most Indian dentists, and made possible by interested church groups, should not be passed up. Bringing other dentists to Bareilly from mission hospitals all over India and training them in short terms of six months to two years, they are making their clinic a center for education and demonstration of the best equipment. Cooperating closely with the Christian Dental Society and the dental school in the Lucknow Medical College, they are able to share both equipment and knowledge with young Indians who will in time become leaders in their field all over the country.

"Are we being irrelevant, having all this fine equipment?" asks young Dr. Torbert, then answers promptly, "No. Indian dentists appreciate and deserve the best. We're preparing them for the day when they'll be able to get it for themselves, and often we're helping to get it for them. And as for the poor villagers who can't afford to pay, we can treat far more of them with this new speedy equipment and do it much better."

Since the Riels left for retirement in 1966, Dr. Petersen was glad indeed of Dr. Torbert's presence when tragedy struck his family. Polly, aged fourteen, was suddenly stricken with a strange malady, a rapid withering of muscles in her left thigh. In October of 1966 they went home on premature furlough, believing she required surgery of the spine. But to their relief further specialized testing in Boston by the noted neurosurgeon, Dr. Poppin, indicated the trouble as acute inflammatory neuritis, and Dr. Poppin felt that with proper exercises she would regain nearly normal use of her leg. To their delight this proved to be so, and in 1967 the family happily prepared to return to India.

Meanwhile, Dr. Thomas and young Dr. Torbert were taxed to

full capacity in the booming dental department. Like his colleagues, Dr. Torbert is an enthusiast for public health. His next project, already planned and implemented by Dr. Riel, would set up another mobile unit which, being smaller, could visit schools high up in the Himalayas. It was a job requiring almost as much pioneering spirit as that which had taken Dr. Riel off to Kathmandu to establish a clinic there.

5

Physiotherapy and rehabilitation, only recently burgeoning into prominence in the West, were still almost untouched areas in India. Although in Bombay there was the All-India Institute of Physical Medicine and Rehabilitation, and in New Delhi the All-India Institute of Medical Sciences had shown interest in starting an institute, the amount of trained leadership was as yet negligible. Yet disabilities resulting from polio, leprosy, tuberculosis, accidents, were legion. The doctors at Clara Swain saw the evidence of them every day. And little could be done either to correct them or to provide vocational assistance for the victims. The need for such work was tremendous.

Ernest was both startled and thrilled when he heard that Dr. Mary Verghese, the young doctor whose terrible accident at Vellore had resulted in paraplegia, had gone to the United States in her wheel chair to study in Bellevue's famous Institute of Physical Medicine and Rehabilitation, and when she came back two and a half years later to assume direction of a new department at Vellore, his own ambitions received a fresh impetus. He would not be content until such a department, however small at first, was started at Clara Swain.

Thanks to Alice Riel, work in occupational therapy was advancing rapidly. In fact, it was she rather than "Doc" who made the most profound and permanent changes at the hospital during their second term of service. The legacy she left was of more enduring substance than filled teeth and a much-used dental van, even than a far-reaching and successful dental health program. For she was responsible for both a fine new building and a new department under well-trained national leadership.

The work in occupational therapy was all of her doing. She had started it in a tiny space with her own limited equipment.

The more adequate room in the new wing had been built and furnished wholly at the Riels' expense. Personally they had made the arrangements and provided the funds for Shanti James to go to the United States, where she was studying at Ohio State University for a degree in occupational therapy. Now Alice Riel, returned from furlough, was cheerfully determined to build up the work she had started.

It was frustrating, however, at first, trying to find interesting and challenging projects of therapeutic value to patients, when her much-needed equipment and supplies were still sitting in a New York warehouse, waiting permission of Indian government officials to be shipped via Church World Service. But if frustration had discouraged her, she would never have returned to India. However, the shipments arrived at last, and they spent days and days unpacking the many trunks and cases and sorting the equipment, some of which had been contributed by the Goodwill Industries of America, with which Mrs. Riel had long been actively connected. Now she could get to work in earnest.

She and her helpers conducted a sheltered workshop type of program, with rehabilitation of the whole patient its goal and reason for existence. Using creative activities, educational and recreational prescriptions, they attempted both to quicken the patients' recovery and, in cases of severe disability, to give aid in acquiring job skills. They began working with most of the patients long before they became ambulatory and continued until they were discharged. (And what an abundance of ingenuity was needed to challenge the interests of the more than a hundred different patients of all age groups and temperaments who might be referred to them for treatment by the doctors and surgeons each month!)

"Would you enjoy going along to the wards with me and my two helpers this morning?" she wrote home in a letter to friends in 1962. "We are showing View-master slides to each patient one by one as we try to cheer them and bring them a glimpse of the outside world. Puzzles and magnetized 'shoes' take their minds from their illnesses for a few minutes. Two of the women doctors have called me to go along on their rounds so that I may understand what is necessary for the patients they want to refer.

"Lakshmi is completely blind and has just had her right leg amputated because of a compound fracture which had neither been set nor treated, and gangrene had set in. Parmeswara is an older patient recovering from a broken hip but very frail and anemic. She is bent and crippled from arthritis. The metal walker that I had the blacksmith make last week will be invaluable as I try to get her on her feet and teach her to walk again. Weaving will exercise her stiffened fingers and help her achieve a sense of progress. Hirawati is a pretty young girl who lost her husband a few months ago with malarial fever. Untrained village midwives had attempted to deliver her baby by unsterile primitive methods. When she arrived here, the baby was dying from tetanus, and she herself almost died. Her bladder had burst during delivery in the village. She still has a high temperature and can do nothing active, but counseling and being an understanding listener build morale and have therapeutic value.

"Shanwati Devi is recovering from severe burns she suffered when her sari caught fire. Her face is still swathed in bandages, but the skin grafted on her hands has nicely healed and the muscles and tendons must be trained to become useful again and to prevent stiffness. As we go into the men's surgical ward with Dr. Das, here is one of the patients, his arm supported by a special sling we have made, sitting up in bed happily weaving a white cord belt. This light active use of a broken arm, which took many months to heal because of a bone infection, is an important step in Mohammed Ali's recovery.

"Some patients become literate during convalescence through our educational program. Caning, basketry, wood carving and woodwork, jewelry making, painting, and drawing become treatments which develop skills, initiative, and self-assurance. We have the intense satisfaction of helping patients overcome despair and discouragement, to discover in themselves talents and interests they never knew they had as they grasp the handle of faith and lose their anxieties."

The arrival in 1962 of the hospital's first resident orthopedic surgeon not only increased the need for occupational therapy but, to Ernest's joy, made imperative the introduction of further techniques of physiotherapy and rehabilitation. Some bone surgery was already being done. Dr. Ronald J. Garst, a pioneering orthopedic surgeon and professor of orthopedics at the Christian Medical College in Ludhiana, had for some time been making bimonthly visits to Bareilly. The city was growing fast industrially. Accident rates were rising. More and more cases were coming to the hospital needing specialized orthopedic treatment. One day Dr. Garst, with the help of Dr. Das, had to perform sixteen operations. Starting at 6:30 in the morning, he was unable to finish all the cases by 7 P.M. before rushing through dinner and catching his train at 7:30.

"A good way for him to get a coronary," Mrs. Garst suggested half jokingly to Ernest Sundaram.

Dr. Ernest knew something must be done. A full-fledged, well-equipped orthopedic department was now imperative. Many board members were skeptical about opening another specialized department without adequate financial support, but they grudgingly gave him permission to explore possibilities. In 1962 an application was received from Dr. J. S. Makhani, M.B.B.S., M.Sc. (Surg.), F.R.C.S., F.A.C.S. He had been a gold medalist of the Mahatma Gandhi Medical College at Indore, then had gone to the Irwin Hospital in Delhi, where he had become interested in orthopedics. Now he was just back from seven years of postgraduate work in the United States and Canada, during which he had qualified for his F.A.C.S. and F.R.C.S. degrees.

Dr. Ernest invited him to come and look over the situation. The young surgeon's face showed both shock and disappointment. Such a great need for an orthopedic department and so little equipment!

"You come and set it up for us," offered Dr. Ernest hopefully.

Dr. Makhani came in October. He was young, in his early thirties, creative, enterprising, and enthusiastic. Immediately the new department burgeoned. Patients came flocking with all kinds of bone problems due to tuberculosis, leprosy, arthritis, fractures, and a host of other disabilities. They came not only from Bareilly and the neighboring area but from points far away. One came from Jamshedpur, near Calcutta. Another, a cripple with rheumatoid arthritis, came from Assam. False joints were inserted in both his hips. His deformities were corrected, and he was able to walk.

Though not a Christian, Dr. Makhani was in full sympathy with the ideals of the institution. He appreciated especially the high integrity of the staff and the trust manifested by the public in a mission hospital because it was known to be completely honest. He had a deep concern for individuals and a keen sympathy for each one of his patients, with their fears of the unknown and their impatience at the long months of treatment required. He made a practice of calling each one by his first name. Like Dr. Perrill, he was a clever improviser, skilled at making use of whatever materials might be available. Bones removed during operations were preserved in ether to be used again for grafting. And he was constantly creating new devices for the therapeutic treatment of his patients.

For with this rapidly developing program, physical as well as occupational therapy became more and more essential. Fortunately, Alice Riel had worked for twenty years in physiotherapy programs of the Goodwill Industries and as national president of the organization's auxiliaries had helped volunteers in their work with home-bound patients, so she and her helpers were soon performing many physical therapy techniques in cooperation with the new department. And with the return of Shanti James (later Mrs. Sanadh) in 1963 with her degree in occupational therapy from Ohio State University, the work expanded still further. Shanti's sister Kamla, who had been a faithful worker in the department for the past two years, was then granted a Methodist Medical Council scholarship and left for Vellore to start a two years' training course in physio-therapy. Later the Riels themselves gave funds for the training of Juggan Singh as a brace maker in Ludhiana.

Suddenly the space they had provided for occupational therapy, which had seemed so sumptuous back in 1957, became hopelessly inadequate. The ever-expanding work in physiotherapy cried for more room and equipment. Even though there were no funds in view and the project must be launched entirely on faith, Alice Riel faced the prospect with her usual undaunted enthusiasm. Like Clara Swain nearly a hundred years before, she knew that if human need and human desire to meet it were sufficiently impelling, the money would somehow be forthcoming. Her enthusiasm was stimulated in the summer of 1963 by a visit from Dr. Sushila Nayar, a former close associate of Gandhi and now the Minister of Health for India, who commended the work in occupational therapy in the highest terms.

With the somewhat cautious blessing of Dr. Ernest and the hospital board Alice Riel and her husband began making plans for a new physical medicine block, which would combine orthopedic wards, occupational therapy, physiotherapy, and brace shop in one efficient unit. In an excess of optimism they hoped to have the building up and ready to move into by the time Kamla should return from Vellore. A year later plans were being finalized.

"We are starting this building on faith," Mrs. Riel wrote her friends in America, "that continuing funds will assure its completion. The building, about 3,400 square feet in size, will cost only about $4 a square foot to build, which certainly is a bargain compared to the cost of the new Kettering Hospital in Dayton! We are sure that many of our friends will want to participate in this project, and you will find a form at the end of this letter which can be detached, completed, and sent in with your gift." Trust the dauntless Alice to provide means as well as incentive! If possible, she would probably have included a ball point pen with the directive.

Mrs. Riel's confidence in her friends was not unfounded, for by the fall of 1964 enough money was in hand to at least start the $18,000 building.

With the growth of the orthopedic department, vocational rehabilitation of disabled patients, especially of amputees, became an absolute necessity. To ask a person after an amputation to go and find himself a job would be like asking him to go and commit suicide. For years the small occupational therapy department had been doing such rehabilitation in a very limited way. But much more was necessary. Now Alice Riel got another inspiration. Why shouldn't some funds be made available through the PL480 program under the Vocational Rehabilitation Association of the United States Public Health Service? One evening she wrote out a rough draft on this subject and read it to her husband and Dr. Ernest.

"Alice, you're crazy!" exclaimed Doc with skeptical good humor. "We're just a small mission hospital. It's a good idea, of course, but just try and persuade the folks in Washington and the Indian Council of Medical Research and the Government Health Ministry!"

Being Alice Riel, she did try. She sent in a formal application. Months passed, and she heard nothing. Still undiscouraged, she wrote to her senator in Washington. Then one day Dr. Ernest received a cable that two American experts were coming to look over the situation. They arrived and stayed for three days. One was an orthopedic surgeon, the other a specialist in public health. They studied the plans of the new building, observed the work already being done, appraised Dr. Makhani's work and his ambitious program for vocational rehabilitation.

"I think," commented the surgeon, "that it's one of the most enterprising projects we have ever been sent to look into. We'll submit our findings to the commission in Washington."

Months passed. Then came a short communication from the American Embassy stating that forms would be sent, and two years after the application was made the funds arrived. The money was designated for the use of patients with tuberculosis of the joints or with paralytic disability from tuberculosis of the spine, in order to provide a program of rehabilitation which would make them self-sufficient. People had always believed the future to be finished for such patients. Now they actually saw many of them develop as great earning power as the able-bodied.

Dr. Makhani and his staff were soon exploring many avenues to arouse interest and cooperation in the community. Work was done through service organizations, such as the Rotary Club. At *melas*, religious festivals, stalls were set up exhibiting handcrafts taught in the rehabilitation center, and articles were sold. Industrialists of the city were approached, and piece work was obtained from several companies, among them the Wimco Match Factory. Work was given out to patients working in their homes, sorting articles, making labels. Two sheltered workshops were set up in connection with the hospital. With the return of Juggan Singh from his training in Ludhiana it was possible to start a workshop for the making of splints and braces. And the work is still barely beginning. The sight of forty smiling children cheerfully and successfully coping with many varieties of disability as they recently enjoyed a party in celebration of the "World Day for Crippled Children" was enough to convince the most skeptical observer that the program holds vast promise for the future.

For Alice Riel these five years in India would have been worth while just for Seetak. A refugee from the Chinese Communist invasion of Tibet and paralyzed from the waist down as a result of polio, she was brought into the hospital one day in late 1964 on a stretcher. A thin but attractive teen-ager, she looked up at them with big bright eyes above the typical high cheekbones and wide characteristic smile of her Tibetan people. She had not heard from her family since her father arranged for her to escape from Tibet by traveling with a caravan over the Himalaya passes into Nepal.

They gave her extensive occupational therapy and physical therapy, then surgery for muscle transplants. After many months she could stand and walk alone with her leg braces and a walker. She was trained to design, cut, and sew simple dresses and children's clothing. Through the interest of a church group in Switzerland, funds were secured to buy her a hand-operated sewing machine and a folding wheel chair. When she was ready to leave the hospital, she would have adequate and comfortable braces and lightweight crutches. Perhaps she would have a chance to live at the Tibetan refugee orphanage at Dharamsala Cantonment, as a ward of His Holiness the Dalai Lama. She would be able to make her own way by sewing for the children there. While at the hospital she gave far more than she received, for the whole department derived strength each day from the bright eyes and smile, knowing how much she suffered physically and how much she sorrowed for the family she would never see again.

There were other Tibetan patients. Jamyan, a ten-year-old, was undergoing treatment to regain some use of his left arm after paralysis. Two other children had been brought by a Swiss doctor, literally carried one under each arm from Kathmandu to Delhi, then by train to Bareilly. One, Jumpto, a so-called "monkey boy" who had never walked upright but always on his hands and feet, made swift progress and it was hoped that he would eventually be able to stand and walk upright. The other, Teshi, was a paralytic. Because of Clara Swain Hospital, all would sometime become useful persons.

Unfortunately, the person most responsible for its existence was unable to attend the dedication in March of 1966 of the Alice M. Riel Physical Medicine Wing, though 2,000 others, including three Methodist bishops, Mr. Henry Lacy, executive secretary of the Methodist Board of Missions for India, the director of health services in the state, the Commissioner of Bareilly, and Dr. Nayar, Minister of Health of the Republic of India, overflowed the multicolored *shamiana* in the hospital quadrangle. Alice Riel was too sick to attend, but her talk, modestly telling the story of her pioneer venture, had been tape-recorded and was played for the audience.

But far better than being present was to see in her mind's eye the four child patients who, she knew, were coming to the stage while her report was being heard, a living demonstration of the difference good treatment could make for those stricken by polio and other disabilities. One child, who could hardly crawl a year before, was now able to move slowly with braces and crutches. As Dr. Nayar patted each small head and put garlands about the little necks, the audience was even more moved than by her later eloquence as she spoke of government efforts through rehabilitation centers.

"The needs of no group of human beings should be ignored if we believe that they all have a bit of God in them," declared the loyal disciple of Mahatma Gandhi.

Alice Riel was well satisfied. The beautiful new building with its white trellis was the fulfillment of all her dreams. Her church friends, with the help of the Harris Foundation, had responded well. The costs had already been met. The equipment, when it all arrived, would be of the latest type, providing for radiation of different kinds, diathermy, electrical muscle stimulation, and ultrasonic therapy. A well-trained Indian staff was already in action. Ten years ago she had started with nothing but a tiny room and a few scraps of equipment. And now look what it had become!

Yes, both she and Doc were leaving their work in good hands. They would return to America next month with many fine memories, much satisfaction, and no regrets. A good investment certainly of their "inactive retirement" years! They were ready to go home. But not to stop working for Clara Swain! Already they had at least a full year of speeches lined up ahead.

6

"Why do you work with this small mission hospital instead of with a government agency?"

The questioner was an important person in the Indian government and one really anxious to secure an answer. Dr. Ernest had been having a conference with the Governor of Uttar Pradesh, its Health Minister, and the Deputy Health Minister of the Government of India. They had made inquiries about a new clinic Ernest had beeen instrumental in establishing at Naini Tal as part of the outreach of Clara Swain Hospital. With them he had visited some endemic areas of chicken pox, measles, and cholera. These were responsible and concerned officials, honestly seeking to find answers. And in the question there was more of bafflement than curiosity. Why a brilliant young doctor should choose to work in a small hospital run by an obscure minority sect when he might head a big institution at twice or three times the salary was simply beyond their comprehension. And they really wanted to know the reason.

Ernest considered. Just why did he make such a choice? And how could he best make them understand? "Well," he said, "let me give you one example. At the time of partition five of us doctors went to Pakistan to take care of fifty thousand Hindu refugees, treating them all the way from Lahore to the banks of the Indus. We were all Christians. Only one Hindu doctor that I know of was willing to volunteer, and he was a classmate of mine who had been trained in a Christian hospital. Because I was Christian and known as such I had a unique opportunity to serve. I think it was then that I made up my mind what my vocation would be and where I could make the best contribution to my country."

The function of the small Christian hospital in a secular society where health with its vast problems was necessarily the province of government—this was a subject to which Ernest gave careful thought during these years of the sixties. Did it still have an important role to play in the new India?

Certainly there was a tremendous need for the small independent hospital. A recent survey by the World Health Organization at the request of the Indian Ministry of Health suggested that every district in each state of the country must have as its goal one hospital of a total strength of 200 beds. It was the official policy of the Ministry of Health to encourage the establishment of a hospital of this caliber in every district headquarters. But even this would provide bare necessities for the densely populated areas, and 70 per cent of the villages in outlying areas would have to be reached through village dispensaries, public health centers, and mobile units. Government statistics showed that even where 100-bed hospitals were available at district level, many were of such poor quality that they did not give adequate service; and for villagers all medical provision was grossly inadequate, in most cases nonexistent. It would be decades, at least, before government and voluntary facilities combined could even begin to meet the minimum health needs of a tragically expanding population.

But what of the *Christian mission* hospital? Was its past, present, and future contribution sufficiently unique to justify its existence? Ernest's answer was an emphatic and unqualified "Yes."

In the last hundred years Christian hospitals had provided the basic core of the nursing personnel for all of India, helping to emancipate her womanhood. In their concern for the total care of the patient they had developed paramedical schools—public health, X-ray and laboratory technicians' courses, occupational and physical therapy, and mental training—in a country where technical training has been and is still sadly lacking. By continuing such schools in the future, even though they were often a financial burden, they could play an even more vital role.

But their really unique contribution derived from their being *Christian mission* hospitals.

"And what is the unique quality which makes such an institution different from every other?" Ernest both asked and answered this question, at least to his own satisfaction. "It is a loving and selfless concern for persons which is not only the essence of true Christianity but also the finest attribute of the healer. Since it is lived rather than preached, it is a form of Christian witness which can be proclaimed even in an institution working in full cooperation with the program of a secular government."

And often the silent witness became the spoken.

"It's different here," a patient might observe wonderingly. "All the doctors and nurses seem to—to care about us."

"We do care. You see, this is a Christian hospital."

"Christian?"

"Yes. We try to be good followers of Jesus Christ, who even gave his life because he cared so much about people."

"I—I'd like to know more about him."

And in a hospital that is truly Christian, even non-Christian doctors chosen for their high skill and character often become so imbued with the spirit of the place that their ministry of healing is exemplary of true Christians. Witness Dr. Das!

7

But it was the nurses even more than the doctors, Dr. Ernest knew, who in their constant daily devotion to patients rendered the uniquely Christian witness. And the quality of nursing training at Clara Swain through the years has been exceptional.

"How I wish I could rub some Aladdin's lamp," wrote Mary Gordon one day in 1962, "so that all of you could join us some morning for chapel, and then follow the girls as they go to their stations in the wards. You could watch them give the patients their morning care and baths, go with the doctors on their rounds, see how they have to work in crowded wards, poorly lighted and ventilated; carry water for baths from a wood-burning water heater in a far corner of the hospital compound, battle flies and mosquitoes due to ill-fitting, warped doors, windows, and screens—cheerfully!"

Mary Gordon herself had been coping with these and worse difficulties, cheerfully, for the last twenty-five years. She had seen vast improvements in the hospital. No longer the need to assist at night operations by the flare of a smoky little gasoline lantern, to sterilize instruments over charcoal, to give baths in 110° temperatures without even the comfort of an electric fan! But there were still plenty of improvements needed, and the items mentioned in her letter home were only a few of them. First and foremost in her mind was *a new school of nursing building*.

She was in her last term of service in that year of 1962, with only three more years to go. Was there time to accomplish her purpose, to convince the authorities who held the purse strings that to meet the needs of this turbulent new India a new school of nursing building for Clara Swain was an absolute essential? In her quiet, smiling, but persistent way she set about making this dream come true. She assembled statistics, compiled painstaking records, designed plans, wrote letters, talked, pulled gently but firmly on every administrative string whose end she could unravel.

Some of the statistics were satisfying. In its nearly sixty years the school of nursing had graduated 317 nurses, and 14 more would be receiving their diplomas that year. Eighty-five mid-wives had completed their training. The graduate nursing staff numbered 37, and there were 68 nursing and midwifery students.

But past programs of training were not good enough. With the advent of specialization in the hospital and the highly trained personnel being engaged in each departmental field, even the A-grade nurses seemed no longer adequate. All over India efforts were being made to upgrade the schools of nursing, and special nursing education had become an urgent problem. The hospital itself was desperately in need of better-trained nurses, either sister tutors or, preferably, those with a B.Sc. degree In addition to her attempts to get a new building, in order to step up the quality of their A-grade training, Mary Gordon worked constantly during this last term to secure adequate nursing service in the hospital.

It was not easy. The first applicant they sent to study for a B. Sc. came successfully to her third year, then married. Miss Allen, the public health nurse, was instrumental in sending some girls to Indore for sister tutor's training, and at one time there were four sister tutors in the hospital, later reduced to two. However, getting admissions into the only two colleges which had a B.Sc. course was extremely difficult, since the number of seats was only sixteen for the whole of India. And financial support was a necessity. It was hoped that Crusade for Christ scholarships could be secured for at least two of the senior nurses, Mrs. Frank and Mrs. Arthur, to take further study in India, perhaps in the excellent Institute of Science at Chandigarh.

But if this problem was not solved during her last term, Mary Gordon was able to fulfill her dream of a new building. By 1963 she had convinced the Woman's Division of Christian Service that a new building for the school of nursing was absolutely essential, and plans were drawn by Russell King of the Methodist Engineering Office in Delhi, including classrooms, dining rooms, kitchen, and library. By the following year the project had been approved by the Board of Missions as an Advance Special, and in October of 1964 Miss Gordon had the satisfaction of seeing the cornerstone laid of the Mary V. Gordon School of Nursing.

At the same time another much-needed new block, the Caroline O. Mondol Maternity Wing, named after the bishop's wife who had helped to establish the department, was dedicated by Bishop Mondol. Dr. Ernest's father, Bishop Sundaram, also participated in the ceremony. At least 2,000 people witnessed the cutting of the ribbon by Mrs. Mondol, since the Annual Conference was meeting at the time in Bareilly.

The former obstetrics and gynecology department had been in the same old building as the surgical cases, many of which were highly infective. The need had long been felt for a separate building, but as usual funds had not been available. Now at last, partly because of the sharing of chest department funds, the ground floor of the new unit had been finished, and it was hoped that the first floor would be completed in another year. Money for the project had all come from local sources.

The new maternity block was almost as much a source of satisfaction to Mary Gordon as the prospective school of nursing. Who could give more fervent thanks for its light, well-ventilated, convenient spaces than one who had spent much of twenty-seven years coping with the inadequacies of the old crowded, dingy, outmoded wards! The new unit had its own labor room, treatment room, delivery rooms, with a night duty room for sisters and doctors. Part of it was even air conditioned! She rejoiced over the neat rows of new beds which had come all the way from California, the gifts of Dr. and Mrs. Don R. King of Long Beach. Other equipment would be coming, since former patients of the hospital had agreed to furnish the unit. Various factories in the area had donated electric fans.

Bishop Mondol had additional reason for pride in this service of dedication, because his niece, Dr. Irene Datt Kutar, was now head of the department of obstetrics and gynecology. Dr. Kutar, a Crusade Scholar who had studied in both England and the United States, winning the advanced degrees of M.R.C.O.G. and F.A.C.S., was eminently qualified for the position and with her three junior doctors soon succeeded in making the department one of the most efficient in the area. Four of her cases of "exchange transfusion" in deeply jaundiced babies, presented to a hospital doctors' clinical meeting which was attended by all private practitioners, army doctors, and other medical personnel in the area, were good examples of progress being made. Dr. Kutar's record in gynecological surgery was outstanding, as well as her work in the field of sterility and habitual abortion. An accelerated program of family planning in cooperation with the public health department of the hospital immediately became one of the department's major emphases.

It was not until March of 1966 that the new school of nursing building was finally dedicated, almost a year after Mary Gordon completed her twenty-eight years of service at Clara Swain and left for retirement in America. However, she was able to see the first set of three rooms completed. Intensely humble, always self-effacing, she requested that she be given no official farewell when she left.

Her service to the hospital had been both constant and sacrificial, with but brief interruptions. Once during the Perrills' regime she had been making her daily evening rounds and for some reason decided to include the basement, as yet unfinished. The workmen had failed to cover a hole before leaving, and she had fallen to a depth of perhaps ten feet. Somehow she had managed to crawl out. A few broken ribs had kept her out of commission for a few days. During her last term she had fallen in a slippery passage and injured her back, necessitating another brief period in bed. None had ever heard her complain, though she had been obviously embarrassed when Dr. Ernest and some of the other young men had insisted on visiting her.

Not long before leaving she suffered a heart attack and was in bed again for several weeks, worrying far more over the trouble she was causing the nurses than over her own condition. Her sensitivity to others' feelings and points of view had always been acute, so much so that even if she was convinced another person was wrong, unless principle was involved she would try to adjust her actions to suit him. She had been an excellent and thorough teacher, and many of her girls had won scholastic prizes. Some of the top positions in the big institutions of Delhi and other cities were held by her students.

"I'd like to be a nurse just like Sister Gordon," her pupils were often heard to say.

"She's like Isabella Thoburn," one student aptly appraised her. "Like her, Miss Gordon has emancipated the young women of our country by giving us not only status but a worthy profession."

One of these emancipated young women was Millicent Frank, who on Mary Gordon's departure became the acting superintendent of nurses. A graduate of Isabella Thoburn's Lal Bagh High School, she had come to Clara Swain in 1943 as a student. Then Miss Lorenz had sent her to Kinnaird Hospital in Lucknow for her midwifery training and on her return installed her as a teacher in the school of nursing. In 1950 she had taken a postgraduate course in Vellore in teaching and supervision, later gone to Delhi for postgraduate work in public health nursing and served as acting head of public health while Miss Allen was on furlough. Her promotion to the new position of responsibility was another step in the hospital's program of increased national leadership.

But she was only one of the Clara Swain nursing graduates to be given further educational opportunities. Several B.Sc. nurses have been sent at the hospital's expense to the College of Nursing in Delhi for graduate training, among them Irene Wheeler and Mercy Jane Harrison. Earlier a male nurse, Mr. J. K. Singh, was the first to receive a Colombo Plan scholarship to study in Australia, selected from an All-India Forum by the government in June, 1958. After a year of study in Sydney, he returned to Clara Swain and is still serving as an excellent teacher and an expert supervisor of the operating rooms, running the latter with the efficiency of a ship's mate.

In fact, the educational aspect of the work at Clara Swain has been one of its outstanding contributions through the years, not only to the hospital itself, but to many other institutions which have profited from its trained leadership. The school of nursing is only one of the departments in which students are being constantly trained. After 1948 there was no period when less than three schools were in operation, and in recent years there have often been as many as seven different schools active at one time, in addition to the school of nursing. Training has been given in anesthesiology, X-ray technology, occupational and physical therapy, laboratory technology, and other paramedical departments.

But perhaps the most dramatic project in education has been an international venture. In recent years holders of Smith Kline and French scholarships, given to fourth-year medical students of the United States, began coming to Clara Swain for a summer semester, working either in general surgery or general medicine, exceptionally keen young students especially interested in tropical disease. Their apprenticeships not only proved a powerful stimulus to the hospital morale and an experience of inestimable value to them, but they could not fail to promote high values of professional fellowship on an international plane. Soon the Canadian Universities Services Overseas requested Dr. Ernest to place candidates in nursing and medicine in various hospitals of north India, and the first CUSO representative, Miss Bonnie Hartley, arrived at Clara Swain in August of 1967 to teach and give clinical instruction in the wards to nursing students. Some German nurses sent out by the "Bread for the World" program were also expected.

Always, in the hospital's various schools of training, the effort has been made to provide the best possible education for physical and spiritual needs as well as the technical knowledge and experience to pass the required examinations. Continuous through the years, of course, and unique in its increasingly high standards and achievement has been the school of nursing.

It was Frances Allen, then adviser for the nursing training, not Mary Gordon, who represented the department when the new building was dedicated, together with the new physical medicine wing, in the spring of 1966, and both buildings were opened by Dr. Sushila Nayar. With the addition of this block, Miss Allen told the 2,000 people assembled, the sixty-year-old school now had all its nursing school facilities concentrated in one unit. Recognized since 1928 for training nurses, accepted since 1945 by the state medical faculty as a center for training A-grade nurses, it had already produced 372 nursing graduates.

"But figures do not tell the whole story," she pointed out. "Beside knowledge and skill, one must instill right attitudes, stimulate high motives, build integrity and high moral character."

Later the Minister of Health reiterated this point when she called on the nursing profession to be free from caste and other prejudices, which sometimes made nurses look on such services as giving the bed pan as the work of a sweeper. Every attention given to patients was essential service, Dr. Nayar emphasized. She recalled Gandhi's statement that no good cause ever suffered for want of funds if dedicated workers were forthcoming, and she sounded a stirring call to the people of India, especially its youth, to look on the problems of the country as challenging opportunities rather than as depressing burdens.

When Frances Allen arrived in Bareilly in 1957 she found little accomplished in the area of public health. She started her work by attempting to introduce the subject in the basic curriculum for students. Presently she was able to send two girls away for further training, Sister Millicent Frank to the Reading

School in Delhi, Mabel Tiwari to the Mid-India Board School for Graduate Nurses in Indore. But as she studied the situation she was more and more convinced that the hospital department could be really effective only if it was incorporated into a program of village extension service. Not only did the students need a practice situation to develop their skills, but so appalling were the conditions of rural India, with its 600,000 poverty-ridden villages, that no Christian hospital could be said to fulfill its mission if it did not go into these areas of greatest need.

Twenty years before, Charles Perrill on his hunting trips had visited the village of Faridpur thirteen miles from Bareilly and become concerned about its extreme poverty. Its people had proved very anxious for good medical care, and through the efforts of its pastor, the Reverend Jhamman Lall, the Deputy Collector Bhakthavar Singh had donated a piece of land for a village health center. But—how find the funds to build it? Years passed, nearly fifteen of them, and still the donated land lay idle.

Returning from furlough in 1964, Frances Allen determined to start the program with such facilities as were available. Plans were made very carefully. She held conferences with government agencies, asking their help and cooperation; secured permission in writing from the district health officer, the civil surgeon of Bareilly, the doctor in the local government dispensary.

"Always work into the existing program," she admonished her students. "Supplement, don't supplant what is already there. And move slowly. Be careful always to maintain good relations."

That year she introduced her first students into the village situation. They lived in the village, two at a time, for the period of a month, visiting homes and each becoming involved in the problems of one particular village family. Also with government permission they operated a small dispensary set up in the church compound.

Here Beatrice Bonjour, "Aunt Beatty," the expert bookkeeper, recreation director, art enthusiast, garden supervisor, guest house hostess, and Jill-of-many-other-trades, took on another duty which was of invaluable help to the program. Taking the two girls who were going into the village each month, she would study with them their personal budgets as nurses, then help each one to compare it with the budget of the village family she was studying. This not only helped them in working with their village families, but gave them guidance in administering their own small incomes.

For most, the latter amounts seemed pitiably small. The allowance of each nurse in training came to about 68 rupees a month (less than $10). Part of this came from mission scholarships. Out of her allowance she would pay her tuition, book expense, uniform requirements, *dhobi* service, and have perhaps 8 rupees left over for personal use, some of which often went to help her parents. The study with Miss Bonjour was revealing. Often the girls found that they had more income than a village family containing six or eight members!

After this program had been in action for some time, there came a wonderful breakthrough. Dr. Ernest met on the train Dr. Manfred Kulessa, South-East Asia Director of the German "Bread for the World." Through him Ernest secured the name of a Mr. Nielsen in Stuttgart and wrote to him. Through his efforts and those of Bishop Wunderlich, the organization agreed to finance the Faridpur project. It took two years to complete negotiations through the India National Christian Council and the World Council of Churches. But in 1966, seventeen years after the plot of land was acquired, the Faridpur Health Clinic of Clara Swain Hospital was completed.

It consisted of two buildings, one containing consultation rooms for male and female doctors, a pharmacy, laboratory, record room, and storage space. The big front verandah with its encircling built-in cement seats made an ideal waiting room, as well as a fine vantage point for nurses to give their public health talks. A huge shade tree between clinic and main road furnished shelter from the sun to passers-by, bullocks, and, occasionally, elephants, as well as patients.

Another small building would provide for an eight-bed maternity ward and delivery room, making possible domiciliary midwifery training for third-year nursing students. Frances Allen's own home church was contributing the basic laboratory equipment, shipping it through Church World Service.

At the same time more land was acquired so that when funds were available, staff quarters could be completed. For to render adequate service to this big area of perhaps twenty-four villages, with a population of up to 50,000, a resident staff was an absolute essential. Already the center was moving toward ambitious goals: simple medical care, immunization, survey work in tuberculosis and other infectious diseases, a dental health program with the use of the mobile unit, antenatal and postnatal clinics including education in family planning, child-care clinics, field experience for students, and village health education. An adventurous enough program for any public health center! But still Frances Allen was far from satisfied.

"It isn't enough," she kept affirming to all who would listen, "for the villagers to come to us. We need to go to them. We should have a bus going out from the center into the villages, like the dental and X-ray vans. We could send out a team every day, a doctor, a nurse, a compounder, who could give simple medical care, immunization, make simple deliveries, give education in child care, sanitation, family planning. Dr. Riel designed the dental van. He could design one for us, too, and how I would like to give him the specifications! If only someone would provide the money!"

8

The traditional pace of India was that of the bullock cart, her symbol of routine activity the patient animal, often blindfolded, treading the ceaseless round of the irrigation well or the oil press. Not so this new generation of highly trained professionals. Like their Western counterparts with whom many of them had studied, they were more like efficient machines, seldom at rest, driven by a furious compulsion to make up for the long lag of the centuries.

Ernest Sundaram was of this new generation. During the first five years of his leadership at Clara Swain he drove himself to accomplish tasks which it should have taken two, perhaps three, men to perform. In administration as well as surgery he was a perfectionist. The hospital had passed through its pioneering stage and achieved what physical growth was necessary. Now specialization must be increased. Every department must be upgraded until it had the best-qualified leadership available, whether national or missionary. He could not be satisfied until he felt that the highest possible standards in every department had been attained. And this was a frustrating and often seemingly impossible task.

But during the years much progress was achieved. When he assumed the superintendency, the departments of dentistry and thoracic surgery were already functioning satisfactorily. The work of Mrs. Riel, together with the new building and the arrival of Dr. Makhani, created an efficient orthopedic department as well as an increasingly adequate department of physical medicine and rehabilitation. A good department of medicine was now functioning smoothly under the supervision of Dr. Zal Kutar, who was also the deputy superintendent. The medical aspects of tuberculosis were being studied very carefully by Dr. Quarashie, who had a first-grade qualification in the subject. The maternity department was giving splendid service under Dr. Irene Kutar, who had three junior doctors working with her, and was ably assisted by a highly trained pediatrician from the Boston Children's Hospital, Dr. Mansukhani, who was doing excellent work in the children's ward.

One day in 1963 Dr. Ernest received a letter from Dr. Donald King, an anesthesiologist at Community Hospital, Long Beach, California.

"Do you think I could make a small contribution to your hospital," the letter inquired, "by coming over to Clara Swain and working for a month?"

Some questioned the value of such a short term, but Dr. Ernest gave immediate approval. Dr. King came at his own expense, spending his vacation in this missionary service. Arriving one morning in November, he went to work the same day.

"You're working harder than most of us," marveled the other doctors, seeing him go to work day after day at 6:30 in the morning and return at 10:30 at night. He brought with him some excellent equipment, especially for giving anesthesia to children, and special assistors and emergency apparatus.

In many small hospitals of India anesthesia was given by compounders without training, but at Clara Swain nurses had long been trained and used for this purpose. This work had been initiated by Miss Sara Harro, an anesthetist from Philadelphia, during the regime of Dr. Perrill, and since its beginning two or three nurses had been trained each year and sent out to other mission hospitals. Since nurses were far more available than doctors in India, their use in this specialized area was highly desirable.

Dr. King immediately examined the work of the anesthetists,

Elsie Singh and Mrs. Paul, together with their two students, and approved their procedures.

"They're giving good anesthesia, including that for chest surgery," he said to Dr. Ernest, "but I feel the next thing is to teach them spinal anesthesia."

In spite of the two doctors' mutual doubts and fears, the nurse anesthetists picked up the new techniques with surprising ease and proved remarkably successful. In subsequent months they proceeded to give 5,000 or more spinal anesthesias without complication. Later Dr. Murphy of the Christian Medical College in Ludhiana instructed them in perfusion anesthesia. The military hospital in Bareilly was soon asking to borrow the new equipment along with the services of the hospital anesthetists. During the India-Chinese conflict seventeen operations were performed there with the aid of Clara Swain personnel and equipment. Short though it was, the month's visit of the Kings was of inestimable value to the department. The school of anesthesia, the only one of its kind available in India, continued to give excellent instruction. Elsie Singh, one of its outstanding products, after studying under Miss Harro and Dr. King, became exceedingly successful in training other students.

And after Dr. King's return to the States, his support continued. He secured for the hospital a respirator and a large operating room light. He aroused the interest of another hospital, the Centenella in Long Beach, which donated beds for the new maternity building. And, best of all, his daughter, inspired perhaps by the enthusiastic reports of her parents, enrolled in the Northwestern Medical School and expressed an interest in giving service some day to Clara Swain. Another of his sons was at the same time preparing for medical school.

The incident highlighted the value of short-term missionary service, even of a few weeks' duration, and suggested limitless possibilities for the use of dedicated specialists in various fields who might be willing to devote a year or less to helping upgrade the program of a mission hospital. Applications began to come from pathologists, dentists, and physiotherapists for similar short-term service.

Pathology was an area of special need for development. During her two terms Mildred Althouse had built up a reasonably good clinical laboratory and had started a school for laboratory technicians in 1949. William Ram, who had come as a student in

1952, had come back to work under her, and because of her efforts he was able to take further training in California and Iowa. Returning from America in 1962, Mr. Ram took over the department, running a successful laboratory, carrying on the blood bank, and conducting a laboratory school, a one-year diploma course open to matriculate students.

Gradually the facilities improved. There was a new spectro-photometer for taking readings for biochemistry, a new hemato-crit machine, which required three minutes instead of a half hour to check the packed cell-volume of blood. Equipment for a bed-side lab was secured, and finally the new two-door blood bank re-frigerator, so desperately needed, was on its way!

But another urgent requirement, for a full-time pathologist, had still to be met. At last the work-study committee of the hospital decided that this need must be given priority. Then, wonder of wonders! No sooner had the decision been made than an application was received from Dr. Dubey, who had worked with the World Health Organization and been trained under one of the best pathologists in India, Dr. Wahi of Agra Medical College. With his M.Sc. in zoology, his first-grade M.D. in pathology, and his six years of teaching experience in a medical college, Dr. Dubey promised to raise the department to the desired level of efficiency.

Surgery continued to be a problem. After carrying a tremendous load in the department for eleven years, Dr. Das suffered a serious heart attack which greatly curtailed his activity. Dr. Roy Coats, who joined the staff as head of the department of general surgery and reorganized it with the help of Dr. Das, Dr. Masih, and Dr. Joshi, was unfortunately obliged to leave. It was hoped that when funds became available Dr. Bimal Masih might go abroad for training in urology, since some 40 per cent of the cases coming to the hospital presented urological problems. It was also hoped that Dr. Roy might obtain a scholarship for study in cardiac surgery, and his wife one for postgraduate work in gynecology and obstetrics.

The pharmacy, until now a small basement room where intra-venous fluids were prepared, with sometimes damp walls and falling plaster, making it impossible to keep the precious fluids sterile and free from ants and other bugs, was transferred to proper tile-walled, air-conditioned quarters adjoining the oper-ating theater, all built with local funds. Under the watchful eye of Mr. Dan, who had been with the department for twenty-four years, excellent fluids could now be prepared without the danger of contamination which might well cause the death of a patient—one like six-year-old Rajendar.

He was brought to the hospital on a stretcher. He could hardly speak and weighed only 16 pounds. When he had typhoid fever, his father explained, the only doctor in the village of Budaun, a quack, had given the boy some herb medicine. It must have contained some corrosive, for it burned the gullet of little Rajendar, who became unable to swallow. He was slowly starving to death.

For his first forty-eight hours in the hospital Rajendar was fed by a vein until his body fluids were stabilized. Then he was given a pint of blood and under a local anesthetic Dr. Das inserted a tube into his stomach. Through this he was fed on a high-caloric diet containing milk, eggs, and soups. He had a special nurse who fed him every two hours around the clock. Two months later he weighed 25 pounds.

X-rays showed that half of his gullet was burned, but fortunately the neck part was still normal. Two teams of surgeons then worked on him simultaneously for four hours, bringing up a loop of small intestine as a substitute for the burned gullet. Four months later Rajendar could eat anything he wanted, and when he left he weighed 30 pounds. Though his father was too poor to pay hospital bills, he was helped by the Chest Charity Fund, donated by patrons in India and America. Another life saved through the cooperative healing ministry of a Christian hospital and its supporters! And by no means least important in the life-giving process was the sterility of those first all-essential intravenous fluids.

Other departments continued to make progress. When Janette Crawford left in 1955 to become treasurer of Lal Bagh School in Lucknow, her place was taken by another missionary, Mr. Wesley Ginn, who put in several years of hard and efficient service. Miss Crawford remained on the board of managers, however, and on both the finance and educational committees of the hospital until her retirement in 1961. Later, when Mr. Ginn was transferred to Vellore, the stores and administration departments were reorganized under the supervision of Mr. Nilajgi, the business manager, who had earned a degree in hospital administration from Northwestern University. Mr. Nizar Masih, the accountant, and Mr. C. K. Tewari in the stores also performed the efficient but constantly frustrating task of keeping the hospital finances on a stable basis.

Some improvements which might seem minor made a vast difference in convenience. It was again Dr. Riel who made one of these possible, raising the money to finance an electric substation from an 11-KV or 11,000-KWA (kilowatt amps) line, providing the whole compound with ample electricity for the next fifty to a hundred years, perhaps the most practical of all the many contributions which this remarkably self-giving missionary had made. This, plus a double water system for the hospital, connected after long negotiations with the State Hydel project, added amazingly to the ease and efficiency of management. Other mundane but highly useful improvements were a male doctors' changing room and an underground sewage system for the new buildings.

It was amazing how much time, imagination, and expense were involved merely in planning and constructing such a modern improvement in a land like India.

"So much money goes down the drain!" remarked one doctor cynically.

In fact, for the superintendent as well as for the accounting department and the hospital board, finances were a constant headache. A mission hospital could take in barely enough fees from patients able to pay to cover the day-to-day operating costs. All other expense—buildings, equipment, instruments—must come from interested friends, groups, or churches, most of them in America. And with the shrinking value of the dollar and the tremendous need of other mission projects all over the world, sufficient funds were never available.

Charges, except to patients in private rooms, had not been increased in twenty years—could not be, due to the stark poverty of most of the patients—yet expenses were constantly mounting. In five years medical costs had increased nearly 300 per cent. Food costs had skyrocketed. The prices of new equipment, of necessary repairs, of labor and building materials had soared. To meet the higher costs of living, salaries and wages had been necessarily raised. The 260-bed hospital had often been stretched, by crowding wards and using corridors and verandahs, to house over 300 patients. And many in the greatest need were totally unable to pay.

This problem of charity patients was one of the most pressing and frustrating. Surely a Christian hospital could not turn away poor patients in dire need of medical help! Yet how could treatment be given free if there were no funds available? It was estimated that if the needs of poor patients applying were properly met, it would take at least 500 beds and 2 million rupees each year for charity alone!

Not that a great deal of free service was not being constantly given! The hospital endeavored to give some kind of medical aid to every poor patient who came. In one recent year its expenditures in charity amounted to 120,000 rupees. In the public health department, Dr. Strete, working at Faridpur, treated 216 leprosy patients without charge, giving them 30,000 tablets of DDS. Three thousand dental patients in the schools were treated free. Flood victims were assisted with food, bedding, clothing, and given free medical treatment in the hospital. Through the Methodist Committee for Overseas Relief tubercular patients were treated at a cost to each individual of only a little more than two rupees a month, less than fifty cents. Yet for many even this was a prohibitive price. With the numbers of poor patients pouring each day through the hospital gates constantly increasing, the amount of charity they were able to give seemed no more than a drop in the ocean!

All these problems were the concern of the combined hospital and medical superintendent, and Dr. Ernest tackled them with his characteristic thoroughness, dynamic energy, and insistence on perfection. His goal, like that of Clara Swain herself, expressed in her first annual report, was to make the institution a truly community hospital, ministering to all cultures, all religions, all strata of society, but expressing in every act its intrinsic Christian concern for human beings. The hospital must be a truly pioneering and teaching center in order to make its greatest contribution in a country where skilled leadership was such a vital necessity. And, since no Christian hospital ministering to the poor in a land like India could expect to be solvent, it was part of his task to explore every possible source of financial aid, missionary, foundation, local, government, private charity.

For the first time in the hospital's history he was able to obtain aid from the government. In the Health Ministry, he discovered, there was a committee charged with dispensing aid through voluntary organizations. He approached Mr. Radha

Raman, its chairman, with two proposals, and obtained grants of some 30,000 rupees for necessary equipment. Plans were made for making future proposals, especially for a new intensive-nursing unit. In its turn the hospital could give guidance and leadership to the government through some of its own pioneering ventures, such as the dental van and the Faridpur Health Center, which could well serve as pilot projects in the areas of public health.

In fact, cooperation with the government in its colossal task of raising the health standards of a startlingly multiplying population was imperative to the program of all mission hospitals. Operating with greater independence and less red tape, they were often able to lead the way in achieving results in shorter time and at less expense. In the vast problem of family planning, much was already being done at Clara Swain to implement the government's extensive program. All female patients who came to the tuberculosis clinic had the "loop" inserted. Education, with opportunity for practical assistance, was constantly dispensed in hospital, all out-patient clinics, the Faridpur Center, and the mobile units. But much more must be done in the future. In a country whose population was increasing by a million each month, the cooperation of every agency with the bold government program of family planning was essential.

There were urgent building priorities also. One, the need for a new private-room complex, was already in process of being met. Undertaken by the West Ohio Conference, Dayton district, another result of the Riels' activity, it would presently be completed at a cost of some $30,000.

Such a unit had become a "must" for the service the hospital was now called to render. Wealthy patients from Bareilly, especially those in the industrial area, expected good accommodations as well as superior hospital care, and they were willing to pay for it. The income thus derived could provide much additional free care for poor patients. If only 30 per cent of the bed strength could be set aside for private rooms, charity work could be at least doubled.

A new surgical ward and operating-room complex were desperately needed. These should include general surgical wards, recovery rooms, operating suites, and orthopedic wards. Present wards were seventy-five years old, insufficient in space, and difficult to keep clean. Cross-infection seriously hampered good medical care. A new building to house X-ray, laboratory, and pharmacy was badly needed, to say nothing of the X-ray machine itself!

The old machines, thanks to the ability and watchful care of Mr. I. C. Singh, the radiographer, had been in useful service for the last twenty years, surely a record even for India. A new 500- or 700-MA machine, with diagnostic facilities associated with it, especially monitoring equipment, would make possible far more advanced cardiac work. But where find the three lakhs of rupees (about $60,000) which would provide it?

And how secure the adequate equipment for the cardiac surgery that was so desperately needed? In all the area containing at least a million people there was not one hospital undertaking to treat cardiac patients amenable to surgical treatment, yet there were times when there were as many as thirty patients at Clara Swain who would have benefited by surgery of the heart. And the hospital had personnel trained in this specialized field! It was a tragic and frustrating deficiency.

An intensive-nursing unit, a second story for the maternity building, staff housing, a mobile dispensary to expand public health work in the villages, a radiologist, a pathologist, a department of anesthesiology, scholarships for advanced training of staff members, a full-time chaplain, staff quarters at Faridpur, a new constitution which would make the hospital more democratic in its working... no wonder that with all these needs crying for fulfillment, the combined office of medical and hospital superintendent was not only a mental and spiritual challenge but a physical headache!

9

But the two jobs of administration were only part of Ernest Sundaram's responsibility. He was also head of the chest department, perhaps the major one in the whole hospital, since such a large percentage of patients were affected by tuberculosis of the lungs. With its 74 beds out of the 260 in the hospital, the department was usually full to capacity. Though Dr. Bimal Roy was an efficient assistant, it was on Dr. Ernest that much of the heavy operating burden fell. So thorough was his training and so excellent his reputation in the whole state of Uttar Pradesh that many patients came for the sole purpose of securing his personal attention.

For instance, there was the son of the wealthy zamindar (landlord) from Shahjahanpur.

"My only son," the father explained with great emotion. "Without him, when I die the family would have no head. All my property—what would become of it? Already the government has taken away what they say we don't need. And—how could I bear to lose him!"

The boy, a sixteen-year-old college student, had suffered severe bleeding and was found to have one lung completely destroyed. He was taken into the hospital and given twenty pints of blood, both the father and mother donating. When he had improved sufficiently to warrant an operation, Dr. Ernest, recognizing the emotional factors involved, was hesitant to perform it.

"Take him to Vellore," he advised the father, "or to Ludhiana. There you will find much larger departments and can get the best surgery available."

The zamindar replied, "Give us one hour to think about it."

He came back. "If he has to die," he said, "let it be at your hands."

Dr. Ernest had no choice. The boy was put on the operating table. Never had his surgeon's skill and confidence been so severely tested. He remembered the words of Dr. Pomeroy, "You do the operation, but it's God who does the healing. Therefore, pray." He did so, fervently, as he lifted the scalpel. At the end of the five or six crucial hours he was more exhausted from nervousness than from the work itself. The boy had lived through the operation, but the success of it was still undetermined. The next day Dr. Ernest had to go to Delhi. "Is he alive?" were his first words when he returned. The affirmative answer was reassuring but not conclusive. Only time would tell whether the disease had really been arrested. Time did. The boy went back to college, obtained his degree, and became a useful citizen of Shahjahanpur.

Even royalty was impressed by the superior techniques and equipment of the chest department. When in 1966 the Maharajah of Rampore became seriously ill due to lung complications, a message came asking for the respirator and ambulance, with an anesthetist, to be sent to the palace, so that he could be brought to Clara Swain. Arriving, the team managed to resuscitate him, but he was in poor condition and died in a few hours.

"We're sorry," came a grateful message from the royal house, "that we didn't know before that you had such good equipment. We would have come to you first."

Then there was the doctor, son-in-law of the Secretary of Finance in the central government at Delhi, who had been operated on in the finest hospital in the city. He came to Clara Swain in massive hemorrhage from a burst liver abscess which had infected his lung. His hemoglobin was only four grams. He was given pint after pint of blood. Then Dr. Ernest performed two operations, followed by more blood transfusions. The patient recovered, later won a scholarship to go to Tokyo and study special techniques in tuberculosis.

The reputation of the chest department spread beyond even state and national boundaries. When the International Congress on Diseases of the Chest met in New Delhi in 1963, Dr. Ernest was invited to read a paper, which was later published by the department in an international magazine, *Diseases of the Chest*, under the title, "Surgical Management of Pleuro-Pulmonary Amebiasis," this same liver ailment on which Dr. Ernest had operated many times. For it was a common malady in India and the Middle East, the bursting of a liver abscess into the lungs, due to the incidence of dysentery.

If Ernest's field of labor had ended at the bounds of the hospital compound, he would still have had sufficient work and responsibility to tax a normal man's energies to the limit. But his interest and concern involved him in projects over a much wider area. Because of his work with refugees at the time of partition, the National Christian Council of India had made him their contact person for emergencies in all of the district surrounding Clara Swain.

One year there was a disastrous flood, and a whole village about sixty miles away was washed out. Ernest immediately went into action. Through local contributions and church agencies, chiefly the MCOR (Methodist Committee for Overseas Relief), he was able to raise 15,000 rupees, enough to completely rehabilitate the villagers. But where to put them? A telephone call to the Commissioner, and land was obtained on higher ground, where new houses could be built for the displaced families. A fifteen-minute transaction which resulted in new life for hundreds of people!

Nor was the hospital's outreach program confined to its own area. When there were similar floods in Assam, two of the staff, Dr. A. Strete and Miss Mabel Tewari, were sent for six months to render aid, ministering to at least 20,000 refugees. They set up an excellent clinic which continued in operation long after they left it.

The ministry of a Christian hospital, Ernest and many of his associates strongly believed, was not only to those crowding through its gates. It was to all the needy within reach of its services. The mobile units, the Faridpur Clinic, the public health visitors were already stretching the bounds of its ministration to include a wide area. Ernest visioned stretching them still further.

An urgent appeal came from people in Naini Tal, the hill resort a hundred miles away where Methodism had taken root in early days and developed a substantial Christian community. But the church property, including a small church building, near the lake had for some time been unused. Bring us a clinic, was the plea, some kind of medical service. But, came the first reaction of the hospital authorities, there were many fine clinics and hospitals in that area. Why take in another? The answer was clear. The existing hospitals and clinics catered only to the wealthy visitors who came to the hill station for their vacation. There was no medical help available to the very poor. Finally the North India Conference Finance Committee placed the whole church property, worth about three lakhs, at the hospital's disposal.

"But we're going too fast," protested some of Ernest's associates. "There are plenty of desperately poor right around us. And we haven't completed our program at the Faridpur Clinic! Surely we should finish the staff quarters there before starting something a hundred miles away!"

The opportunity was too great, the need too compelling. Ernest and others of his associates felt they must respond. Plans were set in motion to start a small consultation clinic at Naini Tal, with a laboratory, X-ray equipment, public health facilities, and at least two specialists available for consultation. Surely the peripheral hospital, small, simple, perhaps no more than a clinic, established in rural centers where India's need was greatest, was one answer to her colossal health problem. Fine and necessary as were the great medical colleges and city hospitals, wonderful as they were to work in, it was with the villages, all 600,000 of them, containing 74 per cent of India's population, that the truly dedicated Christian must be most concerned.

And, as if to vindicate their faith that boldness rather than caution was the divine imperative in attempting to meet human need, the Primate World Relief Fund of the Anglican Church of Canada sent more than two thousand dollars through the World Council of Churches, both unexpected and unsolicited, enough to complete the staff quarters at Faridpur!

But all this accretion of responsibility exacted a severe toll in physical and nervous energy.

"Slow down," Ernest's friends warned. "You're carried away with all these challenges. Take it easier, or the time's going to come when you have to."

The time did come. It was in the summer of 1966 that it happened. He had had no real vacation for six years, no respite even in the hottest season. Indeed, it was then that his work load was likely to be heaviest, as it was in this particular year, with an epidemic of viral encephalitis, a disease endemic to the area, sweeping the district. During its onslaught about three hundred persons died. But Ernest's abundant energy seemed undepleted. He could operate all the morning, attend to administrative duties most of the afternoon, then take his relaxation in recreation, often taking on some of the younger staff or college students for five sets of tennis, after which he would compete with them just as furiously in the swimming pool. Now also he had been given further stimulus for personal success, for after her two beautiful daughters, Anitha and Vinitha, Sheila had given birth to a fine healthy son.

"You're too thin," worried his parents on one of their visits, more infrequent now, for his father had been appointed to the Hyderabad area at the last Central Conference. "You're working too hard."

"Nonsense," he assured them blithely. "Never felt better. If you don't believe it, you should see me outrun the youngsters on the tennis court!"

Then suddenly it came. The attack, whatever its cause, was blinding, devastating. He seemed to dwell for an eternity in the blackest of limbos. Emerging from it was worse. His eyes refused to focus properly. His hands, those delicate and precise surgeon's tools, were weak and uncoordinated. His speech was hesitant. He could not think properly. It was a shocking, terrifying experience. The uncertainty of diagnosis made it seem all the more sinister. What was it? An infection derived from the hospital, the swimming pool, an innocent-looking but deadly mosquito? Encephalitis? Epilepsy? Or merely complete physical and nervous exhaustion?

There followed more attacks, three fits of unconsciousness, weeks—months—of inconclusive tests. It was discovered that he weighed only 125 pounds. He went to Sitapur, a hundred miles from Bareilly, where there was one of the best eye surgeons, a Hindu, in all of India, and had intensive eye examinations. They revealed nothing seriously wrong. He went to Vellore. Under different circumstances it would have been a happy homecoming, reunion with many of the doctors with whom he had spent so many years of training, but now there was little emotion except hope, fear, terrible anxiety.

Then came more weeks of examinations, exhaustive tests, waiting. He was under the personal care of Dr. Jacob Chandy, probably the foremost neurosurgeon in India. The first tests were carotid angiogram and pneumo-encephalogram. To his infinite relief both were negative. He did not have a brain tumor. They took samples of blood for viral studies. It was proved conclusively that there was no sign of epilepsy. His eyes were again tested. There was nothing wrong that new glasses would not correct. What then? Some kind of inflammatory focus was indicated. But what? The doctors in Vellore, the largest medical center in India, admitted they had never seen anything like it. But here in south India the type of encephalitis endemic to Bareilly was not often seen. Ernest himself was certain that he had suffered an endemic form of the disease. He was put on heavy sedation, with Dilantin and Luminal, both sleep-inducing. It was torture to feel energy depleted, vision clouded, especially to see his hands twitch and tremble.

"Suppose—suppose I should never be able to operate again!"

But as all tests proved negative, hope flared, and confidence began to return. Professional interest awakened. It had been ten years since he had studied at Vellore. He was amazed at the huge size of the institution, and there seemed no end to its growth. In spite of the many familiar faces there had been vast changes. The work in leprosy in which he had pioneered with Dr. Paul Brand had grown to enormous proportions, with trainees coming from all over the world to study the new techniques of surgery and rehabilitation, and Dr. Brand himself shuttling from country to country, continent to continent—Africa, South America, India, England, the United States, Australia— promoting the new ideas which had revolutionized the treatment of leprosy.

He saw the work of Dr. Mary Verghese, the paraplegic victim of the accident in 1954, after which he had assisted in giving anesthesia. The story of her remarkable courage and achievement, as well as Dr. Brand's conquest of the ravages of leprosy, had now become familiar to many around the world through the books *Take My Hands* and *Ten Fingers for God*, written by an American author. Dr. Mary was back now from a second trip to the United States, where she had successfully taken her final oral examinations, fully qualifying her to become head of the new department. Ernest inspected the new physical medicine building at the hospital, was enviously impressed with the fine in-patient rehabilitation unit being erected on the college campus, to which Dr. Mary herself would soon be moving. But for the most part the weeks in Vellore inspired him less with envy than with a fresh appreciation of the possibilities capable of achievement at Bareilly.

He could hardly wait to get back and share some of his new insights with his co-workers at Clara Swain. But he had to wait. From Vellore he went to his father's house in Hyderabad, to spend another two months in slow recuperation. They were as therapeutic to mind and spirit as to body. For the first time in his life he learned patience. The healing process could not be hurried. By specialty a surgeon, he was more used to the swift sure thrust of the scalpel in exorcising disease than to the long slow re-creation of health through growth and renewal.

But the lesson of patience was prelude to an even harder one, humility. In spite of his professional interest in the sick, he had had the strong man's contempt for weakness, plus an overconfidence which had often made him impatient with the slower faculties of his associates. Now suddenly he was the patient, the weak one, his own faculties slowed—for how long? Indefinitely? It was a galling experience. Without a renewal of faith it might well have been an embittering one.

There were compensations. Family ties became closer and more precious. The smiling, serene devotion of Sheila was as cheering as a steady candle flame. Enforced leisure gave him more time with his children, and in sharing with them more of his faith and philosophy he gained a new sense of values for himself. A fresh intimacy with parents, aunts, uncles, cousins, inspired by a sudden sense of inadequacy and need, lent reassurance. And slowly he came to know that never again would those who came to him in hospital or clinic be merely "cases," "patients." They would be *persons*, each one with his own peculiar physical and spiritual need, like himself.

It was January before he was able to return to work, and then still under medication and on a very restricted basis. He found many problems. With the failure of rains for a second year the area around Bareilly had been stricken with famine, affecting at least 60 million people. Many in rural districts were subsisting on grass and the bark of trees. Not only was the hospital affected through the destitution of its patients, but Dr. Ernest himself was soon involved through church relief agencies in ministering to needs of the surrounding area.

Frustrated and burdened at first by the weight of unsolved problems and his own weakness, he slowly learned to adjust. Suppose he never did regain all his former energy and skill? Other surgeons had found ways to render service under tremendous physical difficulties. Look at Dr. Tom Dooley, returning to his jungles under a verdict of death! Look at Dr. Mary Verghese in her wheel chair! Except for her accident, hundreds of disabled persons might never have been given the benefits of rehabilitation. Once he had accepted his limitations and subordinated his personal ambition to a willingness to serve according to his new capacities, he felt a profound sense of freedom.

And perhaps his very sense of inadequacy made him a better administrator. He was less critical of the faults of others, less outspoken in condemning them. He learned to delegate responsibility, some of it to his able associate, Dr. Zal Kutar, some to other heads of departments. A new constitution for the hospital, designed to make its functioning more democratic, would provide not only for greater representation from the Conferences and the local community but also for more sharing of responsibility among the staff members themselves.

Perhaps it was this sense of freedom and release from tension which wrought the miracle—or perhaps it was the urgency of tremendous human needs which he alone was qualified to meet. But as the weeks passed, both energy and skill returned. Dr. Bimal Roy, his assistant in the chest department, left to study for his M.S. in Ludhiana. Dr. Ernest found himself alone with both the administrative burden of the hospital and the care of seventy-four in-patients. Emergency operations were necessary, and he performed them. Soon he was operating regularly, carrying the full load of surgery—lung, heart, esophagus, the whole gamut of thoracic emergencies. But the department desperately needed an assistant. In a casual letter to Dr. Tara Chandra, he happened to mention his predicament.

"I'll come and help you," his former pupil and colleague offered promptly, "until you can get an assistant."

Leaving his big hospital, the young surgeon began making the trip to Bareilly each week, on Mondays, and the two operated together, one or the other assisting. It was not the first time there had been cooperation between Clara Swain and the big government sanatorium. Often in recent years Dr. Tara Chandra had invited Ernest to the sanatorium for consultations and had even sent some of the patients from his 400-bed hospital to Clara Swain for treatment.

A "waste," reflected Ernest, remembering the grumblings of some of his colleagues, training this brilliant young surgeon and "losing" him to a government hospital? A waste, all the doctors, technicians, and nurses that Clara Swain had trained and sent out through the years, to enter the life-stream of other, perhaps secular, institutions? As well say that the whole Christian mission was a waste because it did not remain an ingrowing organism, ministering to its core of faithful devotees! The hospital was no little foreign island. It was an integral part of a huge old-new country trying desperately to solve colossal problems through a democratic society. And cooperation in the hospital's larger relationships was as essential as among the diverse faiths and skills and eccentricities of its own personnel.

Cooperation! It was a two-way process. The lines radiating outward in service frequently turned on themselves, radiating inward, becoming circles, feeding more and more energy into the source, that there might be a greater and greater outpouring! So, often in what seemed like remarkable ways, the needs of the hospital were met in order that it might meet the needs of others. Take for instance the matter of the X-ray.

It was no mission board that solved the problem, but OXFAM, a private body of citizens from Oxford, one of the largest charitable organizations in the world, which has fed millions in India with multipurpose food. "Let us build and equip a new X-ray Department at Clara Swain," it offered in 1967 with farsighted generosity. So it was that a new 700-MA X-ray machine would soon be imported at a cost of two lakhs of rupees, that a new laboratory costing another lakh would be built as a top story for the X-ray Department. Together with a new private-room complex whose foundations were already being laid, these would constitute a Centenary project.

And the completion of the Mary V. Gordon Nursing School Building? This also would be accomplished through a gift of $40,000 from the Shanghai University Board in the U.S.A. So the circles of service would continue to radiate, back and forth, interlocking, ever widening, part of that Brotherhood of Sharing which is the sole hope for a better world.

Cooperation, team work! Never had Ernest been more convinced of its necessity than on a day when he stood in the operating room surrounded by doctors, nurses, interns, students, anesthetists. The patient was a girl from the Good Shepherd Agricultural Farm in Tanakpur. While one team of doctors skillfully removed a large tumor from the patient's jaw, another team took out a rib from her left side. Then while the rib was being substituted for the jaw bone, the side was being sutured, closed, dressed. Presently in record time the patient was being wheeled away, a modern miracle of metamorphosis almost as impressive as the creation of new life from the rib of some ancient Adam.

It would take cooperation, Ernest knew, to meet the multiple needs of the hospital in the future, if it in turn was to meet the appalling needs of the area to which it might minister—the combined efforts of mission groups, local charities, Government, and hundreds of concerned Christians in America and India and around the world. It would also take audacity and a consummate faith, those divine imperatives which had driven its founder into what seemed an impossible venture nearly a hundred years ago.

ABOUT THE AUTHOR

Dorothy Clarke Wilson has acquired a large following through the years with her inspirational fiction and nonfiction. Her recent books, *Dr. Ida; Take My Hands;* and *Ten Fingers for God*, are still reaching a wide readership; and *Handicap Race*, published in 1967, is rapidly gaining wide popularity. A native of Maine, Mrs. Wilson has traveled extensively in India and the Bible lands researching her work. She and her husband, a Methodist minister, make their home in Orono, Maine.